BIOPHYSICAL PRINCIPLES OF STRUCTURE AND FUNCTION

Fred M. Snell
Sidney Shulman
Richard P. Spencer
Carl Moos

Designed for use at both the undergraduate and graduate levels, this text presents an introduction to the principles of structure and function in biological systems—with attention focused on the cellular, subcellular, and molecular levels. Its primary purpose is to assist the student of biological and medical sciences in improving his knowledge and appreciation of physical and chemical principles which are important to a better understanding of living things. The book will be valuable either as a primary text in an introductory course in biophysics or as a supplement to courses in cell biology and biochemistry. In addition, it will be of considerable interest to research workers in biology and medicine who are interested in a more quantitative interpretation of their research activities.

In essence, the book is divided into two major parts. The first half is devoted to a treatment of the principles of biological *structure,* building from the atomic and molecular level up to the living cell. The text then proceeds to a consideration of the fundamental principles of chemical thermodynamics and kinetics which underlie the *function* of living cells and organisms.

BIOPHYSICAL PRINCIPLES
OF STRUCTURE
AND FUNCTION

FRED M. SNELL
State University of New York at Buffalo

SIDNEY SHULMAN
State University of New York at Buffalo

RICHARD P. SPENCER
Yale University

CARL MOOS
State University of New York at Stony Brook

ADDISON-WESLEY PUBLISHING COMPANY

READING, MASSACHUSETTS · PALO ALTO · LONDON · DON MILLS, ONTARIO

This book is in

THE ADDISON-WESLEY SERIES
IN THE LIFE SCIENCES

Consulting Editors

EDWARD HERBERT · HERMAN LEWIS

PREFACE

The essence of an understanding of those things we call "living" is a comprehension of the structure of the component parts assembled by life processes and the functional interactions of those parts. Modern biophysical research is largely directed toward clarifying the relation between structure and function, and it is the purpose of this book to bring together and underscore some of the physical, chemical, and physicochemical principles which underlie this approach.

The fundamental unit of living systems is the cell; hence, our understanding of any living system must necessarily be based upon a comprehension of the structures and functions of cells, including not only the common features, such as self-replication, but the enormous diversity of specialized functions as well. In this book, we have chosen to focus attention on the cellular, subcellular, and molecular levels, not because the higher levels are unimportant, but because a consideration of the entire hierarchy of biological organization would have made the treatment either too unwieldy or too superficial.

This book is intended as an introduction to the subject, suitable as a text for an introductory course in biophysics. It will also be useful as a supplementary text for courses in cell biology, biochemistry, physical chemistry and physics, especially if the instructor wishes to broaden the base of the more classical approaches. We have not addressed ourselves to the student of pure physics, of pure chemistry, or of classical biology, because it is our conviction that such disciplinary distinctions have little significance in the current practice of science. Rather, we have in mind upper-division science majors or first-year graduate or professional students who have some background in all these areas and who desire to become more familiar with modern biophysical concepts and approaches.

Outside of formal course work, the book may also be of value to the more experienced biological or medical scientist. Trained as of yesterday, he may wish to clarify and strengthen the foundations of his current investigative endeavors, to deepen and broaden his concepts, and to acquire more of the perspective of the biophysical approach. Similarly, the physical scientist, intrigued by modern biological problems, may find the book helpful in providing a concise introduction to some current biological concepts.

In our organization of the book, we have devoted the first half to a discussion of the *structure* of the living cell, building from the atomic and molecular level up to the whole cell. We then proceed to a consideration of biological *function* on the basis of fundamental principles of chemical thermodynamics and kinetics.

In Chapter 1, we introduce the field of biophysics by outlining some of the problems with which it deals and the conceptual and experimental approaches to their solution. Chapters 2 and 3 review the main features of atomic and molecular structure and the intermolecular interactions which form the basis for the higher levels of biological structure. The ubiquitous and all-important substance, water, is dealt with in some detail in Chapter 4, along with a brief introduction to acid-base equilibria. Protein structure is then developed, beginning with the amino acids in Chapter 5 and continuing through primary, secondary, and tertiary structure in Chapters 6 and 7. Chapter 8 deals with nucleic acids and is followed by a consideration of molecular genetic mechanisms in Chapter 9 and of viruses, as another type of nucleoprotein system, in Chapter 10.

The remaining biological building blocks, the polysaccharides and lipids, are treated in Chapters 11 and 12, respectively, with particular emphasis on the role of lipids in membrane formation. Finally, in Chapter 13, we attempt to summarize the structural arrangements of the subcellular elements which comprise the whole living cell.

The remainder of the book introduces certain principles and concepts of cell function. Emphasis is placed upon an understanding of elementary chemical thermodynamics, which provides the framework for a systematic consideration of many kinds of physical and physicochemical processes. Chapter 14 is thus devoted to a presentation of fundamental principles of thermodynamics, parts of which are given further amplification in Chapter 15 with special attention devoted to the chemical potential. The next three chapters relate to equilibrium processes, both physical and chemical. Proton dissociation reactions are taken up in detail in Chapter 17 as important examples of chemical equilibria; and Chapter 18 deals with various phase equilibria, including osmotic equilibrium and other membrane phenomena.

Nonequilibrium processes are introduced in Chapter 19 with a consideration of diffusion on the basis of thermodynamic "forces" and fluxes. Transport phenomena involving membranes are developed in Chapters 20 and 21, progressing from the relatively simple to the more complex mechanisms. Nonequilibrium chemical reaction processes are treated in Chapters 22 and 23, using a kinetic approach. Elementary chemical transformations are dealt with first, as a basis for the consideration of enzymatic processes, which are the fundamental mechanisms of chemical transformation in biological systems.

Throughout, we have been selective rather than exhaustive in our choice of subject matter. We have attempted to develop concepts rigorously from first principles, but hopefully not at the sacrifice of clarity and intelligibility. Above all we have striven to be accurate and precise in scientific concept and detail.

We are indebted to many who have helped make this book a realization. The first step was a "draft" published in photo-offset, for which we gratefully acknowledge the financial assistance of the National Fund for Medical Education. Portions of this original draft have been utilized for several years in an introductory course in biophysics for medical and dental students at the University of Buffalo (now the State University of New York at Buffalo). We are, therefore, indebted to the classes of students who have used this draft and offered us their criticisms. Many colleagues read portions of this original draft; but in particular, we would like to thank Dr. C. N. Longsworth who gave us many valuable and detailed suggestions. The present book is based on the earlier publication, with extensive revisions, deletions, and additions. We are indebted to many of our immediate colleagues, particularly Dr. R. A. Spangler, for reading and commenting on portions of the manuscript. Dr. J. L. Oncley reviewed the entire manuscript and we are grateful to him for his many cogent criticisms.

We wish to express our appreciation to Mrs. Sandra Moore, Miss Susan Kozmycz and Miss Joanna Ferber for their skillful help in various phases of manuscript preparation. Finally, the cooperation of the entire staff of the Department of Biophysics is most gratefully acknowledged.

Buffalo, N.Y.   F.M.S.
January 1965   S.S.
                                                              R.P.S.
                                                               C.M.

CONTENTS

CHAPTER 1

BIOPHYSICS AND THE LIVING CELL

CHAPTER 1

BIOPHYSICS AND THE LIVING CELL

1-1 Introduction. The fundamental unit of living matter is the cell. No unit of matter is known which is smaller than a cell, yet can carry on the activities associated with life, including metabolism, growth, and reproduction. Even viruses require living cells in which to replicate; in isolated form a virus is quite incapable of performing any life functions. Hence, an understanding of almost any aspect of life must be based on an appreciation of the structure and function of the cell.

Living cells, of course, have not always been present on our planet. Throughout most of its history, the earth was quite "dead," in the sense of being devoid of animate matter, and it is from this inanimate world that life must have originated. The first step in the evolution of life must have been the creation and accumulation in the primitive seas of a wide variety of organic molecules, including some large polymers. Indeed, it has been demonstrated experimentally that many of the complex compounds characteristic of life can arise spontaneously from simpler substances under conditions resembling those of the primitive earth. Some of these molecules must then have gathered together into larger aggregates having new properties distinct from those of their constituents, and this may be regarded as the second stage in the origin of life. Such aggregates probably had the property of selectively attracting particular kinds of molecules from their environment, in a manner somewhat analogous to the growth of a crystal. This sort of phenomenon is well known to the colloid chemist as *coacervation*. We may also suppose that, in some of these aggregates, certain relatively regular and specific structural arrangements predominated. At the very least, we would expect that the molecules at the surface of such aggregates would be subject to forces different from those in the interior. Therefore, a specialized structural arrangement, a primordial limiting membrane, might be expected to appear.

With the existence of enclosed regions differing in chemical composition from their environment, new varieties of chemical reactions become possible, and some of the primitive aggregates must have developed the ability to promote the synthesis of their own constituents from other materials available in the surroundings. We may further hypothesize that when these objects grew to a certain size, they became unstable and divided.

2

At all of these stages something like natural selection must have operated, certain sorts of molecules and aggregates being better able to survive the vicissitudes of the changing environment, and growing at the expense of the others.

The culmination of this chain of events was the appearance of the objects which we characterize as *living organisms*. Exhibiting new properties and obeying new laws, the laws of biology, these organisms are, with few exceptions, clearly distinct from the nonliving world. However, it would be impossible to designate any particular development to mark the moment when life appeared; living matter is distinguished from the nonliving by a variety of criteria, no one of which can be regarded as decisive in itself.

Having arisen as a result of natural processes occurring in the nonliving world, life may be seen to represent no more than a special arrangement of the same kinds of atoms that comprise the rest of the universe. Hence, it is to be expected that living matter must obey the same fundamental laws of physics and chemistry as do other kinds of matter, and this view forms the basis of biophysics. Although this concept may appear trivial, the student of biology knows that many processes occurring in the living world *seem* to violate fundamental laws of nature. Biophysics attacks such puzzles by attempting to elucidate the intimate nature of the life processes and thus to resolve the apparent paradoxes. In many instances, as a byproduct of the application of basic laws of nature to such new situations, our understanding of these laws is broadened and enriched, with consequent benefits for the physical sciences as well.

Obviously, the foregoing comments apply in large part to other branches of biology as well as to biophysics. The distinctive characteristic of the latter, then, is a matter of emphasis. Since living matter exhibits a degree of complexity of structural and functional organization unknown in the inanimate world, new "laws of biology" are required to provide an understanding of life. At the risk of oversimplification, one might characterize biophysics as that branch which gives more emphasis to the application of general "laws of nature" to the elementary processes of life, while other branches of biology endeavor to elucidate the new laws which govern the function of living organisms.

1-2 The study of cell structure. While we generally recognize "life" by its functional attributes, we find that these attributes are in virtually every instance inseparably related to structural organization. Metabolism, irritability, motility, reproduction, and all the other characteristics of living cells can only be understood in the light of the geometrical configuration of the components responsible. Indeed, we might count the presence of an extraordinary degree of structural order as one of the prime attributes of living organisms.

The structure of cells has been under study for nearly three centuries, and until the last two or three decades, the light microscope provided nearly all the available information concerning cell anatomy. Microscopists long ago recognized that cells are by no means homogeneous droplets of "protoplasm." Cells are bounded by a limiting membrane, and nearly always contain a nucleus and a variety of smaller structures such as mitochondria, Golgi bodies, and other organelles. Specialized types of light microscopes have enabled biologists to study further details of cell structure. For example, the phase-contrast and interference microscopes allow the visualization of clear, colorless structures which differ from their surroundings in refractive index. By means of the interference microscope, one can also measure quantitatively the amount of material in various regions within a cell. The polarizing microscope, by measuring the effect of an object on polarized light passing through the instrument, can provide information concerning the regular alignment of molecules or particles in portions of the cell, even though these particles are far too small to be seen individually. The basic concept of the arrangement of lipid and protein molecules in the cell membrane, for example, was originally derived from such observations. (See Chapter 13.)

In seeking to visualize directly the finer details of structure, however, a theoretical limit on the possibilities of light microscopy is reached. The *resolution* of any microscope is defined as the smallest separation, d, between two objects which can just be distinguished from one another. Even with the best lenses, the value of d can never be smaller than a limiting value given approximately by

$$d \geq \frac{\lambda}{2NA},$$ (1-1)

where λ is the wavelength of the light (or other radiation) used (see Section 2-4), and NA stands for the *numerical aperture* of the objective lens, which is a measure of the ability of the lens to collect light emerging from the object.

Numerical aperture is defined by

$$NA = n \sin \alpha,$$ (1-2)

where n is the refractive index of the medium between the object and the lens (1.0 for air; about 1.5 for immersion oil), and α is the angle between the axis and the most extreme ray entering the lens from the center of the object.

Numerical apertures of light microscopes are at best (with oil immersion) only slightly greater than 1.0, so it may be seen that the resolution is limited to about half the wavelength of the light. For example, using visible light with a wavelength of about 5,000 A (0.5 μ), an oil-immersion objective of NA = 1.25 would have a resolution of about 0.5/2.5 = 0.2 μ. It should be emphasized that this result is independent of the magnification, or "power," of the microscope. A magnification of 1,000× or more would be needed to make a separation of 0.2 μ visible. Further magnification, however, would reveal no further detail, but would merely serve to enlarge an unavoidably fuzzy image.

In order to "see" finer details of cell structure, considerably shorter wavelengths must be used; this was the primary reason for the development of the *electron microscope*. The electron microscope is basically similar to the light microscope except that a beam of electrons replaces the light, electrostatic or magnetic "electron lenses" are used, and the magnified image is viewed on a fluorescent screen or recorded on photographic film. The formation of an image by an electron beam is possible because, as will be discussed in Chapter 2, electrons have wave properties. The wavelength of these "matter-waves" depends inversely on the momentum of the electrons, and for most commercial electron microscopes, it is in the neighborhood of 0.05 A. Unfortunately, due to practical limitations on the design of electron lenses, the best resolution actually obtained with ideal objects is currently no better than about 5 A. But this is obviously a major step beyond the figure of 0.2 μ (2,000 A) derived above for the light microscope and will undoubtedly be further improved during the coming years.

The electron microscope has opened an entirely new realm of micro-anatomy, which is being vigorously explored throughout the world. Many hitherto unknown features of cell structure can now be seen, and it has become evident that virtually the entire cell is organized in a complex and highly structured manner. In essence, the cell is divided into many physically distinct compartments, or phases, which take a variety of forms, such as particles, membranes, tubules, and vesicles. Smaller objects, too, such as viruses, and even large molecules of protein and nucleic acid, can be seen, and their sizes, shapes, and internal structures can be directly observed (see Chapters 7, 8, and 10). The most serious limitation on electron microscopy is the requirement that the specimen be fixed and dehydrated, which precludes continuous observations of cell function such as are possible with the light microscope.

As an alternative method of improving resolution over that obtainable with visible light, x-rays have been used, since they have wavelengths of the order of 1 A. However, since no satisfactory x-ray lenses exist, it is not possible to form a high-resolution x-ray image directly.* Instead, with

---

* Work is under way in several laboratories on the development of an x-ray microscope using curved x-ray reflectors for focusing, but progress has been slow, and the resolutions presently achieved are not better than that of the light microscope. (See Ref. 5.)

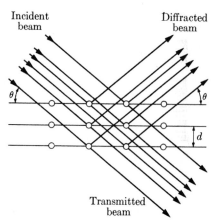

Fig. 1-1. Diffraction of x-rays by a crystal with spacing d between layers of atoms (lattice planes).

objects having periodic order, such as laminated structures, crystals, and the like, the technique of *x-ray diffraction* is applied. When x-rays impinge upon any object, the electrons in its atoms scatter the x-rays in all directions. If the atoms are arranged in evenly spaced layers as in a crystal lattice, however, the x-rays scattered in certain directions from all the layers are in phase with each other and add up by constructive interference to give diffracted beams in these particular directions. The directions of diffraction, as shown in Fig. 1-1, are given by Bragg's Law,

$$n\lambda = 2d \sin \theta, \qquad (1\text{--}3)$$

where n is any positive integer and is called the *order* of the diffraction, λ is the wavelength of the x-rays, d is the spacing between atomic layers in the object, and θ is the angle indicated in Fig. 1-1. Since the angle θ is the same for the incident and the diffracted beams, the latter are sometimes referred to as "x-ray reflections," although in principle, diffraction is quite different from reflection at a plane surface. From measured values of θ for a given wavelength of x-rays, the spacing between the layers of atoms in the crystal may be calculated by means of Eq. (1–3). Together with an analysis of the relative intensities of different diffracted beams, this technique can reveal the location of every atom in a perfect three-dimensional crystal, and hence the detailed geometrical structure of the molecules composing it.* Interatomic distances in smaller molecules are commonly

---

* Hydrogen atoms are so small, and scatter x-rays so weakly, that their positions are usually not determinable except by the use of indirect methods.

determined in this way with an accuracy of a few hundredths of an angstrom unit, and bond angles are determined with an accuracy of one degree or better.

In more complex molecules such as the proteins, however, it is not so
simple to compute the position of every atom. This is true because the
x-ray diffraction pattern from a single crystal does not contain all the
necessary information; the intensities of the scattered rays are recorded,
but their relative phases are not, and these phase relations must be known
if the complete structure of the crystal is to be computed directly. The
approach in the case of small molecules is, in essence, to make educated
guesses, on the basis of chemical information, of what the structure might
be, and then to compute the expected diffraction pattern of each possible
structure and determine which matches the observed diffraction data best.
This is impossible in the case of macromolecules which contain hundreds
or thousands of atoms, especially when most of these are the relatively
small carbon, oxygen, and nitrogen atoms, which do not differ greatly in
x-ray scattering power; so in these cases other "tricks" must be employed.

Among such tricks, one which has been used successfully with proteins
involves the use of heavy-atom markers in the molecule. If a small number
of large heavy-metal atoms, such as mercury or silver, can be chemically
added to the protein molecule without altering the overall arrangement of
molecules in the crystal, then an analysis of the resulting *changes* in the
diffraction pattern can provide a basis for a complete determination of the
structure. Using this method, complete three-dimensional structures have
been determined for myoglobin and hemoglobin, the oxygen-carrying proteins of muscle and blood (see Chapter 7), but the method is exceedingly
laborious and requires very extensive computations. And its most serious
limitation is that it is applicable only to compounds of which relatively
large, well-ordered crystals can be prepared, and for which suitable heavy-
atom substitutions can be made.

If the object is not a perfect crystal but has a regularly repeating structure in one or two directions, then x-ray diffraction can be used to determine repeat spacings in these directions. For example, the method has been
applied to the elucidation of the regular structural periodicities along fibrous
molecules of protein and nucleic acid (Chapters 7 and 8), and the spacing
between layers in lamellar structures like the myelin sheath of nerve fibers.
However, no information can be obtained regarding structural features
which are not regularly repeated in the object; this imposes very severe
limitations on the applicability of x-ray diffraction to biological samples.

1-3 The study of cell function. The ultimate goal of the biophysicist,
as of any other biologist, is not merely the description of the structure of
the parts of the cell, even down to a molecular level. Rather, his interest

is in the interpretation of the observed structural relationships in terms of the dynamic functional roles of the various components. We shall attempt here to outline some general concepts which illustrate the approach of the biophysicist to problems of biological function at a cellular and molecular level.

The evolution of living organisms is characterized by two seemingly contradictory tendencies—*constancy* and *change*. It is a familiar feature of life that the complex mechanisms of genetics operate to assure that offspring will resemble their parents in the multitude of structural features and functional capacities that identify a biological species. And yet, within this very mechanism for maintaining constancy lies the mechanism of change—the possibility of mutation and natural selection leading to the diversification of living forms corresponding to the diversity of environments in which life has existed and now exists in various places on our planet. The study of the molecular mechanisms of genetic information transfer is an area of biophysics which has experienced particularly rapid advances in recent years. It is evident now that the genetic information is "coded" in the form of specific chemical structures, the nucleic acids; and the replication of these specific structures is the result of intermolecular interactions no different fundamentally from those familiar to physical and colloid chemists.

Aside from genetics and evolution, the activities of the individual organism and its component cells are also characterized by the two features of constancy and change. Constant internal conditions are necessary to life; but, on the other hand, definite changes are involved in the special functions of particular cells, such as the electrical excitation of nerve, the contraction of muscle, or secretion by a gland.

The constancy of the "internal environment" of the cell is maintained, in the face of changes in chemical composition in the surroundings, by the regulation of the passage of chemical substances into and out of the cell. An essential aspect of cellular function is the ability to obtain from the environment those substances needed for life, even when they are available only at low concentrations, and to exclude or eliminate waste products and other harmful agents, even when these are present at relatively high concentrations in the surroundings. The properties of the cell envelope are therefore crucial to the existence of the cell itself. In studying the properties of cellular membranes, the most direct approach is the measurement of the passage of substances across the membranes in either direction. This may be done chemically or with the aid of radioactive tracers. In addition, when the penetrating material is an ion, its passage across a membrane may often be measured electrically, since a flow of ions constitutes an electric current.

Another aspect of the regulation of the "internal environment" is the control of the extremely complex biochemical reaction systems in the cell. In most cases, a given substance has the possibility of entering any of a variety of different chemical reaction "pathways," and having undergone one transformation, it may face a new set of alternatives for the succeeding steps. To maintain the proper concentrations of the various cell components, to provide materials for growth, repair, and secretion, and to supply energy from chemical sources for cellular activities, the rates of all the countless chemical reactions in the cell must be adjusted with extraordinary precision. This control of the rates, or *kinetics*, of chemical reaction systems resides primarily in the fact that virtually all biochemical reactions are mediated by enzymes—specialized proteins, each of which catalyzes a certain reaction with great specificity and effectiveness. Further regulatory influences may result from the structural organization of the cell contents into compartments, so that various compounds may or may not have access to other molecules with which they might react. This brings us back to the role of membrane permeability in controlling cell function, but now we are referring to the membranes separating regions within the cell. Of course, membranes need not be regarded merely as passive partitions. Enzyme molecules may constitute part of the membrane structure, and essential processes may occur at the membranes themselves.

The kinetics of chemical reactions may be studied in many different ways. The most direct is the actual measurement of reaction rates by determination of time rates of change in the concentrations of substances which are consumed or produced by a given process. A second approach, which has been especially useful in the study of chemical reaction systems in the intact living cell or in complex mixtures derived therefrom, is based on measurement of the *steady-state* concentration of various substances. In a steady-state, the concentration of a substance remains constant in time, not because it is inert, but because it is produced and consumed at equal rates. From the steady-state concentration of a substance in the cell under various conditions, one can derive information regarding the rates of the reactions involved in the formation and the utilization of the substance.

In many cases, substances of interest absorb visible or ultraviolet light, or are fluorescent; therefore, the concentrations of these materials can be recorded continuously by optical means without destroying the cells for chemical analysis. Such techniques have been applied widely in measuring both steady-state concentrations and time rates of change for certain substances in intact cells and tissues, and in correlating these observations with the functional state of the cells.

In addition to maintaining the constancy of the "internal environment," we have referred to a second fundamental aspect of cell function: cells generally have the ability to change drastically and often abruptly some of their properties. Muscle cells can suddenly alter their physical dimensions and mechanical properties; nerve cells can undergo sudden changes in membrane permeability leading to the propagated electrical impulses so essential for coordinating the function of the various parts of higher animals; gland cells may suddenly release secretions into the blood-stream or the digestive tract; and the cells of many animal and plant tissues may suddenly begin to grow and divide in the healing of a wound or as part of a reproductive cycle. The study of the intimate molecular basis of the regulatory mechanisms responsible for the constancy of intracellular conditions is thus inseparable from the investigation of how sharp changes in function are initiated and brought about. Both kinds of behavior must be related to the nature and properties of the molecules of which living matter is composed and to the physics and chemistry of their interactions. The biophysical approach, the effort to apply the concepts and methods of physics and physical chemistry to biological problems, is therefore an essential aspect of the overall effort of biologists to understand living cells and organisms.

1-4 Simplifications and idealizations. A living cell (not to mention a multicellular organism) is an overwhelmingly complicated thing, and any attempt to understand it in every detail all at once is obviously foredoomed. However, particular problems can be attacked successfully if they can be separated, conceptually or physically, from the myriad of other related problems. Conclusions can often be obtained subject to the familiar condition of "other things being equal." In actual fact, of course, other things practically never do remain "equal." The entire organism, and even its immediate environment, is such a closely integrated entity that almost no change can be made which does not simultaneously affect all aspects of the system. Does this render useless all approaches to particular problems in isolation? It does not. But the investigator must not lose awareness of the assumption he is making about "other things being equal." For example, in investigating the utilization of cellular energy resources for a particular function, such as transporting a substance into the cell, we must not forget that any change in the energy demanded for this purpose is certain to alter the amount of energy available from the same resources for other apparently unrelated functions.

Often it is necessary to remove a portion of the cell or organism from its normal surroundings for investigation of its special properties. Here, too, it is essential to keep in mind that the properties being studied may be altered by the unaccustomed environment, and the application of the results of such studies to a consideration of events in the intact cell must be made with caution.

Another matter about which some preliminary comments should be made is the application of general physical and physicochemical principles to biological situations. Although these principles are often derived for "ideal" cases, they are extremely useful in the consideration of real phenomena. As an example, consider the familiar Ideal Gas Law, which relates the pressure, temperature, and volume of an ideal gas. No real gas obeys this law exactly, except perhaps in the limit as the pressure becomes very small, but nevertheless the relation is applicable in two principal ways. First, since it is approximately true, it can be used for the approximate prediction of the behavior of real gases under ordinary circumstances. And second, the actual deviation of real gases from the predicted ideal behavior yields additional information regarding the sizes of the gas molecules and the forces of interaction between them. In biological systems, the application of the laws of physical chemistry has similar purposes. First, these laws serve to predict the behavior to be expected from the system, assuming a given mechanism for the process under investigation, and second, deviations from the expected behavior provide clues to a fuller understanding of the actual mechanism of the process. To mention only one example, which is treated in greater detail in Chapters 20 and 21, the direction and rate of penetration of substances through the cell membrane may be predicted from physical principles, assuming the membrane is merely a passive barrier. For those substances which are observed to behave in a very different manner, in some cases even moving in the "wrong" direction, one can unequivocally conclude that the real mechanism is more complex than mere passive diffusion through "pores" in the membrane and involves the dynamic functional properties of the membrane and the cell as a whole.

In summary, biophysics is built on the assumption that living cells and organisms, having originated from nonliving matter, must be subject to the same principles of physics and physical chemistry as those which apply to the inanimate world. By using the methods and concepts of the physical sciences in the study of biological problems, the biophysicist endeavors to "understand" life processes, that is, to know what kinds of molecular structures and interactions are responsible for observed biological phenomena.

REFERENCES

1. A. V. HILL, "Why Biophysics?" *Science* **124**, 1233-1237 (1956).
2. A. I. OPARIN, *Life—its Nature, Origin and Development.* Academic Press, New York, 1961.
3. G. OSTER and A. W. POLLISTER, *Physical Techniques in Biological Research,* Vols. 1 and 3. Academic Press, New York, 1956.
4. R. W. G. WYCKOFF, *The World of the Electron Microscope.* Yale University Press, 1958.
5. V. E. COSSLETT, A. ENGSTROM, and H. H. PATTEE (Eds.), *X-ray Microscopy and Microradiography.* Academic Press, New York, 1957.
6. F. H. C. CRICK and J. C. KENDREW, "X-ray Analysis and Protein Structure," *Advances in Protein Chemistry* **12**, 133–214 (1957).

CHAPTER 2

THE ATOM

2-1 INTRODUCTION
   Atoms in biological structure
   Nucleus and electrons
   Dimensions

2-2 ELEMENTARY PARTICLES
   Protons, neutrons, and electrons
   Atomic number and atomic weight
   Isotopes and radioactivity

2-3 ELECTRON ORBITALS AND ENERGY LEVELS
   Orbitals
   Energy levels
   Electron shells

2-4 ELECTROMAGNETIC RADIATION
   Wavelength, frequency, and velocity
   Types of radiation
   Quanta and energy
   Spectroscopy and atomic structure

2-5 ELECTRONS AS WAVES AND THE STRUCTURE OF ATOMS
   The wave nature of matter
   Quantum numbers
   Pauli exclusion principle
   Structure of atoms

2-6 THE STABILITY OF NOBLE GAS STRUCTURES
   The noble gases and the "complete octet"
   The origin of ions
   Electron sharing and the covalent bond

CHAPTER 2

THE ATOM

2-1 Introduction. All the properties included under the adjective "living" are presumed to arise from the combination and interaction of atoms in certain specific ways. Of course, a knowledge of atomic structure alone does not permit the calculation of the behavior of a living cell; indeed, the direct extension of atomic structure theory even to simple molecules soon becomes prohibitively complex. But certain essential properties of cells and their constituents can be understood only in terms of the intimate structure of atoms. To give only a few examples, the unique behavior of the ubiquitous and all-important water molecule, the intermolecular forces which hold together the structural elements of the cell, and the interactions of organisms with radiation of various sorts must be approached from the point of view of atomic structure.

Atoms are composed of two portions. Centrally located is a *nucleus* in which resides most of the mass of the atom (more than 99.9%); surrounding this is a cloud of *electrons*. The whole atom has a diameter of the order of 10^{-8} cm (1A), while the diameter of the nucleus is near 10^{-13} cm, so that most of the atomic volume is almost devoid of mass. Thus even solid matter appears to be largely "empty space." However, it is a familiar fact that strong forces resist the intrusion of other atoms into this "empty space" within the atom.

2-2 The elementary particles. Over one hundred different chemical elements are known, but the atoms of all of them are built of the same three types of elementary particles: protons, neutrons, and electrons. Protons and neutrons are the constituents of the nucleus and are therefore called *nucleons*. The *proton* has a positive electric charge of 4.8×10^{-10} electrostatic units (esu), often represented by e, and a mass of about 1.7×10^{-24} gm. The *neutron*, although approximately equal in mass to the proton, carries no electric charge. The number of protons in a nucleus, Z, is the *atomic number*, and determines the chemical identity of the atom and its place in the periodic chart of the elements. The total positive charge of the nucleus, then, is given by Ze, where e is the electrical charge on each proton.

The mass of a single *electron* is $\frac{1}{1836}$ of that of a nucleon, but each electron carries a negative charge equal in magnitude to the positive charge of a proton. Neutral atoms, such as those of a pure element, contain a number

14

of electrons equal to Z, the atomic number. If the number of electrons does not equal Z, the atom possesses a net electric charge, and it is then an *ion*.

Since the nucleons account for almost the entire mass of the atom, the total number of neutrons and protons in the nucleus is called the *mass number*, A, of the atom. The approximate weight of the atom in grams may be obtained by multiplying the mass number by the nucleon mass of 1.7×10^{-24} gm. More precise values of atomic weight are generally given in *atomic mass units* (amu), which are defined by assigning an atomic weight of exactly 12 amu to the commonest form of carbon for which $A = 12$.* On this basis, one amu is equal to 1.6603×10^{-24} gm. As an example, we may consider the atom of sodium. Its nucleus contains 11 protons and 12 neutrons; so its mass number, A, is 23. Its precise atomic weight, however, is 22.9898 amu.

All the atoms of a given chemical element have the same number of protons, Z, but the number of neutrons in the nucleus may vary. In such cases, atoms having the same Z but different A are called *isotopes*, and are usually identified by adding the mass number as a superscript to the chemical symbol. For instance, the commonest form of carbon mentioned earlier would be designated C^{12}, but natural carbon also contains small amounts of C^{13} and C^{14}. For an element which has several naturally occurring isotopes, the atomic weight generally refers to the average value for that mixture of isotopes which is found in nature. The atomic weight of natural carbon, for example, is not precisely 12, but is 12.0111, due to the presence of small amounts of C^{13} and C^{14}. Certain isotopes are unstable and transform spontaneously into different isotopes, or sometimes different elements, with the concomitant emission of various sorts of radiation. Such isotopes are said to be *radioactive*. The isotope C^{14} is an example of a radioactive isotope; it decays spontaneously into N^{14} with the emission of a β^{-}-particle from the nucleus. A β^{-}-particle is similar to an electron; hence β^{-}-emission leads to a unit increase in Z with no change in A. Other radioactive nuclei emit β^{+}- or α-particles. The β^{+}-particle (positron) resembles a positively charged electron, so β^{+}-emission results in a unit decrease in Z with no change in A. An α-particle is a helium nucleus, and when a nucleus releases an α-particle, Z is decreased by two units and A is decreased by four units. In addition, many radioactive isotopes also emit γ-rays, which are electromagnetic radiation similar to high-energy x-rays. (See Section 2–4.)

---

* The definition of the amu on the basis of carbon-12 was adopted as of 1962 by the International Union of Pure and Applied Chemistry. Prior to that time, the unit was defined by assigning a value of 16 to oxygen, and older tables use these units. However, the difference between the two values is only about 40 parts per million.

Radioactive isotopes have found wide application in biology. For instance, they are commonly used as a means of "tagging" or "labeling" particular atoms of a given element to help ascertain the biochemical "pathways" or sequences of reactions involved in cellular metabolism. Different isotopes of the same element behave virtually identically in chemical reactions, and the radiation emitted by radioactive atoms may be measured by means of a Geiger counter or other suitable detector. As a hypothetical illustration of one type of experiment, a compound X, in which some carbon atoms are replaced with C^{14}, might be added to a biochemical system (organism, tissue, cell suspension, or cell extract). Another compound, Y, might subsequently be isolated from the preparation, and if Y is radioactive (contains C^{14}), this would indicate that the system under consideration converted X to Y.

2–3 Electron orbitals and energy levels. For many purposes, the electrons in an atom may be considered to be revolving around the nucleus in orbits, just as the planets revolve in the solar system. However, the atom is not simply a miniature solar system. In the solar system, a planetary object can establish an orbit at any given distance from the sun. But for

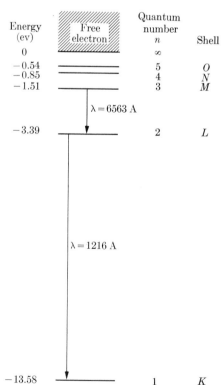

Fig. 2–1. The energy levels of the hydrogen atom. The energy of each quantum state is given in electron-volts (ev). (1 ev = 1.60×10^{-12} erg.) The wavelengths of the radiation corresponding to two transitions are also shown. The state $n = \infty$ represents the electron free of the atom and at rest.

the electrons in an atom, only a certain set of discrete orbits are possible. These "allowed" orbits are referred to as *orbitals*.

Since the electron has a negative electric charge and the nucleus a positive charge, a force of attraction exists between them tending to pull the electron into the smallest available orbital. Work must be done against this force (energy must be absorbed from the environment) when an electron moves from an orbital near the nucleus to another orbital farther out. This work increases the potential energy of the electron, and for this reason, the electron is said to be at a higher *energy level* when it is farther from the nucleus. Each orbital corresponds, therefore, to a certain energy level of the electrons in it.

These energy levels have significance only in terms of the changes in energy associated with transitions from one level to another. Hence, to specify quantitatively the energy level for each orbital, some arbitrarily chosen reference level must be defined. In dealing with electronic energy levels in atoms, it is customary to assign zero energy to the free electron, at rest, infinitely far from the nucleus. Relative to this reference level, all the atomic orbitals have negative potential energies, the most negative being the closest to the nucleus. As an example, the energy levels of the hydrogen atom are illustrated in Fig. 2–1. The principal energy levels, or *electron shells*, are identified by letters beginning with the K-shell nearest the nucleus, and followed by L, M, and so on, with increasing energy. Within each shell, there is one or more orbitals, as will be explained in Section 2–5.

2–4 Electromagnetic radiation. When an electron absorbs energy and is raised to a higher energy level in an atom, the atom is said to be in an *excited state*, and it will tend spontaneously to return to the *ground state* of minimum potential energy. The extra energy is re-emitted as the electron "falls" back to the lower energy orbital. In these processes energy is generally absorbed or emitted as electromagnetic radiation (light or x-rays), so it will be appropriate at this point to discuss briefly the fundamental properties of such radiation.

Electromagnetic radiation is an alternation of electric and magnetic field which propagates through space as a wave. It may be represented, as in Fig. 2–2, by plotting the strength of the electric field as a function of

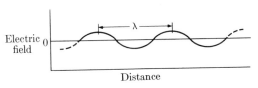

Electric field

Distance

FIG. 2–2. An electromagnetic wave of a wavelength, λ.

distance at one instant of time. One of the characteristics of any wave phenomenon, the *wavelength*, λ, as indicated in Fig. 2–2, is the distance in space between successive "peaks" of the wave. On the other hand, an observer may stand at one position in space and, figuratively speaking, watch the wave go by. He can then determine its *frequency* ν as the number of peaks that pass him each second. Likewise, he could measure the *velocity* v with which any particular peak moves past. Upon consideration of these concepts, it becomes evident that frequency, wavelength, and velocity are related by

$$v = \lambda\nu. \tag{2-1}$$

If v is measured in cm/sec, then for dimensional consistency, ν must be measured in $\sec^{-1}$, and λ in cm. Another commonly employed unit is the *wave number*, which is the number of waves in each centimeter, or simply $1/\lambda$, where λ is in cm. The units of *wave number* are cm^{-1}.

The velocity of electromagnetic radiation in a vacuum is an important constant of nature, generally represented by c, and its value is 3×10^{10} cm/sec (about 186,000 miles/sec). In a medium, the velocity is generally less than c and is given by

$$v = \frac{c}{n}, \tag{2-2}$$

where n is the *refractive index* of the medium. For visible light, the refractive index of air is about 1.00 ($v \approx c$ in air). Various optical glasses have refractive indices between 1.46 and 1.96, and that of water is 1.33.

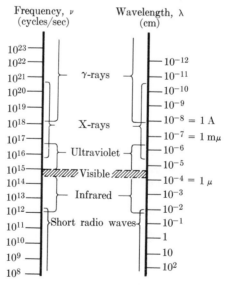

FIG. 2–3. The electromagnetic spectrum.

The chart in Fig. 2–3 shows the values of λ(*in vacuo*) for the various regions of the electromagnetic spectrum commonly encountered. The various types of radiation are not different in principle, but are distinguished from each other by the manner in which the radiation is generated or detected. The longer wavelengths (radio waves) are produced by alternating electric currents in antennae, and are of little interest in the present context. Infrared radiation originates from vibrational and rotational motions of the molecules of a hot body, and the measurement of infrared absorption by substances is an important means of studying molecular structure and intermolecular bonds. Visible and ultraviolet light and x-rays result from transitions of electrons between energy levels in atoms, and γ-rays originate from radioactive decay of certain unstable nuclei.

The wave theory of electromagnetic radiation suffices to explain many of its properties, such as refraction, diffraction, and polarization. However, especially at shorter wavelengths (infrared and below), phenomena are observed which do not fit a simple wave concept. As a result of studies of the photoelectric effect and of the infrared radiation from hot bodies, it was deduced that light has the properties of particles as well as waves. A light ray may be regarded as a series of individual "wave packets" called *quanta*, or *photons*, each possessing an energy E related to its frequency ν by

$$E = h\nu, \qquad (2–3)$$

where h is a universal physical constant equal to 6.62×10^{-27} erg-sec. In honor of Max Planck, the originator of the quantum theory, h is called Planck's constant. From Eq. (2–3), it is evident that higher frequencies (and hence, shorter wavelengths) denote higher energy. It is important not to confuse the energy of each photon with the intensity of the radiation. The *intensity* of a light source, or its total power output, depends not only on the energy of each quantum but also on the number of quanta emitted per unit time.

We can now apply the quantum concept to the radiation associated with electron transitions in atoms. Each time an electron "jumps" from one level to another, a single quantum of light or x-rays is emitted or absorbed. The energy of this photon, as given by Eq. (2–3), is always just equal to the change in energy level undergone by the electron. Each of the various possible transitions between energy levels in an atom is associated with a particular frequency of light; larger "jumps" in energy level correspond to light of higher frequency and shorter wavelength. In Fig. 2–1, the wavelength of the light associated with two such transitions is indicated. It is evident that for the larger jump, from the L- to the K-shell, the emitted light has the shorter wavelength. A wavelength of 1216 A is in the ultraviolet region of the spectrum, while 6563 A represents a visible red color.

With a spectroscope, one can measure the frequencies of light emitted by excited atoms, for instance, in an electric spark, as their electrons drop from higher to lower energy levels. Likewise, an atom in its ground state will absorb light or x-rays of just those energies corresponding to possible upward "jumps" by its electrons; and again by means of a spectroscope, it is possible to determine the frequencies which are absorbed by the atoms of a given substance. Such spectroscopic observations have been the primary source of quantitative information concerning atomic energy levels.

2–5 Electrons as waves and the structure of atoms. By analogy with the demonstrated wave-particle duality in the properties of light, it was suggested in 1924 by the physicist Louis de Broglie that matter might also possess a dual nature. He made the assumption that Eq. (2–3) might apply to material particles as well as to photons, and on this basis he showed that moving particles (for instance, an electron beam) should have a wavelength given by

$$\lambda = \frac{h}{p}, \tag{2-4}$$

where p is the momentum of the particles, the product of their mass and velocity. Three years later, Davisson and Germer obtained the first experimental support for this bold proposal. They found that a beam of electrons could be diffracted from a crystal just like x-rays, behaving as though they had exactly the wavelength predicted by Eq. (2–4). Since that time, wave properties have been unequivocally demonstrated for heavier particles as well, such as nucleons and helium nuclei. The wave nature of electrons has been the basis for many practical developments, including the electron microscope, in which the electron beam obeys laws of optics like those originally derived for light.

The mathematical treatment of electrons as waves (quantum mechanics) provides an explanation for the existence of discrete energy levels and orbitals in atoms. In a crude sense, one treats the various electron orbitals as standing waves, analogous to the vibration modes of a violin string, but in three dimensions instead of one. Only for certain wavelengths, corresponding to certain energy levels, will the electron wave "fit" around an atom in a so-called "stationary state." As a consequence of this theory, the picture of an electron as a small object moving around the nucleus in a precise orbit is replaced by the idea of an electron cloud spread throughout the space around the nucleus, with a certain density distribution for each orbital. (Photographic representations of some of the orbitals of the hydrogen atom are shown in Fig. 2–4.) This density distribution represents the probability that the electron can be found at various points in space. The maximum in the density distribution then indicates the location where

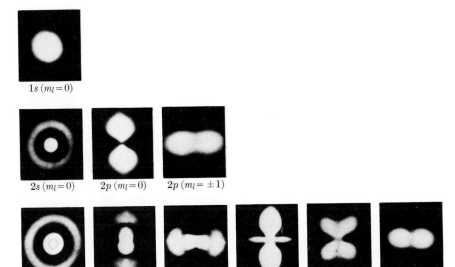

1s ($m_l = 0$)

2s ($m_l = 0$)   2p ($m_l = 0$)   2p ($m_l = \pm 1$)

3s ($m_l = 0$)   3p ($m_l = 0$)   3p ($m_l = \pm 1$)   3d ($m_l = 0$)   3d ($m_l = \pm 1$)   3d ($m_l = \pm 2$)

FIG. 2-4. Photographic representations of the electron density distributions in orbitals of the K, L, and M shells. The nucleus is located at the center of each picture. [From H. E. White, *Phys. Rev.* **37**, 1416 (1931).]

the electron is most likely to be, but as is evident from Fig. 2-4, it has a definite probability of being quite far from this position.

From the equations for the electron wave, it is possible to calculate a series of stationary states corresponding to electron orbitals in an atom. Each of these orbitals is characterized by a set of values for certain parameters in the equation, which are called *quantum numbers*. The first of these is the principal quantum number, n, and its values represent the electron shells with which we are already familiar. The values of n are positive integers beginning with 1:

$$\text{Shell: } K \ L \ M \ N \ O \ \ldots$$
$$n = \ 1 \ 2 \ 3 \ 4 \ 5 \ \ldots$$

The second quantum number, l, is related conceptually to the angular momentum of the electron as it moves around the nucleus, and l may take on any integral value from 0 to $n - 1$. Thus, in the K-shell, l can only be zero, and in the L-shell, where $n = 2$, l may be 0 or 1. In the hydrogen atom, the energy level of an orbital is determined solely by the value of n; within a given shell, orbitals of different l have the same energy. This is not true, however, of atoms containing more than one electron, in which the value of l also influences the energy of an orbital. In an intuitive sense,

TABLE 2–1

QUANTUM NUMBERS OF ELECTRON ORBITALS

POSSIBLE VALUES OF THE QUANTUM NUMBERS n, l, m_l, AND s
FOR ELECTRONS IN THE K-, L-, AND M-SHELLS

Shell	K	L				M								
n (integers $n \geq 1$)	1	2				3								
Number of electrons ($2n^2$)	2	8				18								
Subshell	$1s$	$2s$	$2p$			$3s$	$3p$			$3d$				
l (integers, $0 \leq l \leq n-1$)	0	0	1			0	1			2				
Number of electrons	2	2	6			2	6			10				
m_l (integers, $-l \leq m_l \leq +l$)	0	0	-1	0	$+1$	0	-1	0	$+1$	-2	-1	0	$+1$	$+2$
s, spin ($+\frac{1}{2}$ or $-\frac{1}{2}$)	$\pm\frac{1}{2}$	$\pm\frac{1}{2}$	$\pm\frac{1}{2}$	$\pm\frac{1}{2}$	$\pm\frac{1}{2}$	$\pm\frac{1}{2}$	$\pm\frac{1}{2}$	$\pm\frac{1}{2}$	$\pm\frac{1}{2}$	$\pm\frac{1}{2}$	$\pm\frac{1}{2}$	$\pm\frac{1}{2}$	$\pm\frac{1}{2}$	$\pm\frac{1}{2}$

one could imagine that the shape of an orbital, which depends on its l value, might determine the extent to which it is "screened" from the nucleus by the other electrons of the atom. This effect of l on energy level will be especially important when we consider the arrangement of the electrons in atoms beyond argon in the periodic chart.

Spectroscopists had earlier recognized that some of the electron shells were really groups of two or more *subshells* with close, but not identical, energy levels. They identified these subshells by the letters $s, p, d, f, g, \ldots$, and this notation is still retained. (This apparently random sequence of letters originated from the description of spectral lines as *s*harp, *p*rincipal, *d*iffuse, or *f*undamental. After f, the sequence is alphabetical). The values of the quantum number l correspond to these subshells as follows:

$$\text{Subshells: } s \quad p \quad d \quad f \quad g \quad \ldots$$
$$l = 0 \quad 1 \quad 2 \quad 3 \quad 4 \quad \ldots$$

In naming the orbitals, it is customary to combine the value of n with the letter designation of the subshell. For example, in the K-shell there is only a $1s$-orbital, and in the L-shell there are $2s$- and $2p$-orbitals.

It can be seen in Fig. 2–4 that s-orbitals are spherically symmetrical, while those with l greater than zero are not. Therefore, for all orbitals except s-orbitals, there is another quantum number, m_l, whose values represent different orientations of the electron cloud in space. The value of m_l may be any integer from $-l$ to $+l$. For example, p-orbitals $(l = 1)$ may have $m_l = -1, 0,$ or $+1$. Orbitals with the same n and l, but different m_l, ordinarily have the same energy.

The last quantum number to consider is associated with the electron itself. It is found experimentally that the electron behaves like a tiny magnet, and this is explained by regarding it as spinning on its axis. Since it is charged, such rotation would constitute a circular electric current and produce a magnetic moment. The quantum number s represents the electron's *spin*, and s has only two possible values, $+\frac{1}{2}$ or $-\frac{1}{2}$, representing opposite orientations of the magnetic moment of the electron. Table 2–1 summarizes the quantum numbers that we have mentioned.

Now we are ready to consider the distribution of electrons among the various orbitals in an atom. We shall deal only with the ground state, the state in which all electrons have the lowest possible potential energies. Of course, in excited atoms, electrons may occupy higher-energy orbitals temporarily, but such electrons will eventually "fall" back to the lowest energy levels available.

The fundamental principle upon which atomic structure is based, in addition to the rules of quantum mechanics already outlined, was postulated by Wolfgang Pauli in 1925. It is that *no two electrons in an atom can*

TABLE 2–2

ELECTRONIC STRUCTURE OF ELEMENTS SHOWING
NUMBER OF ELECTRONS IN EACH SUBSHELL

Period	Element	Symbol	Z	K	L		M			N
				$1s$	$2s$	$2p$	$3s$	$3p$	$3d$	$4s$
I	Hydrogen	H	1	1						
	Helium	He	2	2						
	Lithium	Li	3	2	1					
	Beryllium	Be	4	2	2					
	Boron	B	5	2	2	1				
II	Carbon	C	6	2	2	2				
	Nitrogen	N	7	2	2	3				
	Oxygen	O	8	2	2	4				
	Fluorine	F	9	2	2	5				
	Neon	Ne	10	2	2	6				
	Sodium	Na	11	2	2	6	1			
	Magnesium	Mg	12	2	2	6	2			
	Aluminum	Al	13	2	2	6	2	1		
III	Silicon	Si	14	2	2	6	2	2		
	Phosphorus	P	15	2	2	6	2	3		
	Sulfur	S	16	2	2	6	2	4		
	Chlorine	Cl	17	2	2	6	2	5		
	Argon	A	18	2	2	6	2	6		
	Potassium	K	19	2	2	6	2	6		1
IV	Calcium	Ca	20	2	2	6	2	6		2
	Scandium	Sc	21	2	2	6	2	6	1	2

be in the same quantum state, as defined by the set of quantum numbers, n, l, m_l, s. From this principle, known as the Pauli exclusion principle, it follows (see Table 2–1) that the maximum number of electrons that can occupy the K-shell is 2, for the L-shell it is 8, and, in general, for the nth shell it is $2n^2$.

In building up the electronic structure for atoms of increasing atomic number, the subshells tend to fill in the order of increasing energy, the exclusion principle allowing only two electrons (with opposite spin) in each orbital. Table 2–2 shows the electronic structures, in the ground state, of atoms up to scandium. As the atoms are built, electrons are added to the orbitals in order of increasing energy level. In the first two elements, hydrogen and helium, the electrons occupy the $1s$-orbital, which has the lowest energy. In keeping with the Pauli principle, the two electrons in helium must, of course, have opposing spins. In the next atom, lithium, we find that, since only two electrons can occupy the $1s$-orbital, the third must enter the $2s$-orbital to begin filling the L-shell. To form beryllium, one more electron can enter the $2s$-orbital, and with boron the $2p$-orbitals must begin to fill. There are three $2p$-orbitals ($m_l = -1, 0$, and $+1$), so there is room for six $2p$-electrons, and atoms up to neon may be built. With sodium, since the L-shell is filled, one electron must enter the M-shell in a $3s$-orbital, and the $3s$ and $3p$-orbitals are then used to build atoms from sodium to argon, as shown in the table. The structure of potassium may appear to be anomalous, but actually the $4s$-orbital has a lower energy than the $3d$, and hence it fills next after the $3p$-levels. When the $4s$-orbital is full, the $3d$-levels begin to fill, beginning with scandium as shown in the table; and at the end of period IV of the periodic chart, we find krypton, in which all levels through $4p$ are filled making a total of 36 electrons, 18 more than in argon.

2–6 Stability of noble gas structures. It will be recalled from the study of chemistry that helium, neon, and argon are members of a group of chemically unreactive elements, the noble gases.* It is evident from Table 2–2 that the outermost shells of the atoms of neon and argon have their s- and p-orbitals completely filled with a total of 8 electrons, and this is referred to as a *complete octet*. The explanation for the chemical inertness of noble gases is that these 8-electron configurations are extremely stable. That is, the potential energy of electrons in complete octets is lower than it would be in any other configuration, and low potential energy denotes great stability. Although, strictly speaking, the term "octet" does not describe the filled K-shell of helium, the same principle applies.

It is also a familiar fact of chemistry that atoms in which the outermost shell contains 7 electrons, or only one electron, are extremely reactive; examples are the halogens (for instance, F and Cl) with 7 electrons in the outer shell, and the alkali metals (for instance, Li and Na) with just one. The formation of sodium chloride from sodium metal and chlorine gas results from the transfer of the "extra" electron from sodium to chlorine to fill the vacancy in the outer shell of the latter. The electronic configuration around the sodium nucleus is now like that of neon, and the configuration around the chlorine nucleus is that of argon. Hence, the potential energy of the electrons is considerably lower than it was in the original neutral atoms of sodium and chlorine, and therefore the compound NaCl is much more stable than sodium metal and chlorine gas. Of course, although an electron has been transferred, the nuclear charges have not been

---

* Although relatively unreactive, the rare gases are not completely inert. The synthesis of stable compounds of xenon and radon has recently been reported.

changed; so the sodium and chlorine atoms now bear net electric charges, and are called *ions*. The process is summarized by

$$
\begin{aligned}
\mathrm{Na}^0 &\rightarrow \mathrm{Na}^+ + \mathrm{e}^- \\
\underline{\mathrm{e}^- + \mathrm{Cl}^0} &\underline{\rightarrow \mathrm{Cl}^-} \\
\text{Net: } \mathrm{Na}^0 + \mathrm{Cl}^0 &\rightarrow \mathrm{Na}^+ + \mathrm{Cl}^-
\end{aligned}
\qquad (2\text{-}5)
$$

The formation of ions is only one possible way in which atoms can achieve the more stable "complete octet" configuration for their electrons. It is also possible for two atoms to "share" a pair of electrons by forming a *covalent bond*. The simplest example of covalent bond formation is the union of two atoms of hydrogen to form the molecule, H_2. In this molecule, the two electrons contributed by the two atoms are distributed around both nuclei forming an electron-pair bond. The two electrons serve to fill the K-shells of both atoms and therefore have the lower potential energy characteristic of the helium-like structure.

REFERENCES

1. G. GAMOW, *Mr. Thompkins Explores the Atom*. Macmillan, New York, 1944.

2. L. PAULING, *The Nature of the Chemical Bond*, 3rd Ed. Cornell University Press, Ithaca, N. Y., 1960.

3. F. K. RICHTMYER, E. J. KENNARD, and T. LAURITSEN, *Introduction to Modern Physics*, 5th Ed. McGraw-Hill, New York, 1955.

4. M. RUSSELL WEHR and J. A. RICHARDS, JR., *Physics of the Atom*. Addison-Wesley, Reading, Mass., 1960.

5. M. D. KAMEN, *Isotopic Tracers in Biology*, 3rd Ed. Academic Press, New York, 1957.

6. L. PAULING, *General Chemistry*, 2nd Ed. Freeman, San Francisco, 1953.

CHAPTER 3

CHEMICAL BONDS AND INTERMOLECULAR INTERACTIONS

CHAPTER 3

CHEMICAL BONDS AND
INTERMOLECULAR INTERACTIONS

3–1 Introduction. Atoms, functioning as independent entities, are extremely rare in biological systems. The major portion of the living cell is composed of molecules, many of which are quite complex. Even ions, like Na^+, K^+, and Cl^-, nearly always occur in combination with other ions or molecules. Therefore, following our brief survey of the essentials of atomic structure, we must proceed to a consideration of the forces between the atoms within a molecule and among molecules, atoms, and ions which are responsible for the highly organized structure of cells and their components.

The strongest bonds, and hence, those most familiar to the student of elementary chemistry, are ionic and covalent bonds, often referred to as *primary bonds*. These primary bonds arise from the fact that the electron configuration of an atom is most stable when the outermost shell has a "complete octet" of eight electrons, as in a noble gas. As we saw in Chapter 2, atoms may achieve this configuration either by the transfer of one of more electrons from one atom to another to form ions, or by sharing one or more pairs of electrons in a *covalent bond* in which the shared electron pairs, so to speak, do double duty, serving to form "complete octets" around both atoms.

Ionic bonds between oppositely charged ions, such as the Na^+ and Cl^- ions in a salt crystal, can be understood quite well in terms of classical electrostatics, while covalent bonds are best interpreted in terms of quantum-mechanical considerations of electron orbitals. There are also bonds with some features of both of these types, i.e., covalent bonds with partial ionic character, which play an essential role in molecular organization.

Biological structure is dependent not only on these primary bonds, however. Weaker *secondary interactions* link molecules to each other and are responsible for the precise arrangement of matter in the cell in the form of membranes, fibers, granules, and other structural elements, as well as the detailed configuration of macromolecules such as the proteins and nucleic acids.

3–2 Bond energy and the ionic bond. In comparing the strengths of different types of interatomic and intermolecular interactions, we shall have occasion to refer to *bond energy;* hence we must pause at this point to develop clearly the meaning of this concept. As an example, we shall

28

consider the ionic bond because, of all the bonds, it is most easily treated in terms of classical physics.

If two objects carrying electric charges are brought near each other, a force will exist between them. This force is given by Coulomb's law:

$$F = \frac{q_1 q_2}{Dr^2},\qquad (3\text{--}1)$$

where F is the force, q_1 and q_2 are the charges, and r is their distance of separation. The *dielectric constant* D is a characteristic property of the medium between the charges, and its values have been determined for many different materials. If F is measured in dynes, r in centimeters, and q in electrostatic units, then D is unity for a vacuum. The dielectric constant of a medium may then be defined as *the ratio of the force between two charges in a vacuum to that between the same two charges in the medium.* Since D appears in the denominator in Eq. (3–1), the higher the value of D, the weaker the force, or in other words, D is a measure of the extent to which the force between charges is reduced by the intervening medium. In order to keep signs consistent, it is helpful to remember that a force which tends to increase r (a repulsion) is considered positive, and conversely, a negative force indicates an attraction. For example, if q_1 and q_2 are of opposite sign, their product will be negative, and since D and r^2 are always positive, the force between opposite charges will be negative, i.e., attractive.

The form of Coulomb's law in terms of force (Eq. 3–1) is useful in dealing with macroscopic systems; however, when considering atoms and molecules, it is usually impossible to measure directly the forces between particles. For several reasons, a formulation giving *potential energy* is more useful. First, energy changes can be directly measured for collections of atoms (macroscopic matter) in the form of heat, electrical energy, and so on. Second, energy has the important property of being conserved, so that quantitative relations may be predicted between energy changes in different kinds of processes. For instance, from the energies of interaction among carbon, oxygen, and hydrogen atoms, one can estimate the heat or work obtainable from the combustion of coal or the metabolism of foodstuff.

To convert Coulomb's law into a form giving energy instead of force, we ask, "What is the electrical potential energy of two charged particles at a separation r, assuming zero potential energy at infinite separation?" This question may be rephrased, "What work must be done on two charges to bring them together from infinite distance to a distance r from each other?" Work may be calculated as the product of a force and the distance through which it acts, and Eq. (3–1) gives the force between the two particles. We can, therefore, write the work done in moving one of the charges a small distance, $-dx$, closer to the other, or, in other words, the work required to decrease the distance of separation from $(x + dx)$ to x. (The distance moved is negative because the particles are moving closer together, i.e., in the direction of decreasing x.) If the force is regarded as constant over the small distance dx, this work is simply

$$dw = (F)(-dx) = -\frac{q_1 q_2}{Dx^2}\, dx, \qquad (3\text{-}2)$$

where F is the force existing at a distance x. To obtain the total work done in moving the charges from infinite separation $(x = \infty)$ to a separation $x = r$, we must add up the small elements of work, dw, corresponding to all the elements of distance dx from $x = \infty$ to $x = r$. Although we have assumed the force to be constant over the small distance dx, it is certainly not constant over the entire distance from r to ∞. Hence, it is necessary to integrate Eq. (3–2) as follows:*

$$W = \int_{x=\infty}^{x=r} dw = -\int_{x=\infty}^{x=r} \frac{q_1 q_2}{Dx^2}\, dx = \frac{q_1 q_2}{Dr}. \qquad (3\text{-}3)$$

The amount of work, W, which must be put into the system to bring the two particles together will be positive if the particles have similar charges, i.e., if the product $q_1 q_2$ is positive. In this case the potential energy V of the system is increased by bringing the particles together; and if, as is customary, we assign a value of zero to the potential energy at infinite separation, the two charges at distance r have a potential energy of interaction given by

$$V = \frac{q_1 q_2}{Dr}. \qquad (3\text{-}4)$$

If q_1 and q_2 are of opposite sign, it is evident that V will be negative, which means that the system has a lower potential energy when the particles are together than when they are separated. Hence, to separate oppositely charged particles, energy must be put *into* the system to raise its potential energy *up* to zero. Under these circumstances, a *bond* exists, and the *bond energy may be defined as the amount of energy required to completely separate the particles to infinite distance.* The bond energy, then, is given by $-V$. While the evaluation of V from Eq. (3–4) is valid only for ionic bonds, the foregoing definition of bond energy is applicable to all interatomic and intermolecular forces. Since r appears in the denominator of Eq. (3–4), the bond energy between two charged particles increases as the distance between them decreases. Figure 3–1 shows the dependence of V on r for two ions of opposite charge. In accordance

---

* The reader lacking a knowledge of calculus will find a more extensive discussion of integration in the appendix.

with the arbitrary assumption made earlier, V is seen to approach zero at large values of r. As r decreases, V becomes more and more negative, according to Eq. (3–4), until the ions are close enough to "bump into each other," i.e., so close that their outer orbitals interfere. At this point a repulsive force appears, and the curve bends sharply upward for further decreases in r. In general, the two ions will tend to assume the equilibrium position of minimum potential energy, designated r_e. A particle in such a situation is often referred to as being in an "energy well," since the curve in Fig. 3–1 resembles the shape of a hole or well, from which the particle can be removed only by "lifting" it out with the expenditure of energy. The "depth" of the well, then, represents the bond energy.

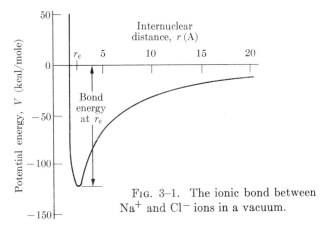

FIG. 3–1. The ionic bond between Na^+ and Cl^- ions in a vacuum.

As an example, let us calculate the ionic bond energy between Na^+ and Cl^- ions at the distance found in the NaCl crystal, or $r = 2.81$ A $= 2.81 \times 10^{-8}$ cm. The charge on each ion is equal in magnitude to the electronic unit charge, 4.80×10^{-10} esu, and D will be taken equal to 1, the value for a vacuum. Using Eq. (3–4), we have

$$V = \frac{(-4.80 \times 10^{-10})(4.80 \times 10^{-10})}{(1)\ (2.81 \times 10^{-8})}\ \text{erg} = -8.20 \times 10^{-12}\ \text{erg.}$$

This is the potential energy of one bond. A more useful unit of energy is kilocalories per mole, since chemical energy is most often measured as heat and one normally deals with large numbers of atoms which are conveniently measured in moles. Using the fact that 1 mole $= 6.02 \times 10^{23}$ individual molecules or atoms (Avogadro's number) and that 1 kilocalorie (kcal) $= 4.18 \times 10^{10}$ ergs, we have

$$V = -\frac{(8.20 \times 10^{-12})(6.02 \times 10^{23})}{(4.18 \times 10^{10})} = -118\ \text{kcal/mole.}$$

The bond energy, $-V$, is thus 118 kcal/mole. Direct measurement of the heat evolved in forming NaCl crystals from Na^+ and Cl^- ions gives 181 kcal/mole, and the difference between this value and 118 kcal/mole is probably due almost entirely to the fact that each ion in the crystal interacts with many other ions rather than only one.

It is of interest to note that in water, which has a dielectric constant of approximately 80, the bond energy is reduced 80-fold to $118/80 = 1.47$ kcal/mole. Anticipating the discussion in Chapter 4, we can see that the high value of D in water contributes to the great effectiveness of this substance as a solvent for ionic crystals, since the bond energies holding the crystals together are so greatly reduced in this medium.

3–3 The covalent bond. In a covalent bond, as was pointed out in Chapter 2, atoms achieve the stable noble gas configuration by sharing electrons to form "complete octets" in their outer shells. The bond energy in this case represents the decrease in potential energy of the electrons in going from incomplete octets in the separate neutral atoms to noble gas configurations. The H_2 molecule, in which the K-shells of both atoms are filled by the shared pair of electrons, has a bond energy of 104.2 kcal/mole, and other covalent bonds have comparable energies (C—C, 83.1 kcal/mole; O—H, 110.6 kcal/mole; C—H, 98.8 kcal/mole). These values are seen to be comparable to the energy calculated above for a typical ionic bond.

The covalent bond is the only bond with which true *molecules* are constructed. A bond between a given atom and another *particular* atom is formed by the sharing of an electron pair, in contrast to an ionic bond, which is a force exerted by an ion upon *any* oppositely charged ion in its vicinity. Thus a covalently bonded molecule, such as H_2O or CO_2, remains a single chemical entity unless it is altered by a chemical reaction, while the formula NaCl, for example, is only a representation of a stoichiometric ratio of Na^+ and Cl^- ions in a solution or a crystal. Separate NaCl "molecules" do not exist in either case. In the crystal, each Na^+ ion is bonded to six neighboring Cl^- ions, and each Cl^- to six neighboring Na^+ ions, so that the whole crystal is a single bonded unit. And in solution, Na^+ and Cl^- ions function independently, as shown by the fact that the solution conducts electricity by the motion of cations and anions in opposite directions. Even pure molten NaCl conducts electricity, showing that here, too, the ions are free to move independently.

The formation of a covalent bond between two atoms may be viewed as an overlapping of the orbitals of the two atoms to form a combined bond orbital for the shared electron pair. Roughly speaking, the direction in which a bond is formed is determined by the shape of the atomic or-

TABLE 3-1

BOND ANGLES IN COMPOUNDS OF C, O, AND N*

Compound	Angle	Value
Methanol, CH_3OH	H—C—H	109.3°
Methyl iodide, CH_3I	H—C—H	111.4°
Glycine, $H_2N—CH_2—COOH$	C—C—N	111.8°
Water, H_2O	H—O—H	104.45°
Dimethyl ether, $H_3C—O—CH_3$	C—O—C	111°
Ammonia, NH_3	H—N—H	107.3°
Trimethylamine, $(CH_3)_3N$	C—N—C	108°

* Data from Pauling, *The Nature of the Chemical Bond*, 3rd Ed., Chapter 4.

bitals involved, since the strongest bond (lowest potential energy) is formed when the orbitals overlap maximally. Actually, however, it is generally not possible to predict bond angles in a simple manner. The free carbon atom, for instance, has two 2s- and two 2p-electrons in its outer shell (Table 2-2), but when these electrons are shared to form single covalent bonds, the four bonds formed are all equivalent; the chemistry of carbon shows no distinction between "s-bonds" and "p-bonds." This is because each bond is formed not with a separate s- or p-orbital, but rather with a hybrid of s and p, since, in this way, the participating electrons attain a lower potential energy. The four single bonds on carbon are directed toward the corners of a regular tetrahedron, forming angles of approximately 109.5°, due to a corresponding orientation of the four s-p hybrid orbitals which form the bonds. Some representative bond angles are given in Table 3-1 and it can be seen that the actual angles between single bonds on a carbon atom may vary slightly depending on the nature of the four groups bonded to it. The angles between bonds on oxygen and nitrogen are also near the tetrahedral value, but in these cases the theoretical explanation of the observed angles is not definitely established at the present time.

The configurations of the bonding orbitals determine the distance between the bonded atoms as well as the angles between bonds. The length of a particular bond (single, double, or triple) between two given atoms is found to be remarkably uniform regardless of the molecule in which the two atoms occur. It is possible, therefore, to assign to each element a *covalent radius* such that the bond distance between any two atoms is approximately equal to the sum of their covalent radii. A few typical covalent radii are listed in Table 3-2.

TABLE 3–2

COVALENT RADII, IN ANGSTROMS, FOR VARIOUS ATOMS

	C	O	N	H
Single	0.77	0.66	0.70	0.30
Double	0.67	0.62	0.62	–

This convenient fact makes possible the construction of scale models of atoms which may be attached together to form quite accurate models of molecules. Figure 3–2 shows some examples of one commercially available type of atom models. The atoms are represented by spherical balls with flat faces where covalent bonds may be formed. The radius of the sphere represents, to scale, the so-called *van der Waals radius* of the atom, or the radius to which the electron orbitals of the atom extend with appreciable density. Roughly speaking, the van der Waals radius indicates the space which is "filled" by the atom, that is, the space into which other atoms cannot easily penetrate (except when forming covalent bonds). With the models, "covalent bonds" are formed between the "atoms" by means of small metal fasteners at the centers of the flat faces of the "atoms," and these couplings are so designed that the resulting "bond" between two "atoms" represents, to scale, the correct interatomic distance between their centers. Likewise, the angles between the faces are such as to form "bonds" at the correct angles. Of course, single,

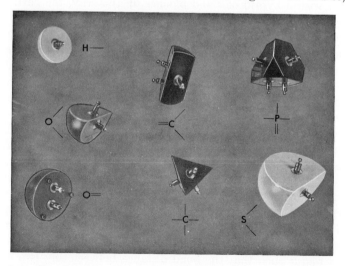

FIG. 3–2. Examples of scale models of atoms. The scale of these Courtauld models is 1 A = 0.8 inch.

double, and triple bonds differ in bond length and angle, so different model "atoms" are required to represent different bond configurations of a given element. Many photographs of "molecules" built of such models are shown in Chapters 5 and 8.

Measurements of bond angles and distances are obtained in a variety of ways. The oldest and most common is the x-ray diffraction study of crystals, which was mentioned in Chapter 1. By observing the angles and intensities of reflection of x-rays of a particular wavelength from a crystal, the spacings between identical layers of atoms in the crystal may be deduced, and if such determinations are made for many different directions in the crystal, the location of each atom may be computed. Spectroscopic methods using ultraviolet, infrared, or microwave radiation may also be used.

3–4 Partial ionic character of covalent bonds. In a covalent bond between unlike atoms, one of the two atoms may have a greater affinity for electrons, or *electronegativity*, than the other. This means that the bond orbital for the shared electrons is more dense near that atom; that is, the shared electrons have a greater probability of being near the more electronegative atom. The "center of gravity" of negative charge is, therefore, slightly displaced relative to that of positive charge. Such a bond is said to have *partial ionic character*, because an electrostatic attraction, like that between two ions, exists between the displaced centers of positive and negative charge. This electrostatic attraction increases the bond energy above that which would be predicted from the covalent bond energies of the same atoms with other partners. The effect of partial ionic character on bond energies is illustrated in Table 3–3 for four bonds which are especially common in biological compounds. As the bonds are

TABLE 3–3

PARTIAL IONIC CHARACTER OF COVALENT BONDS*

| Bond | Bond energy (kcal/mole) | | Approximate percent ionic character |
	Predicted for pure covalent bond	Observed	
C—O	52.5	84.0	22%
H—O	68.8	110.6	39%
C—N	56.5	69.7	6%
H—N	63.3	93.4	19%

* Data from Pauling, *The Nature of the Chemical Bond*, 3rd Ed., Chapter 3.

written in the table, the atom on the right is the more electronegative partner, i.e., the one which acquires a slight net negative charge. The approximate percentage of ionic character in each bond, given in the last column of Table 3–3, indicates the magnitude of this charge compared to the charge on one electron. Obviously, if an electron were completely transferred from one atom to the other, oppositely charged ions would result and the bond would have "100% ionic character." The partial ionic character of some covalent bonds has particular importance because the slight displacement of charge in such a bond creates an electric dipole. The role of such dipoles in intermolecular interactions will be dealt with in the following section.

3–5 Secondary interactions and dipoles. We have pointed out that ionic and covalent bonds, having energies of the order of 100 kcal/mole, are primarily responsible for the structure of molecules and ionic crystals and are referred to as *primary bonds*. In addition, however, there are a variety of *secondary interactions* which are extremely important for biological structure and function. As we shall see, these are generally much weaker than the primary bonds; but in macromolecules and other large organized structures, where many secondary forces may operate, their total effect often becomes decisively significant. Furthermore, the very weakness of these bonds gives them added importance from the point of view of function, since they can be broken and rearranged with relatively little expenditure of energy.

Actually, the distinction between primary and secondary interactions is at times rather arbitrary. Intermolecular bonds which are generally regarded as secondary interactions may in some instances be stronger than the covalent bonds within the molecules. This is true, for example, of amino acids (see Chapter 5), as shown by the fact that their crystals cannot be melted without concomitant chemical decomposition.

All the secondary forces depend to a large extent on the electrostatic interaction of dipoles with ionic charges or with each other; hence we shall now examine the properties of dipoles. An *electric dipole* is a pair of equal and opposite charges, $+q$ and $-q$, separated by a distance d, and the characteristic property of a dipole is its dipole moment μ, which is defined by

$$\mu = qd. \qquad (3–5)$$

The energy of interaction of a dipole and an ion can easily be calculated by adding up the values of V given by Eq. (3–4) for each charge in the dipole. This problem is portrayed in Fig. 3–3 for a positive charge q_1 located at a distance r from a dipole with $\mu = q_2 d$. Applying Eq. (3–4), the total potential energy is

$$V = \frac{(q_1)(-q_2)}{Dr} + \frac{(q_1)(q_2)}{D(r + d)}. \qquad (3–6)$$

FIG. 3-3. Ion-dipole
interaction.

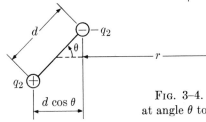

FIG. 3-4. Ion-dipole interaction with dipole
at angle θ to direction of ion.

Combining terms and substituting μ for $q_2 d$ (from Eq. 3-5), we have

$$V = -\frac{q_1 q_2}{D}\left(\frac{1}{r+d} - \frac{1}{r}\right) = \frac{q_1 q_2}{D}\left[\frac{r-(r+d)}{r(r+d)}\right]$$

$$= -\frac{q_1 q_2\, d}{Dr(r+d)} = -\frac{q_1 \mu}{Dr(r+d)}. \tag{3-7}$$

If d is much smaller than r, then $(r+d)$ is approximately equal to r,
so we obtain

$$V = -\frac{q_1 \mu}{Dr^2} \quad \text{for} \quad d \ll r. \tag{3-8}$$

Equation (3-8) applies only when the dipole is oriented with its axis
pointing toward the ion. If the dipole axis makes an angle θ with the line
between the dipole and the ion, as in Fig. 3-4, then Eq. (3-8) becomes

$$V = -\frac{q_1 \mu}{Dr^2} \cos\theta. \tag{3-9}$$

This equation may easily be derived by substituting $d \cos\theta$ for d in Eq.
(3-7). When $\theta = 90°$, the net bond energy becomes zero, as would be
expected, since the charges $+q_2$ and $-q_2$ are then at equal distances from
q_1. And if $\theta = 180°$, i.e., if the dipole is reversed, then V becomes positive,
indicating a repulsion rather than a bond.

The energy of interaction for two dipoles, μ_1 and μ_2, when their axes
are aligned, can, in a similar way, be shown to be

$$V = -\frac{2\mu_1 \mu_2}{Dr^3} \quad \text{for} \quad d \ll r. \tag{3-10}$$

Again, if the dipole axes are oriented at angles to the line between them,
the bond energy is decreased.

Of course, a charge, or another dipole, will exert a torque on a dipole
in its vicinity, tending to rotate the latter toward the orientation of

minimum potential energy. If it is free to rotate, as would ordinarily be the case for a molecule in a solution or a gas, it will assume the preferred orientation.

An essential point to note regarding Eqs. (3–8) and (3–10) is the dependence of bond energy on distance. While the magnitude of the ionic bond energy decreases with the first power of distance (Eq. 3–4), the ion-dipole and dipole-dipole interaction energies depend on the inverse square and cube of distance, respectively. This means that these interactions weaken more rapidly with increasing distance than does the ionic bond. In the subsequent discussion of other types of bonds, it is important to note how their bond energies vary with distance.

Permanent dipoles are extremely common in biological materials, lending great significance to the interactions just described. To list only a few examples, all amino acids and many lipids and proteins have dipole moments due to the distribution of charged (acidic and basic) groups in these molecules. Furthermore, any covalent bond with a large degree of partial ionic character (see Section 3–4) is a dipole. For instance, water, as we shall see in the next chapter, owes many of its unique properties to its dipolar nature, which depends on the partial ionic character of the O—H bond. Among the phenomena which arise from interactions of such dipoles with each other, and with ions, are the hydration of ions, the binding of ions to amino acids and proteins, and many features of the organization of protein and nucleic acid molecules and lipid and polysaccharide structures.

To illustrate the magnitude of such forces compared to primary bonds, consider a sodium ion and a water molecule at a distance of 5 A. The dipole moment of water is 1.84×10^{-18} esu. From Eq. (3–8), taking $D = 1$ as in a vacuum, we have

$$V = -\frac{(4.80 \times 10^{-10})(1.84 \times 10^{-18})}{(1)\ (5\times10^{-8})^2} = -3.53 \times 10^{-13}\ \text{erg.}$$

Converting units as in Section 3–2, we obtain

$$V = -\frac{(3.53 \times 10^{-13})(6.02 \times 10^{23})}{4.18 \times 10^{10}} = -5.08\ \text{kcal/mole.}$$

This calculation, of course, is only approximately valid, because Eq. (3–8) depends on the assumption that the distance r is much greater than the dimension of the dipole, d. Here the distance was 5 A, and d for the water dipole is of the order of 1 A.

3–6 The hydrogen bond. One particular dipole-dipole interaction, the hydrogen bond or H-bond, has unique properties that give it special significance, as will become evident in later chapters. We have seen in

Section 3–4 that the covalent bond between hydrogen and a strongly electronegative atom, such as oxygen or nitrogen, has a high degree of partial ionic character. Accordingly, such a bond forms a dipole, with the H-atom as its positive pole and the electronegative partner, which we shall designate by the general symbol X, as its negative pole. If this dipole approaches another bond having partial ionic character, such as another H—X bond or a C—X bond, with the proper orientation, a dipole-dipole bond will be formed (Fig. 3–5).

The H-atom, however, has the unique property of possessing only a K-shell, so when its single electron is largely removed, as in the H—X bonds above, only a bare proton remains. Since the proton is so much smaller than any other atom, the two atoms X_1 and X_2 can approach each other very closely, forming a bond with several unique and important features. First, the atoms X_1 and X_2 are so close to each other that the approach of a third electronegative atom is effectively precluded. Therefore, the H-bond can involve only two atoms (besides the hydrogen) and never three or more. Second, due presumably to the repulsion between the electronegative atoms X_1 and X_2, the H-bond is nearly always linear (see Fig. 3–5).

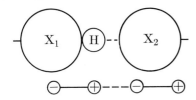

FIG. 3–5. The hydrogen bond as a dipole-dipole interaction.

Third, since the atoms are so close, the H-bond cannot be treated simply as an electrostatic interaction between dipoles. Although a completely satisfactory theory of the H-bond has not been developed, it is clear that a definite role is played by the quantum-mechanical properties of the electron orbitals of the X_1—H bond and the X_2-atom. In particular, the energy of an H-bond is considerably greater than a purely electrostatic theory would predict; most H-bonds have energies between 2 and 6 kcal/mole. Furthermore, H-bonds have definite interatomic distances and are formed at definite angles to the other bonds on the atoms X_1 and X_2. In water, for example, intermolecular H-bonds are formed on the oxygen at approximately tetrahedral angles to the covalent O—H bonds, at a distance from oxygen to oxygen of 2.76 A (see Fig. 4–4). This tetrahedral arrangement of the four bonds in water (two covalent bonds and two H-bonds) will be seen in the next chapter to be the key to an understanding of many properties of this substance. H-bonds also form the basis for current concepts of the structure of proteins and nucleic acids (see Chapters 6 to 8).

3–7 Induced dipoles. The electronic configuration of all atoms and molecules is, to a certain extent, deformable, and the ease with which the electrons can be displaced within an atom or molecule is represented by its *polarizability*, α. When an uncharged atom or molecule is brought near a positively charged ion, the electrons of the former are attracted and its nuclei are repelled, producing a slight relative displacement of positive and negative charges within it (Fig. 3–6). This creates an *induced dipole* which is then attracted to the inducing ion. A negative ion would, of course, induce a dipole of opposite orientation, again giving rise to an attractive force. The magnitude of the induced dipole moment depends, as shown in Eq. (3–11), upon the magnitude q and distance r of the inducing charge, as well as α:

$$\mu_{\text{ind}} = \frac{\alpha q}{Dr^2}. \qquad (3\text{–}11)$$

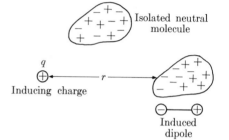

Isolated neutral molecule

q

Inducing charge

Induced dipole

From Eqs. (3–11) and (3–8), it may be seen that the potential energy of interaction of an ion with a polarizable particle, in which the ion induces a dipole, is given by

$$V = -\frac{\alpha q^2}{D^2 r^4}. \qquad (3\text{–}12)$$

Fig. 3–6. Induced dipole.

A permanent dipole also exerts a force on the electrons and nuclei of a polarizable substance, and hence it too can induce a dipole. The energy of interaction of a permanent dipole with an induced dipole is

$$V = -\frac{2\alpha\mu^2}{D^2 r^6}. \qquad (3\text{–}13)$$

It can easily be seen that the orientation of an induced dipole is always such that the maximum attractive force arises between it and the inducing charge or dipole, regardless of the sign or orientation of the latter.

As was true for Eqs. (3–8) and (3–10), these relations are quantitatively correct only when the distance r is much larger than the dimensions of the atoms or molecules themselves, a situation which rarely applies. This matter is discussed further in Section 3–9.

3–8 Transient dipoles and London dispersion interactions. Although the charges in an atom or molecule may, on the average, be symmetrically distributed, the electrons are in constant motion, and at any given instant, the charge distribution will generally not be symmetrical. Therefore, the atom or molecule will have a *transient dipole moment* due to the motion of the electrons. It was pointed out by F. London in 1930 that such a transient dipole will induce dipoles in neighboring matter, and although the transient dipole is constantly changing its strength and orientation, the dipoles which it induces are always so oriented as to be attracted to it. This phenomenon gives rise to *London dispersion forces*. Although such interactions taken singly are extremely weak, because of the tiny magnitude of the dipole moments involved, they are of such ubiquitous occurrence that their cumulative effect may assume great importance. This is particularly true of large molecules, for instance, certain lipids, in which other types of interaction do not occur. (See Chapter 11.)

It can be shown that the energy of the London interaction, like that between a permanent dipole and an induced dipole, is proportional to r^{-6} when the distance r between the particles is much larger than the size of the particles themselves. However, the exact energy expression for this interaction is of little value because some of the parameters involved are not well known.

3–9 Long-range and short-range interactions. The dependence of interaction energy on distance, summarized in Table 3–4, is a particularly important basis of comparison among different interatomic and intermolecular forces. An ionic bond, whose energy decreases in proportion to the first power of the distance, is regarded as a *long-range bond*. On the other hand, interactions near the bottom of the list in Table 3–4, which decrease in energy more rapidly as the distance increases, are considered to be *short-range interactions*. As a hypothetical example to illustrate this point, it may be seen that when the distance between two interacting molecules is doubled, an ionic bond between them has half its original bond energy. The transient dipole interactions, however, would be reduced to $1/2^6$ or $1/64$ of their initial energy.

Many biological interactions between molecules depend on a close "fit" between the surfaces of the molecules; examples are the "lock and key"

TABLE 3–4

DEPENDENCE OF BOND ENERGY ON DISTANCE r
FOR PARTICLES WHICH ARE SMALL RELATIVE TO r

Bond	Energy proportional to
Ion—ion	r^{-1}
Ion—dipole	r^{-2}
Dipole—dipole	r^{-3}
Ion—induced dipole	r^{-4}
Dipole—induced dipole	r^{-6}
Transient dipole—induced dipole	r^{-6}

concepts of enzyme-substrate and antigen-antibody interactions, which may be familiar to the reader. This is a direct result of the short-range nature of many of the forces involved, since any nonconformity between the surface configurations of two molecules may decisively weaken the interaction between them.

As a qualification of these comments, it should be mentioned that when the distance between particles is *not* much larger than the dimensions of the particles, the quantitative relations we have given above for inter-action energies are not strictly applicable. This may occur either because the molecules, or portions of molecules, are very close together or because the particles in question are very large compared to atomic dimensions. In such cases, as a rule, the dependence of interaction energy on r is less steep. For instance, when two dipoles are very close together, their inter-action must be considered in terms of the ionic interactions among the individual charges of which they are composed, which depend, of course, on the inverse first power of distance. In the case of London dispersion forces between particles which are large compared to the distance be-tween them, one must add up the interaction of *each* atom in one particle with *every* atom in the other particle. When this is done, the total energy is found to depend roughly on $1/r$ or $1/r^2$ rather than $1/r^6$. For this reason, the dispersion forces between large particles like cells or membranes may, under certain conditions, be significant even at distances as great as several hundred angstrom units.

For very small distances, further uncertainty arises in regard to the choice of a dielectric constant. For instance, when there can only be a few water molecules between two interacting solute particles, it is quite doubtful that the bulk dielectric constant of water, which is approximately 80, is applicable in calculating the energy of interaction between the par-ticles. And when no solvent molecules at all can "fit" between the particles in question, it may be that a dielectric constant of unity, for empty space, is the correct choice, regardless of the actual solvent.

REFERENCES

1. L. PAULING, *Nature of the Chemical Bond*, 3rd Ed. Cornell University Press, Ithaca, N. Y., 1960.

2. R. B. SETLOW, and E. C. POLLARD, *Molecular Biophysics*, Chapter 6. Addison-Wesley, Reading, Mass., 1962.

3. G. C. PIMENTEL, and A. L. McCLELLAN, *The Hydrogen Bond*. Freeman, San Francisco, 1960.

4. G. S. HARTLEY, and C. ROBINSON, "Atomic Models, Part I, A New Type of Space-Filling Atomic Models," *Trans. Far. Soc.* **48**, 847–853 (1952).

5. J. TH. G. OVERBEEK, "Attractive Forces Between Colloidal Particles," *Colloid Science*, Part I, Chapter VI. Edited by H. R. Kruyt. Elsevier, New York, 1952.

CHAPTER 4

WATER

CHAPTER 4

WATER

4–1 Introduction. None of the processes associated with the living state can occur in the absence of water. The earliest forms of life appeared in an aqueous environment, and the evolution of modern land organisms depended in large part on the development of devices to maintain this status internally so that life processes could continue. The fact that life has evolved on this planet, where water is so abundant in all its states of aggregation (liquid, solid, and vapor), and the fact that living organisms have continued to be so dependent on this substance suggest that it must possess unique properties which are essential for life.

From the point of view of the physical chemist, water is indeed an exceptional substance. We shall here explore some of its properties, emphasizing those with the greatest biological significance. Then we shall discuss the explanation of these properties which can be suggested on the basis of the structure and interactions of water molecules. It should be remembered that our understanding of this seemingly simple substance is far from complete; in fact, water is currently the subject of active investigation in many laboratories throughout the world.

4–2 Properties of water. Among the first properties that a chemist determines for any substance are its *melting point* and *boiling point*, and these values for water are familiar as reference points on our temperature scale. Closely related to these characteristics is the molal *heat of vaporization*, which is the heat required to vaporize one mole of a substance. Let us compare these values for water with those for certain other substances. In Fig. 4–1 the values for water are plotted together with those of other compounds of similar chemical structure (dihydrides), proceeding down column VI of the periodic table. It is evident that there is a trend for the melting and boiling points and the heat of vaporization to decrease with decreasing molecular weight. However, water deviates markedly from this pattern in all three properties. Similar plots would show that the properties of NH_3 deviate from those of the hydrides of other elements in group V and that the same is true of HF among the group VII hydrides (hydrogen halides). Alternatively, we may compare substances having the same total number of electrons per molecule, or an "isoelectronic series," which takes us across a row in the periodic table. Figure

44

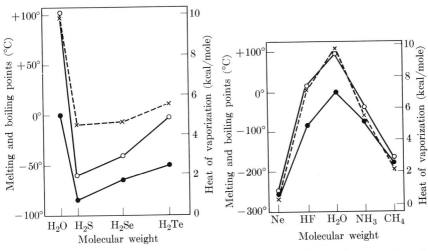

FIG. 4–1. Physical properties of water and other dihydrides. (● = melting point; ○ = boiling point; ✕ = molal heat of vaporization.)

FIG. 4–2. Physical properties of compounds in isoelectronic series with water. (● = melting point; ○ = boiling point; ✕ = molal heat of vaporization.)

4–2 shows that in the series, Ne, HF, H_2O, NH_3, and CH_4, water has the highest values for all three thermal properties. Extrapolating back in Fig. 4–1 from H_2Te, H_2Se, and H_2S, we might expect water to have a melting point near −100° instead of 0°, a boiling point of about −80° rather than +100°, and a molal heat of vaporization near 4 kcal/mole rather than the observed 9.75 kcal/mole. If heats of vaporization are compared on a weight basis, the superiority of water is even more striking (Table 4–1), since its molecular weight is relatively low. Another important thermal property included in Table 4–1 is the *specific heat capacity*, or the number of calories of heat required to raise the temperature of one gram of a substance by one degree celsius.* In this property, too, water is unusual.

Life processes cannot proceed normally unless a relatively constant temperature is maintained, either in the environment or internally, and in this regard the thermal properties of water are of fundamental importance. The metabolic processes of life continually generate heat, but by virtue of the fact that actively metabolizing tissues are at least 75% water with its high heat capacity, the consequent temperature increase is minimized. From Table 4–1, it can be seen that, were the body composed primarily of an organic liquid like alcohol instead of water, the temperature rise caused by a given amount of heat would be almost doubled.

---

* Also called degree "centigrade."

TABLE 4–1

PHYSICAL PROPERTIES OF VARIOUS LIQUIDS*

Substance	Heat of vaporization, cal/gm	Specific heat capacity, cal/gm-deg	Surface tension, erg/cm^2	Dielectric constant, esu	Viscosity, millipoises
Water, 0°C.	595.9	1.009	75.64	88	17.921
Water, 10°	584.9	0.999	72.75	80	10.050
Water, 100°	539.6	1.006	58.85	48	2.838
Ammonia†	296.5 (17°)	1.125	18 (34.1°)	15.5 (20.5°)	2.66 (−33.5°)
Methyl alcohol	262.8 (64.7°)	0.600	22.6	33.1	5.93
Ethyl alcohol	204.3 (78.3°)	0.581 (25°)	22.3	—	11.943
Ethylene glycol	191.1 (197°)	0.571 (14.9°)	47.7	41.2	173.3 (25°)
Formic acid	119.9 (101°)	0.511 (15.5°)	37.6	58.5 (16°)	17.844
Acetic acid	96.8 (118.3°)	0.468 (0°)	27.8	7.1 (17°)	12.22
Acetaldehyde	136.2 (21°)	—	21.2	22.2 (10°)	2.307
Acetone	131.9	0.528	23.7	21.4	3.311
Pyridine	107.4 (114.1°)	0.431 (21°–108°)	38.0	12.5	8.775 (25°)
Benzene	103.6 (25°)	0.406	29.0	2.3	6.47
Ethyl ether	83.9 (34.6°)	0.547 (30°)	17.0	4.3	2.448
Chloroform	60.9 (40°)	0.234	27.1	5.05	5.63

* Values for a temperature of 20°C unless otherwise specified. Data from Lange, *Handbook of Chemistry*, 8th Ed., 1952.

† Ammonia, of course, is a liquid at ordinary temperatures only under pressures greater than one atmosphere.

A similar argument can be made for the environment of water-dwelling organisms, which protects them from the extreme fluctuations in temperature which might otherwise occur with night and day and with the seasons.

Furthermore, because of its high heat of vaporization, the evaporation of a very small weight of water can dissipate a considerable amount of heat. Vaporization of one gram of water relieves the organism of more than 500 calories of heat; or, viewed in another way, to reduce the body temperature by one degree, the body needs to evaporate less than two grams of water per kilogram of total weight. Again, the common organic liquids are at best only half as effective. Actually, the evaporation of water is the most important physiological mechanism of heat dissipation for the human body.

Two other properties included in Table 4–1 are the surface tension and the dielectric constant. *Surface tension* arises from the fact that molecules in the interior of a liquid are bonded to neighboring molecules on all sides by secondary intermolecular bonds, while those in the surface must be unattached on one side. Consequently, the transfer of a molecule from the interior to the surface of a liquid involves the rupture of some intermolecular bonds, which requires energy. Increasing the surface area means increasing the number of molecules in the surface, and the amount of energy consumed per unit increase in area, expressed in $ergs/cm^2$, is called the surface tension. Surface tension is closely related to heat of vaporization in that an increase in surface area requires the breakdown of a portion of the same bonds which must be broken to vaporize the substance.

The high surface tension of water is vital to the formation of films of lipid and protein which comprise the cellular membranes. (See Chapters 12 and 13.) And, in view of the ultimate dependence of animals upon green plants for food, we must recognize the role of surface tension in transporting water and dissolved nutrients through the soil and through the tissues of plants.

The *dielectric constant* was defined in Chapter 3. There it was pointed out that the unusually high dielectric constant of water makes this liquid a very effective solvent for ionic substances, since the strength of ionic bonds is so greatly reduced that ionic crystals become unstable. Most biochemical reactions take place in water solution, and clearly, the solubility in this medium of a wide variety of substances, both organic and inorganic, is of great biological importance.

One further property of water which deserves mention is its unusual quality of increasing in volume (decreasing in density) on freezing. As water is cooled, a maximum in density is reached at about 4°C, after which its volume expands, ice being only about nine-tenths as dense as water. This is the reason why it is possible to go ice-skating on a deep lake in winter and swim in it in summer, and it is also a reason why our oceans and lakes provided a suitable environment for the early evolution of life. If water behaved like most ordinary substances, ice would be more dense than the liquid and would sink, so that bodies of water would freeze from the bottom up. It has been speculated that this would lead to the accumulation of a considerable bulk of ice, which would be partially melted at the surface in summer, only to freeze solid again with the return of winter.

4–3 The water molecule and its intermolecular bonds. The many physical and physical-chemical properties of water that set it apart from analogous compounds can be understood in terms of its molecular structure and intermolecular configuration. The two covalent O—H bonds form an angle of 104° in water, and the O—H bond has nearly 40% partial ionic character (see Section 3–4), giving the hydrogen atoms a slight positive charge and the oxygen a slight negative charge. As shown in Fig. 4–3, this makes the molecule a dipole. Furthermore, intermolecular H-bonds can be formed between neighboring molecules.

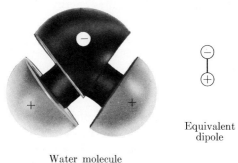

Equivalent
dipole

Water molecule

FIG. 4–3. The water molecule as a dipole.

Melting and evaporation involve the rupture of intermolecular bonds, and substances in which these bonds are unusually strong have exceptionally high melting and boiling points and heats of vaporization. It was noted in the previous section that this is the case for HF, H_2O, and NH_3, all of which are capable of forming intermolecular H-bonds. Of these substances, water has the highest values (Fig. 4–2), because only in the water molecule are the numbers of H-atoms and "acceptor" sites (unshared electron-pairs on the oxygen) both equal to two, so that an average of two H-bonds per molecule can be formed. This, in turn, permits the existence of a three-dimensional network rather than merely the linear and branched chains which are possible in HF and NH_3. Intermolecular H-bonding also contributes to the high surface tension which, like the heat of vaporization, is related to the energy of intermolecular bonds. At high temperature, the thermal kinetic energy of the molecules ruptures some of the H-bonds, and this is the explanation for the high heat capacity of water. That is, to raise the temperature of water, energy is consumed not only in increasing the kinetic energy of the molecules but also in breaking H-bonds.

The high dielectric constant of water results in part from the fact that the molecule is a dipole. The orientation of dipoles between charged particles reduces the force between them, and this effect is represented, in terms of Coulomb's law (Eq. 3-1), by a high dielectric constant. However, not only is the water molecule itself a dipole, but also H-bonded groups of molecules form even larger dipoles, giving water a dielectric constant considerably higher than can be accounted for simply on the basis of the dipole moment of the single molecule.

The energy of the H-bonds in water has been estimated from the energy required to vaporize ice (heat of sublimation), i.e., the energy needed to remove molecules from the maximally H-bonded structure. This is 12.2 kcal/mole of water. Values for similar but non-H-bonded substances, such as methane, indicate that about 2 kcal/mole can be attributed to London dispersion forces, leaving about 10 kcal/mole due to H-bonding. Since there are two bonds per molecule, the bond energy is about 5 kcal per mole of bonds. Other methods of estimating bond energy yield similar values.

A liquid in which the molecules are strongly bonded to each other might be expected to have a high viscosity,* since it ought to be difficult to distort such a structure. However, referring to the last column of Table 4-1, it is evident that water does not have an unusually high viscosity. There are at least two possible explanations for this apparent anomaly. It may be that although many intermolecular H-bonds exist at any instant, they are continually being broken and re-formed at a high rate. Hence, the distortion of the liquid requires only that the bonds be re-formed in a new arrangement. An alternative possibility is that the water molecules in the liquid form small, discrete "clumps" rather than a continuous structure. Further consideration of the structure of liquid water is given in the following section.

4-4 The structure of ice and liquid water. The angles and distances at which H-bonds are formed on an electronegative atom are determined by the configuration of its outer electron orbitals, as will be recalled from Section 3-6. In the case of water, the two covalent bonds and two H-bonds arrange themselves roughly tetrahedrally (Fig. 4-4), and in agreement with

---

* Viscosity is discussed more fully in Chapter 19.

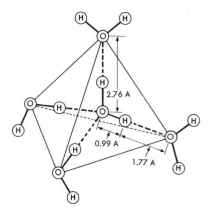

FIG. 4-4.   Tetrahedral arrangement of water molecules
in ice.

this picture, the structure illustrated in Fig. 4–5 has been derived for ice
from x-ray crystallographic data. An important feature of this tetrahedral
ice structure is that it is quite open, having a calculated density of about
0.9 gm/cm³.   This is quite evident from the photograph in Fig. 4–5,
because the atom models used there represent, to scale, the full extent
of the space occupied by each atom.   Therefore, the presence of empty

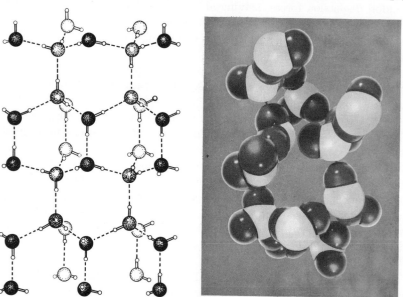

FIG. 4–5. The arrangement of molecules in the ice crystal. The orientation of
the water molecules in the drawing is arbitrary; there is one proton along each
oxygen-oxygen axis, closer to one or the other of the two oxygen atoms. (The
drawing is reproduced, with permission, from Pauling, *Nature of the Chemical
Bond*, 3rd ed.)

space in the model assembly indicates that the molecules are not packed so closely as they could be if there were no intermolecular bonds. When ice melts, the breakdown of this structure would lead to an increase in density, but it is opposed by the increased thermal motion of the molecules with increasing temperature, which tends to decrease the density. Below 4°C, the first effect predominates, while at higher temperatures, the latter effect becomes dominant. This provides a possible explanation for the anomalous expansion of water which occurs as it is cooled below 4° and is frozen.

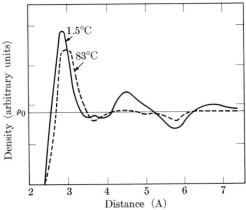

Fig. 4–6. Density distribution of water molecules around any given molecule in liquid water at 1.5° and 83°C. Curves show the relative density of neighboring water molecules as a function of distance from the center of any given molecule, as determined by x-ray scattering measurements. (ρ_0 = average bulk density of water.) Peaks at 2.9 A and 4.5 A indicate that these intermolecular distances predominate in the structure of liquid water. [Data from J. Morgan and B. E. Warren, *J. Chem. Phys.* **6**, 666 (1938).]

It was mentioned earlier that the total energy of the H-bonds in ice is about 10 kcal/mole of water. Since the heat of fusion is only 1.44 kcal/mole, it appears that less than 15% (1.44/10) of the H-bonds in ice are broken on melting. Thus, cold water is still approximately 85% H-bonded. Whether liquid water has the same tetrahedral structure as ice is not definitely established, but x-ray scattering experiments have yielded supporting evidence. In the tetrahedral structure of ice (Fig. 4–4), the distance between each water molecule and its nearest neighbor (measured between centers of oxygen atoms) is 2.76 A, and the next nearest neighbors are 4.51 A away from any given water molecule. If the same intermolecular spacings predominate in liquid water, then x-ray scattering experiments should reveal their presence. The curves in Fig. 4–6, calculated from x-ray scattering data, show the distribution of

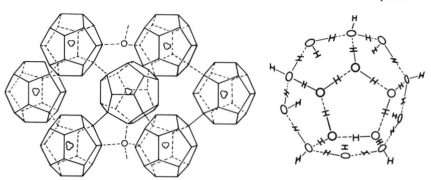

FIG. 4–7. The proposed "clathrate" structure of water. At each corner of the pentagonal dodecahedra is a water molecule, and each edge is an intermolecular hydrogen bond. The dodecahedra are hydrogen bonded to each other through additional water molecules between them, and the center of each dodecahedron is occupied by a single, unbonded, water or solute molecule. [Reprinted by permission from L. Pauling, *Science* **134**, 16 (1961).]

spacings between positions of maximum electron density (oxygen atoms) in liquid water at various temperatures. If the water had no regular structure, then all intermolecular distances should be equally likely beyond a distance of closest approach determined by the size of the molecules. Hence, in this case, the curves would be flat. The actual curves, however, show a pronounced peak at about 2.9 A and another at 4.5 Å, indicating that these distances predominate in the liquid. This suggests the presence of H-bonded regions (perhaps in a tetrahedral configuration), which persist even at a temperature as high as 83°.

The tetrahedral arrangement of ice may not be the only possibility for the structure of liquid water. It is known that small inert molecules form hydrates in which twenty water molecules are arranged in an H-bonded "cage" around each foreign molecule; these structures, called "clathrates," are illustrated in Fig. 4–7. Linus Pauling has recently proposed that such a structure might exist in pure water as well, with the inside of the clathrate cage occupied by a free water molecule. According to this theory, the increase in density which accompanies the melting of ice does not result from partial breakdown to non-structured random packing. Rather, it is suggested that the tetrahedral ice is completely rearranged into the clathrate structure, which would have a calculated density near 1.0 gm/cm³, the correct value for cold water.

Although the existence of a clathrate-type structure in pure water is still a matter of speculation, the formation of such arrays of water molecules around certain solute molecules is a well established fact and may have important implications for biology. For instance, Pauling has suggested that the anesthetic activity of noble gases and other biochemically inert substances, which has long baffled physiologists, might be due to their effect on the structure of water in the vicinity of certain crucial nerve endings in the brain. Also, the formation of clathrate hydrates around some chemical groupings on the surface of proteins has been invoked by Klotz recently to explain some puzzling properties of these molecules.

4–5 Dissociation of water. We have regarded the hydrogen atom in the O—H $\cdots$ O bond as being covalently bonded to one particular oxygen atom. Occasionally, however, the hydrogen nucleus (proton) "jumps" across and becomes covalently bonded to the other oxygen atom (Fig. 4–8). The result of this event is the formation of H_3O^+ and OH^- ions, i.e., the *dissociation of water*. Subsequently, the proton may reunite with a hydroxyl (OH^-) ion to re-form water, so we write the reaction in Fig. 4–8 as a reversible one. Under constant conditions, as is familiar from elementary chemistry, such a reversible chemical reaction reaches a dynamic equilibrium in which the rates of the forward and reverse reactions are the same. The concentrations of H_3O^+ and OH^- are then constant.

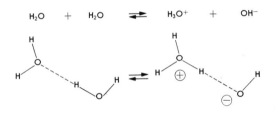

FIG. 4–8. Dissociation of water.

From the electrical conductivity of pure water, which is a measure of the number of free ions present, it is known that at 25°C the concentrations of H_3O^+ and OH^- ions are both 10^{-7} molar (M). The concentration of H_3O^+ ion (or, if the attached water molecule is neglected, H^+ ions) is most often expressed logarithmically as pH, which is defined approximately by

$$\text{pH} = -\log c_{H^+} = \log \frac{1}{c_{H^+}}, \qquad (4\text{–}1)$$

where c_{H^+} is the molar concentration of hydrogen (or H_3O^+) ions.* In

---

* For a precise definition of pH, the concentration in Eq. (4–1) should be replaced by an "effective concentration," or *activity*, as is discussed in Chapter 17.

pure water at 2.5°C the pH is therefore 7.0, and this value is referred to as a neutral pH.* From these facts, it can easily be calculated that the transfer of a proton from one water molecule to another is actually a rare event (although when it does occur, it is one of the fastest chemical reactions known; see Ref. 4). At a given instant, only about one out of every 10^9 protons will have made this transition.

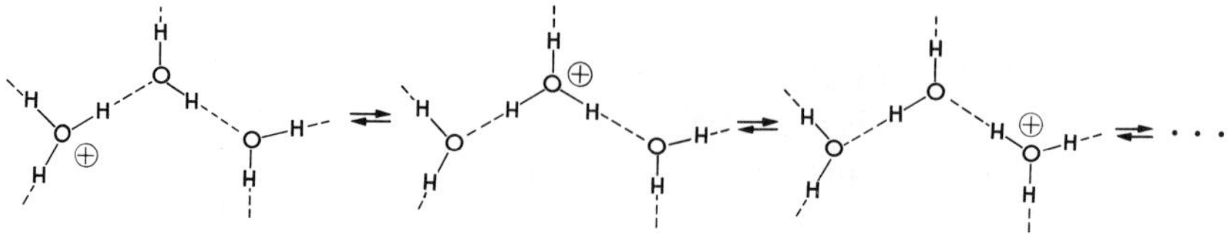

FIG. 4–9. Conduction of protons through water.

When a hydronium (H_3O^+) ion has been formed by the reaction of Fig. 4–8, it may lose its extra proton by reversal of this same reaction, i.e., recombination with a hydroxyl ion to form two water molecules. Or, on the other hand, the H_3O^+ ion may transfer one of its protons to another water molecule, as in Fig. 4–9. Such transfers, occurring repeatedly along a hydrogen-bonded chain of water molecules, have the effect of carrying a proton through the water without the actual motion of individual hydronium ions or water molecules. That such a "bucket brigade" process occurs is indicated by the observation that the passage of protons through water appears to be extremely rapid, much more rapid than that of other ions. Table 4–2 shows some actual values for the mobilities of lithium ions and protons in water and in ice. The precise meaning of the numbers given is not important in this context; it will suffice to say that the mobility is the velocity with which the ion moves when driven by an electrical potential gradient of 1 volt/cm. (A more detailed treatment of mobilities appears in Chapter 19.) It is evident from this table that in liquid water, protons can move some nine times faster than lithium ions, which are the smallest ions other than protons. The importance of the H-bonded structure for the transfer of protons is particularly emphasized by the measurements in ice, in which the H-bonded structure extends much further without interruption and is much more stable than in liquid water. As would be expected, lithium ions are practically immobile in ice; however, the mobility of protons in ice is actually almost a hundred-fold *higher* than that in water!

---

* Direct measurement of the pH of "pure" water hardly ever gives a value of 7.0, because traces of CO_2 from the air or NaOH from the glass are generally present.

TABLE 4–2

APPARENT MOBILITIES OF PROTONS AND LITHIUM IONS
IN ICE AND WATER*

	Water	Ice
H^+	0.0036	0.3
Li^+	0.0004	$<10^{-8}$

* Mobilities are given in $cm^2 \cdot volt^{-1} \cdot sec^{-1}$, or velocity $(cm \cdot sec^{-1})$ per unit potential gradient $(volt \cdot cm^{-1})$.

The rapid mobility of protons in water may have significant consequences for biology, since many important biochemical reactions in the living cell involve the transfer of protons from one organic compound to another. And in view of the suggestion, mentioned in the previous section, that water in the immediate vicinity of proteins and other biological structures may be organized in more stable H-bonded hydrate structures, the extraordinarily high mobility of protons in ice may also have great biological importance.

4–6 Acids and bases. Although a detailed consideration of the properties of acids and bases will be postponed to Chapter 17, it is appropriate at this point to introduce briefly some aspects of the subject in preparation for the discussion of amino acids and proteins in the succeeding chapters. As we stated earlier, in pure water at 25° the concentration of H_3O^+ is 10^{-7} M. However, the presence of certain solutes may alter this concentration. Some substances are *acids*, or "proton donors," which means that they tend to liberate free protons in water. These protons, of course, are immediately bound to water molecules to form H_3O^+ ions; the over-all reaction is

$$HA + H_2O \rightleftharpoons A^- + H_3O^+, \qquad (4–2)$$

where HA is the acid. Other solutes combine with protons, as in Eq. (4–3), and these are *bases:*

$$B + H_3O^+ \rightleftharpoons H_2O + HB^+. \qquad (4–3)$$

These reactions are reversible, and it should be noted that the reverse of reaction (4–2) is quite similar to reaction (4–3), and vice versa. Hence, A^- is referred to as the conjugate base of HA, and similarly, HB^+ is the conjugate acid of the base B. To give concrete examples, a typical acid is acetic acid, CH_3—COOH, and its conjugate base is the acetate ion, CH_3—COO^-. Ammonia, NH_3, is a base, and ammonium ion, NH_4^+, is its conjugate acid. In the following discussion, we shall treat only the case of the acid HA, and the reader should keep in mind that identical considerations apply to the acid HB^+.

It will be familiar to most readers that reversible reactions, such as (4–2) and (4–3), tend to reach an equilibrium state in which the reaction proceeds forward and backward at equal rates, the concentrations of the reactants and products remaining constant in time. For reasons which will be better understood when the elements of physical chemistry have been presented (Chapters 14 to 16), such chemical equilibria are character- ized by a constant relationship among the concentrations of products and reactants. For the dissociation of the acid HA (Eq. 4–2), this relation is

$$K = \frac{c_{A^-} \cdot c_{H_3O^+}}{c_{HA}}, \qquad (4\text{–}4)$$

where c represents the molar concentrations of the various chemical species involved in the reaction, and K is called the *acid dissociation constant*. The value of K is a characteristic property of any particular acid, and it is essentially independent of the composition of the solution, although it usually varies with the temperature.

Since $c_{H_3O^+}$ is generally expressed logarithmically as pH (Eq. 4–1), we shall convert Eq. (4–4) into logarithmic form:

$$\log K = \log c_{H_3O^+} + \log \frac{c_{A^-}}{c_{HA}}. \qquad (4\text{–}5)$$

Rearranging, and utilizing the definition of pH (Eq. 4–1), we obtain

$$pH + \log K = \log \frac{c_{A^-}}{c_{HA}}. \qquad (4\text{–}6)$$

It is common practice to express the dissociation constants of acids as pK values, which are defined, by analogy with pH, as follows:

$$pK \equiv -\log K. \qquad (4\text{–}7)$$

Using this notation, Eq. (4–6) becomes

$$pH - pK = \log \frac{c_{A^-}}{c_{HA}}. \qquad (4\text{–}8)$$

Equation (4–8) is a form of the Henderson-Hasselbalch equation, which will be treated at length in Chapter 17. It is expressed here in this form to emphasize the effect of pH on the degree of dissociation of the acid. If the pH is equal to the pK of a given acid, then according to Eq. (4–8), $\log (c_{A^-}/c_{HA}) = 0$, and $c_{A^-}/c_{HA} = 1$. In other words, *the pK is that pH at which the acid is half dissociated*, i.e., the concentrations of the dissociated and undissociated forms are equal.

Let us consider the example of acetic acid,

$$CH_3COOH + H_2O \rightleftharpoons CH_3COO^- + H_3O^+, \qquad (4\text{-}9)$$

which has a pK of about 4.7. At a pH lower (more acidic) than 4.7, Eq. (4–8) tells us that log $(c_{CH_3COO^-}/c_{CH_3COOH})$ is negative, so the concentration of CH_3COOH is greater than that of CH_3COO^-. If the pH is increased, for instance by the addition of sodium hydroxide, then $c_{CH_3COO^-}$ increases and c_{CH_3COOH} decreases until, at pH = 4.7, the two concentrations are equal. When the pH exceeds 4.7, log $(c_{CH_3COO^-}/c_{CH_3COOH})$ becomes positive, i.e., $c_{CH_3COO^-}$ is greater than c_{CH_3COOH}. For the ammonium ion,

$$NH_4^+ + H_2O \rightleftharpoons NH_3 + H_3O^+, \qquad (4\text{-}10)$$

similar changes occur as the pH is varied around its pK of 9.2. At a pH below 9.2, $c_{NH_4^+} > c_{NH_3}$; when pH = 9.2, the concentration of NH_4^+ and NH_3 are equal, and at more alkaline pH values (pH > 9.2), $c_{NH_3} > c_{NH_4^+}$.

An important feature of these relationships is the effect of pH on the *charge* of the groups in question. In both the examples discussed, it can be seen that increasing the pH has the effect of converting the groups to less positively or more negatively charged forms ($CH_3COOH \rightarrow CH_3COO^-$, and $NH_4^+ \rightarrow NH_3$). Of course, there is never a net charge in the solution. If the pH is raised by adding NaOH, the increasing negativity of the acetate and ammonia groups is always just counterbalanced by the added Na^+ ions. Conversely, if the pH is lowered by the addition of HCl, the increasing positive charge of the acetic acid and ammonium ions is just balanced by the added Cl^- ions.

The importance of the changes in the charge of groups like acetic acid and ammonia will become evident in Chapter 5, where it will be seen that similar groups occur as parts of the amino acid structures of which proteins are composed. Hence, changes in pH influence the net charge on protein molecules, and this has important consequences for the properties of these molecules, although the charges on the protein are always balanced by "counter-ions" in the solution, such as the Na^+ and Cl^- ions mentioned above.

REFERENCES

1. L. J. HENDERSON, *The Fitness of the Environment*, Chapter 4. Beacon, Boston, 1958.

2. L. PAULING, *The Nature of the Chemical Bond*, 3rd Ed., Chapter 12. Cornell University Press, Ithaca, N. Y., 1960.

3. J. T. EDSALL and J. WYMAN, *Biophysical Chemistry*, Vol. I, Chapter 2. Academic Press, New York, 1958.

4. M. EIGEN and L. DeMAEYER, "Hydrogen Bond Structure, Proton Hydration, and Proton Transfer in Aqueous Solution," *The Structure of Electrolytic Solutions*, Chapter 5. John Wiley, New York, 1959.

5. L. PAULING, "A Molecular Theory of General Anesthesia," *Science* **134**, 15–21 (1961).

6. I. M. KLOTZ, "Water," *Horizons in Biochemistry*. Academic Press, New York, 1962.

7. L. PAULING, "The Structure of Water," *Hydrogen Bonding*. Pergamon Press, New York, 1957.

8. J. MORGAN and B. E. WARREN, "X-Ray Analysis of the Structure of Water," *J. Chem. Phys.* **6**, 666 (1938).

CHAPTER 5

AMINO ACIDS AND PEPTIDES

CHAPTER 5

AMINO ACIDS AND PEPTIDES

5-1 Introduction. Throughout all the cells and fluids of living organisms we find molecules of very diverse types. It is of special interest to note that among these are many which are of exceedingly high molecular weight. These giant molecules, or *macromolecules*, are found to have a very extensive range of structural patterns as well as an extremely diversified set of functional reactions and inter-reactions with each other. On closer inspection it can be seen that these macromolecules are primarily to be considered as members of three distinct groups. These are the *proteins*, the *nucleic acids*, and the *polysaccharides*. It is of further usefulness to observe that each molecule of this type is actually composed of a definite pattern of arrangement of atoms. These molecules, in other words, are not found to have a complex and completely irregular arrangement of atoms. Instead, they can always be seen to involve a sequence of small units that have been attached by primary chemical bonds to each other to form a continuing structure which is the large molecule. These macromolecules can therefore be considered as *high polymers* in the same way that synthetic high polymers are constructed to give us the ordinary plastics of commerce and in-industry. A polymer is formed by the condensation of a large number of one of several *monomers*, or low-molecular-weight units. One can distinguish between *homopolymers*, in which a single kind of monomer unit occurs, and *heteropolymers*, in which several monomer types are found. In all three families of macromolecules, this condensation is formed in such a way that the elements of water are split out from the original monomer units, and therefore the resultant bond is sometimes known as an *anhydro bond*. An anhydro bond is a common denominator for all the macromolecules and indicates once more the very great significance of the water molecule in biological systems.

It will be necessary to devote several chapters to these extensive families of biological polymers. In the present chapter we will begin our consideration of these groups by studying the monomer units of the proteins and some of the simpler and smaller polymers that occur as natural substances.

5-2 The proteins. The defining characteristics of proteins are that they are of high molecular weight and that they are composed of α-amino acids. When a protein is hydrolyzed, that is, split by the addition of the elements

60

of water (a process which is the reverse of the formation of the anhydro bond), the products that result are either entirely or predominantly α-amino acids.

There are three additional important attributes of proteins. For one thing they constitute an indispensable basis of living matter. It is true that carbohydrates and lipids are also involved, and that minerals and vitamins and other types of molecules are necessary in the proper function of living systems. However, for growth and reproduction and the controlled liberation of energy in the activity of cells and tissues, proteins are of primary importance. Secondly, they have a characteristic property of specificity. This means that different species of plants and animals contain characteristic proteins which can be distinguished from each other. This should be contrasted with urea or glucose, which are molecules that are identical in different types of plant or animal. Thirdly, proteins have a property of denaturation. This means that they are very labile molecules and that the exact architecture of the molecules can be easily altered, leading to changes in the properties of the protein. Such changes may or may not be reversible to the original state.

The functions which different types of proteins fulfill in the body economy are quite numerous and diversified. Some examples can be discussed at this point. One of the major functions of certain groups of proteins is to provide the structural and supporting elements of the body. This includes the major components of hair, wool, silk, and horn. These substances assist in providing the necessary rigidity and strength whereby the animal can be lifted to various distances above the surface that would otherwise be crawled upon. Another important function of protein is contractility. The contraction of muscle is the function of certain protein systems. The contractility properties of flagella and of cilia also involve protein substances. A third function is that of enzymatic activity. An enzyme is an organic chemical which is a catalyst. All enzymes are proteins, and there are an enormous number of examples. A simple division of this group can be made by distinguishing between intercellular and intracellular enzymes. The former group are instrumental in the chemical breakdown of foods in the gastro-intestinal tract; the enzymes promote the digestion process. The latter group largely regulates the metabolic and biosynthetic processes inside all cells; these enzymes are responsible for the necessary production of energy. Later chapters will describe in detail the influence of enzymes on reaction rates and the mechanism of their behavior. A fourth important group of proteins are certain hormones of the body, and especially those of the pancreas, thyroid, and pituitary glands. An additional necessity of organized animal bodies is that of oxygen transport. In simple one-celled animals and plants, the transport of oxygen is mediated by diffusion from the surface of the cell to all the interior parts of the unit. But in more complex multicellular animals, since the volume of the body increases more rapidly than its surface area, processes of diffusion would be totally inadequate, and the necessity for a specific means of transporting oxygen is quite apparent. Such transporting systems exist in various molecular forms, but all of these are specialized proteins which are intricately developed for this particular purpose. One example of such a protein is hemoglobin, which is the red, iron-containing protein within the red blood cells. Many other types of functional behavior could be discussed. It is to be expected that these properties will be more rationally understood only when we have a complete understanding of the detailed structure of each protein molecule. This is still far from achievement in almost all cases.

5–3 The amino acids. As indicated above, a group of approximately 24 different α-amino acids are involved in the construction of all proteins found in nature. All proteins are made from these amino acids and apparently no others. Of this group, three or four are only infrequently observed. In neutral aqueous solution, the structure of an amino acid is predominantly that of a dipolar salt or zwitterion. The amino acid molecule is, in other words, a double salt containing both a negative and a positive charge which can be diagrammed as shown in Fig. 5–1, where the "R" represents various differing side chains (or "R" groups) that constitute the only distinction between the various α-amino acids.

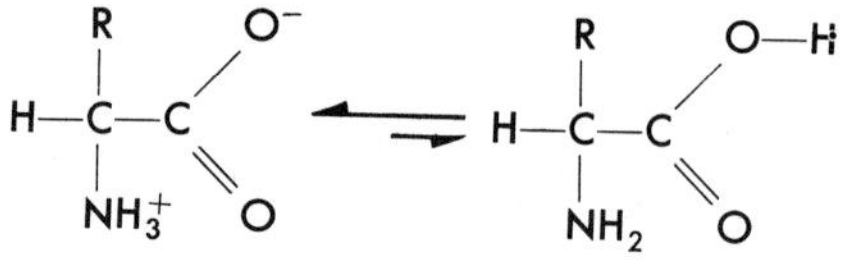

(a)   (b)

FIG. 5–1. Generalized formula for the α-amino acids.

An amino acid, such as the one shown in Figure 5–1, is a dipole of very high electric moment. The dipole moment is approximately eight times as great as that of the water molecule. This form (Figure 5–1a) is the predominant one, although small amounts of the uncharged form, shown as (Figure 5–1b), do exist. Actually, these forms are in equilibrium with each other, but the double salt form is far more plentiful. There are many kinds of evidence for this conclusion. One type of evidence is the fact that the crystal of an amino acid has a very high melting point, of the order of 300°C., and, in fact, the molecules decompose at the same time that the crystal melts. This indicates that the intermolecular forces are very strong indeed, and that they are about the same strength as the intramolecular covalent forces holding each molecule together. This can only be explained in terms of intermolecular forces involving electrostatic forces of attraction between charged carboxyl and charged amino groups, and the fact that this electrostatic attraction, superimposed on hydrogen bonding between the amino acid units, constitutes a force that is much stronger than the bonds between similar organic molecules. Additional evidence for the dipolar form of the molecule can be obtained from infrared spectra and Raman spectra. Certain wavelengths of light are absorbed or scattered, and each of these characteristic wavelengths, or frequencies, is related to a particular covalent link in the molecule. Ionized and un-ionized forms of the carboxyl group and of the amino group will behave differently with regard to whether certain frequencies are shown. In this way, one can prove that only the ionized forms are significant for amino acids in the neutral pH region.

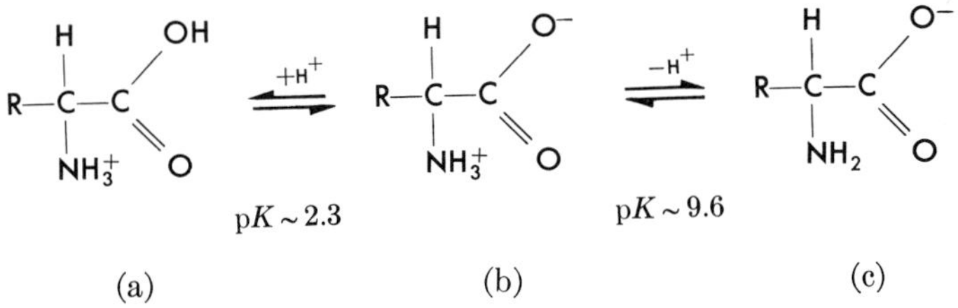

Fig. 5–2. Acid-base equilibria of amino acids.

In the region of neutral pH, an amino acid is in the forms illustrated in Fig. 5–1. It should also be understood, ignoring for the moment the R groups, that this molecule contains both an acid and a base group, and that therefore two sets of acid-base ionizations can occur. At very low pH, both groups are in the form of acid groups, that is, proton-dissociating groups. The carboxyl or —COOH group can reversibly dissociate a proton to become a carboxylate ion, —COO$^-$. The COOH group is therefore an acid, and the COO$^-$ is its conjugate base. In a similar and reciprocal fashion, the amine group or —NH$_2$ group is a base and the —NH$_3^+$ group is its conjugate acid. These relations were discussed in Chapter 4, and the nature of acid-base phenomena in general is discussed in much greater detail in Chapter 17. We can expect that the state of an amino acid and its net electric charge will change (exclusive of any properties within the R group) in accordance with the pH of the solution in which it is dissolved. The set of equilibria would be as shown in Fig. 5–2. At very low pH, i.e., below the pK for the —COOH, an amino acid is predominantly a cation. At very high pH, i.e., above the pK for the —NH$_3^+$, an amino acid is predominantly an anion.

Figure 5–3 lists the formulas for all the amino acids. The portion of the molecule which is common to them all, namely the α-carbon and its at-

Name	Symbol	R-group	Model
Glycine	Gly	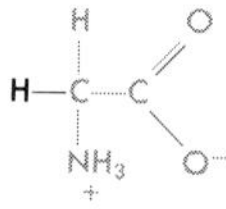	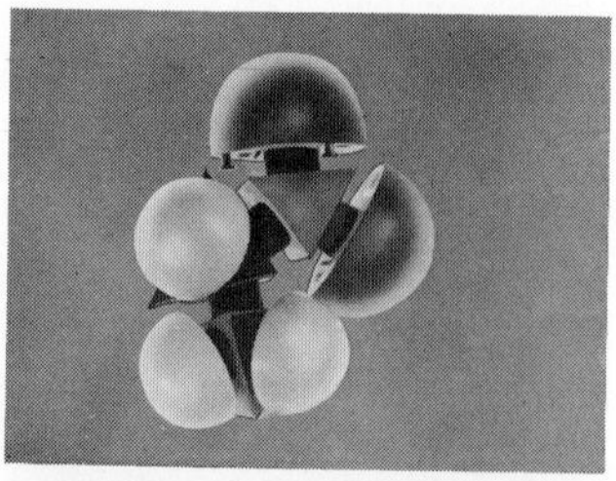
Alanine	Ala	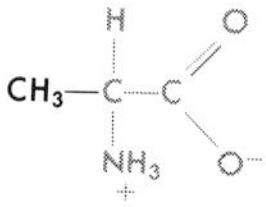	
Valine	Val	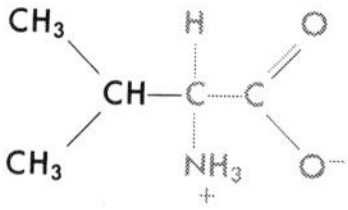	
Leucine	Leu	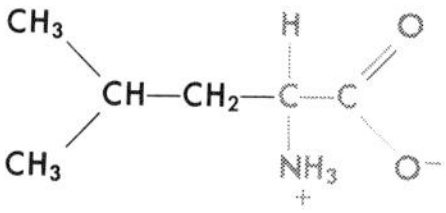	
Isoleucine	Ileu	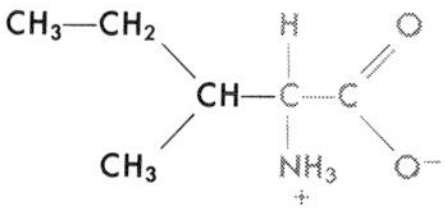	

Fig. 5–3. Amino acid formulas. The side chains (R-groups) are shown in darker print. The photographs show Courtauld space-filling atomic models that have faces cut according to the number of bonds for each atom and their angular spacings. The scale is 0.8 inch per angstrom unit, or approximately 2×10^8 to 1.

Name	Symbol	R-group	Model

Serine — Ser

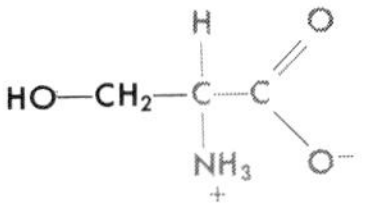

$$HO-CH_2-C(H)(NH_3^+)-C(=O)-O^-$$

Threonine — Thr

$$HO-CH(CH_3)-C(H)(NH_3^+)-C(=O)-O^-$$

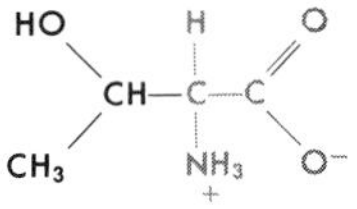

Phenylalanine — Phe

$$C_6H_5-CH_2-C(H)(NH_3^+)-C(=O)-O^-$$

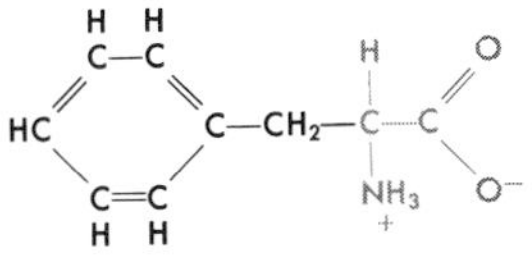

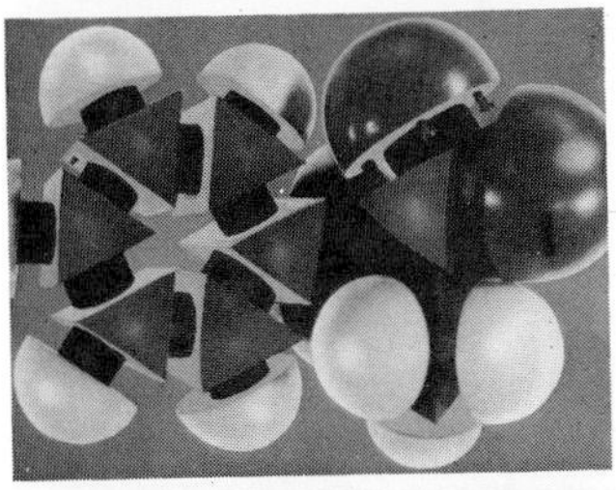

Tyrosine — Tyr

$$HO-C_6H_4-CH_2-C(H)(NH_3^+)-C(=O)-O^-$$

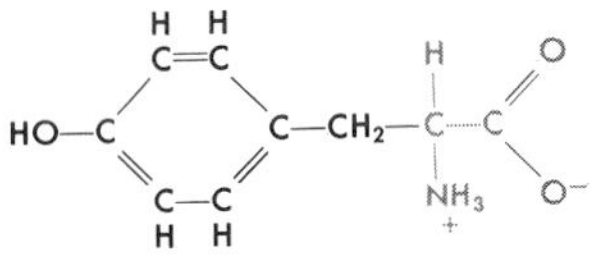

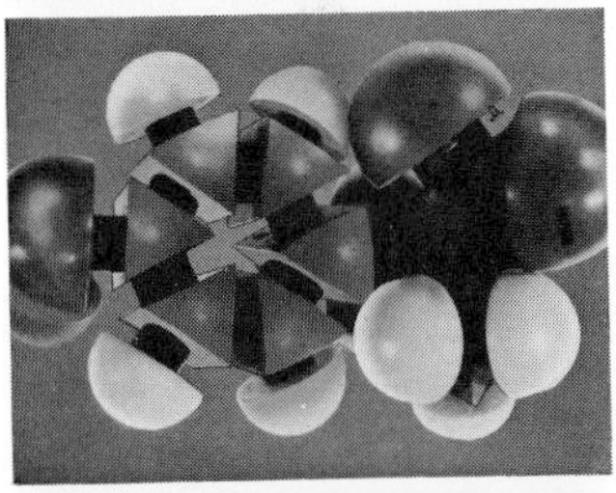

Tryptophan — Try

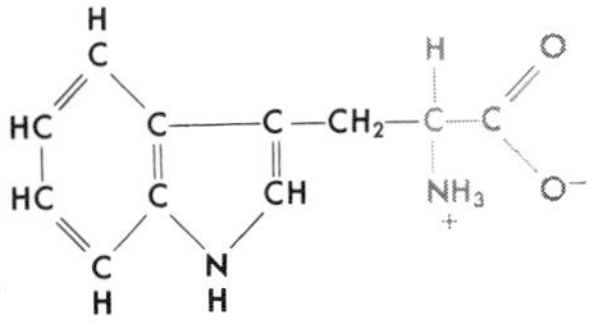

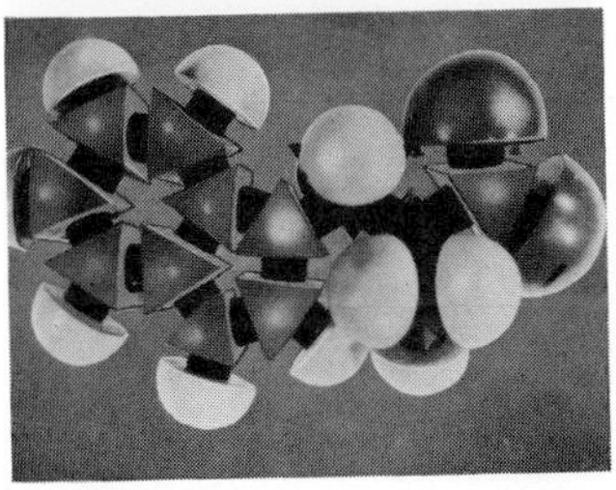

FIGURE 5–3 (Cont.)

Name	Symbol	R-group	Model

Cystine $(CyS)_2$

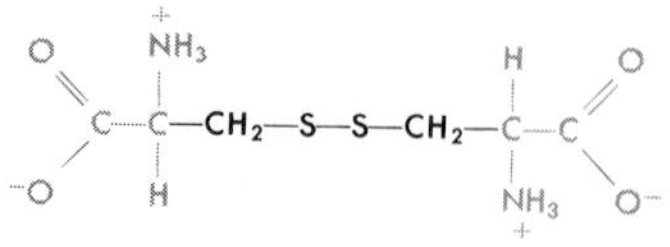

Cysteine   CySH

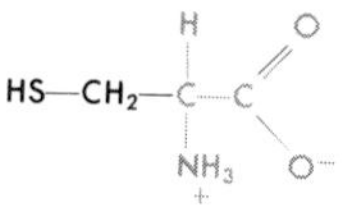

Methionine   Met

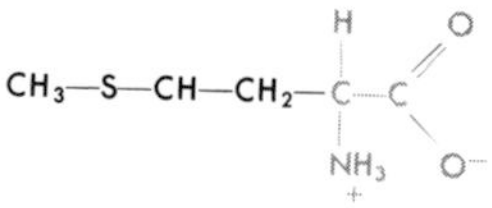

Proline   Pro

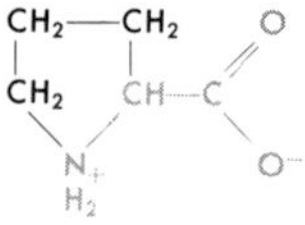

Hydroxyproline   Hypro

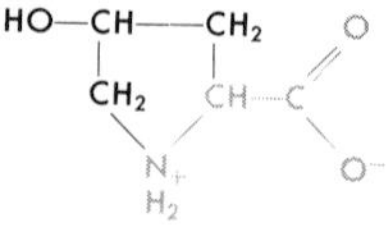

FIGURE 5–3 (Cont.)

Name	Symbol	R-group	Model
Aspartic Acid	Asp	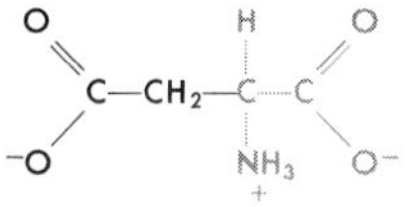	
Glutamic Acid	Glu	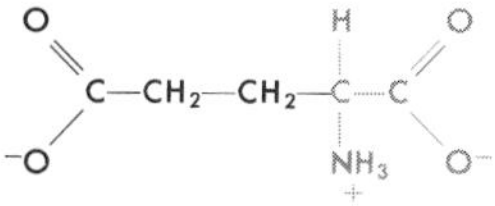	
Asparagine	Asp-NH$_2$	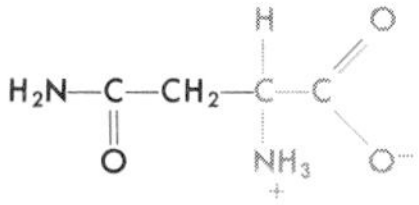	
Glutamine	Glu-NH$_2$	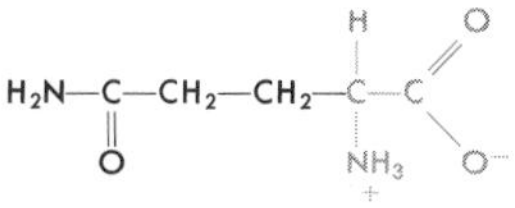	
Histidine	His	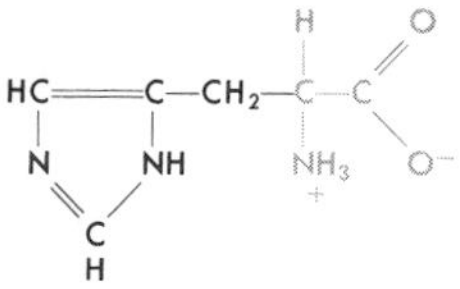	

FIGURE 5–3 (Cont.)

Name	Symbol	R-group	Model
Arginine	Arg	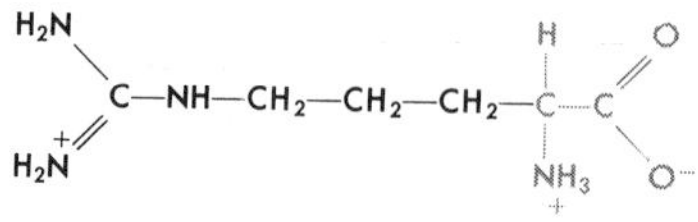	
Lysine	Lys	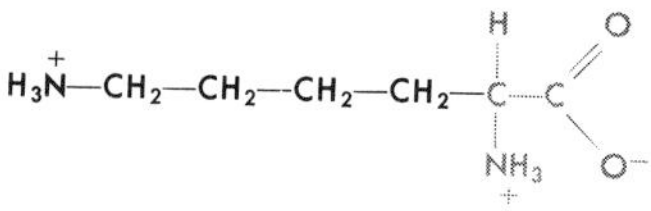	
Hydroxylysine	Hylys	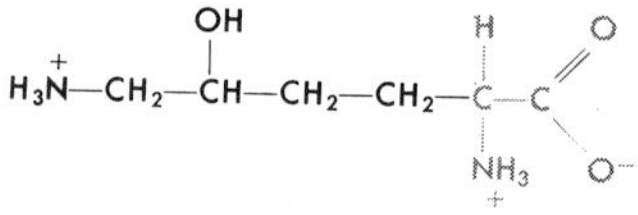	
Diiodotyrosine		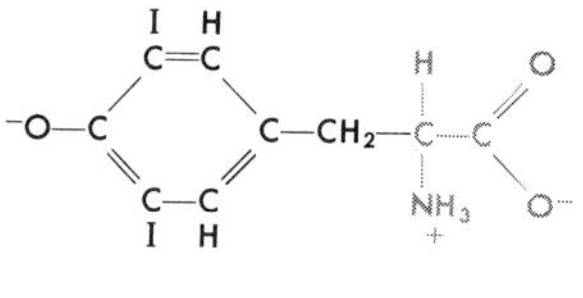	
Thyroxine		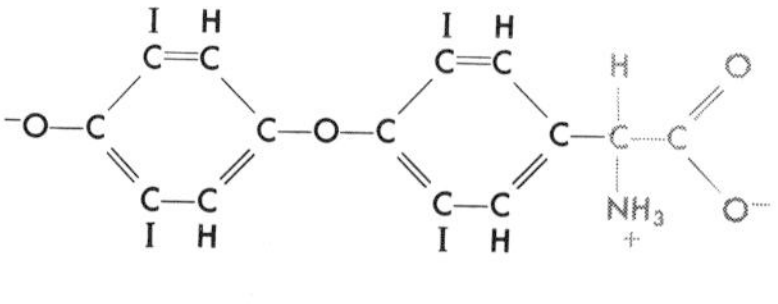	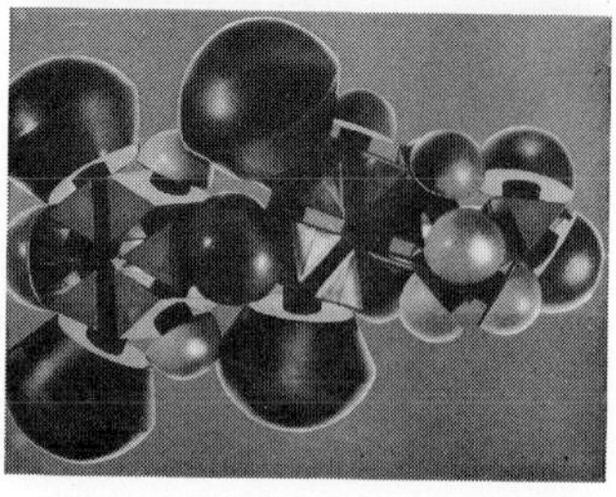

FIGURE 5–3 (*Cont.*)

tached amino and carboxyl groups, are set in lighter print. For each amino acid there is a standard abbreviation, generally three letters. A column of photographs is also shown which illustrates the actual three-dimensional structure of each amino acid as assembled from Courtauld Atomic Models. It should be noted first of all that, except for glycine, every amino acid contains four different substituents attached to the α-carbon atom. This means that this is an asymmetric carbon atom, and it will cause the substance to show optical activity. When a beam of polarized light passes through a solution of an optically active substance, the plane of light is rotated through a certain angle. This may be either to the right (+) or to the left (−). A more extensive discussion of optical activity can be found in Chapter 11. Each substance that is optically active occurs in two forms, called *optical isomers*, which are essentially identical, except that they have, under the same experimental conditions, equal and opposite influence on the plane of the light. All the amino acids (except glycine) have been put into two sets of pairs, the D-series and the L-series. The designation of the series does not necessarily indicate the direction of light rotation. In fact, some members of, say, the L-series may turn the plane of light to the left, and other members to the right. The very same substance may well show this variation under different conditions of solution. The designation, L- *or* D-, is fixed, however, since this is a token of the structural arrangement in the molecule. All the compounds of a series have the four groups, H, R, COO^-, and NH_3^+, arranged in one way around the α-carbon atom, and the amino acids of the other series have these four substituents arranged in the other way. For guidance in the construction of molecular models, it can be stated precisely that in an amino acid of the L-series (if one looks down on the α-carbon tetrahedron), arranged so that the hydrogen atom is at the top of the pyramid, one will see, in clockwise order around the base of the pyramid, the groups, R-group, amino, and carboxyl. For the D-compound, one need only interchange any two of the four substituents. The two arrangements are such as to give a mirror image of each other, but they are not superimposable on each other. The designations of L and D were derived from structural comparisons with L-glyceraldehyde and D-glyceraldehyde. These were designated L and D according to their levo and dextro rotations, and the amino acids and the sugars have all been put into L and D families by means of structural comparisons with them. This is described further in Chapter 11.

All amino acids found in proteins belong to the L-series. The D-amino acids are found in certain lower molecular weight configurations, especially in some antibiotics, but not in proteins. Moreover, it should be noted that the side chains of proteins may also include an additional acidic group or an additional basic group. These are, of course, polar groupings. They serve, however, to provide additional positive or negative charges, varying according to the pH of the solution. There may also be polar groupings which are not acidic or basic; that is, they are not ionized. Finally there may be side chains which are nonpolar or hydrophobic in character. The amino acids therefore provide a variety of functional groupings as well as a variety of shapes and sizes in the protein when they are condensed to form this large structure.

A number of individual comments should be made about certain amino acids. There are two amino acids which contain alcoholic groups. These are serine (with a primary hydroxyl group) and threonine (with a secondary hydroxyl group). Possibilities of ester formation and ether formation should be kept in mind. Esterification with phosphoric acid is especially important, and the serylphosphate group is found to occur in certain proteins called phosphoproteins. Similar esterification is of great importance in the reaction of some proteins with organic phosphates, such as diisopropylfluorophosphate. This reagent inactivates many enzymes, and this effect is the result of such an interaction with a serine residue in the protein molecule. There are three structures that contain aromatic rings. These are phenylalanine, tyrosine, and tryptophan. These three amino acids absorb ultraviolet light in the wavelength region of approximately 275 to 280 mμ(2750 to 2800 A), and they are therefore responsible for the general property that proteins show of absorbing light of this wavelength. There are three amino acids that contain sulfur. Methionine contains a fairly inactive form of sulfur which is covalently linked to two carbon atoms. Cysteine, however, contains a sulfhydryl group and is therefore a very active unit. It is easily oxidized and so constitutes a reducing agent. It can also react and combine with a number of metals. It can be oxidized to form cystine, which contains the corresponding disulfide linkage, and which can in turn be reduced to provide cysteine again. Cystine can serve the important function of providing branched chains on a protein structure.

There are two amino acids which are secondary amines rather than primary amines; in other words, they are *imines*. The nitrogen is present in a pyrrolidine ring. These amino acids are proline and hydroxyproline. They are also unlike other amino acids in being quite soluble in alcohol. The fact that one less hydrogen atom is attached to the nitrogen atom than is true in the other amino acids is of considerable importance when the various amino acids are combined in a protein structure, as discussed in Chapter 7. It means that the customary possibility of H-bond formation is *not* available for the prolines, and this gives them a special place in the principles of protein structure. The hydroxy derivative occurs only in a few proteins. The acidic amino acids are aspartic acid and glutamic acid. Each of these is capable of providing additional negative charges on the protein molecule. They may, however, occur alternatively in the form of the amides, which are named, respectively, asparagine and glutamine. In this form they cannot provide a negative charge, no matter what the pH of the solution. The basic amino acids are histidine, lysine, and arginine. These can provide additional positive charges for the molecule, but they have considerably different pK levels. Each of them is characterized by a specific type of group, which is either imidazole (with a $pK \sim 6$), an additional primary amine group (with a $pK \sim 10$), or a guanidine group (with a $pK \sim 12$). One generally speaks of the guanidine group as being "strongly basic," although, for the purpose of discussing ionization and titration properties, one should rather think of it, in its cationic form, as an acid, able to liberate a proton, over a certain range of pH. Hydroxylysine may also be included in this list, but it has only been found in collagen and gelatin, and in no other proteins. Diiodotyrosine and thyroxine have been found only in a very few proteins. They are very important, however, in the constituents and hormones of the thyroid gland.

These various patterns of structure can be better appreciated by assembly and inspection of the three-dimensional models. When these pairs of atoms are linked, the proportional van der Waals radius for each atom and the proportional covalent bond distance between their centers are properly scaled.

5–4 Structure of peptides. The fundamental linkage in the structure of proteins is the peptide bond, or peptide link. This can be thought of as a condensation between the carboxyl group of one amino acid and the amino group of another, splitting out the elements of water. For example, alanine and tyrosine can be condensed to give alanyltyrosine, abbreviated Ala.Tyr. The information can be written schematically as in Fig. 5–4. When this reaction is reversed, as occurs under certain conditions, we have an example of a hydrolysis reaction. The peptide bond is split by reaction with water, and the amino acid molecules are liberated. Alanyltyrosine is a dipeptide, meaning that there are two amino acids linked together by one peptide link (shown in the dashed outline in Fig. 5–4). It should be clearly noted that tyrosylalanine (Tyr.Ala) is a completely different compound,

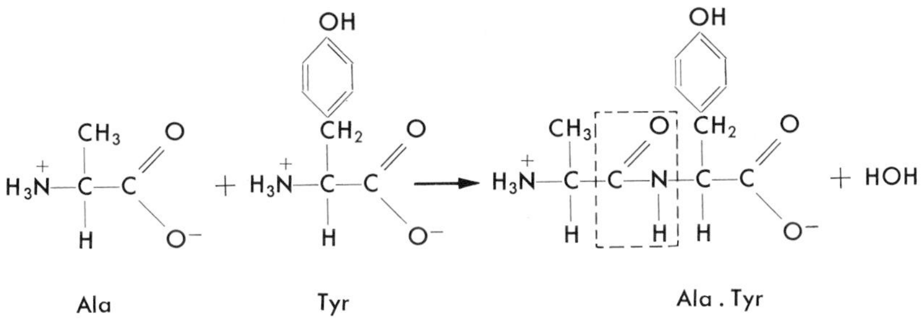

FIG. 5–4. Formation of a dipeptide (schematic equation).

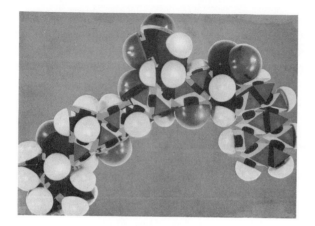

$$
\begin{array}{c}
\text{CH}_3 \quad \text{CH}_3 \\
\text{CH} \\
\text{H}_3\overset{+}{\text{N}}-\text{CH}-\underset{\underset{\text{O}}{\|}}{\text{C}}-\text{N}-\cdots
\end{array}
$$

Valyl————alanyl————glycyl————glutamyl————tryptophan
Val .   Ala .   Gly .   Glu .   Try

Fig. 5–5. A hypothetical pentapeptide. The peptide chain, shown in three-dimensional atomic models, is illustrated in two of its many possible configurations.

although made from the same monomer units. The process of condensation can be considered to proceed further with additional units, and we might consider the hypothetical pentapeptide, Val.Ala.Gly.Glu.Try, shown in Fig. 5–5. This peptide contains the same sequence of amino acids as is found in the end segment of the chain occurring in the protein myoglobin, which will be discussed in more detail below. In Fig. 5–5, five amino acids are linked together to form four peptide bonds. It is seen that the chain of this peptide contains one free amino group and one free carboxyl group. The amino acid providing the free amino group (valine) is called the N-terminal amino acid, and the amino acid providing the free carboxyl group (tryptophan) is called the C-terminal amino acid. The other units (and even the terminal ones) are usually termed *residues*, since several atoms (equivalent to HOH) have been removed from each amino acid. It is purely arbitrary, but an accepted convention is to write such formulas so that the N-terminal amino acid is on the left. The figure also shows this structure as it would appear in three dimensions and as it is constructed with the aid of atomic models, so that the relative bulk and shape of each substituent, as well as the randomly twisted and kinked nature of the chain, can be visualized. The chain can take many different positions; two of them are illustrated. A polypeptide then would be a molecule containing a large number (n) of amino acid units linked together, if the structure is unbranched, by $(n - 1)$ peptide bonds. The number n is well above 100 for all but the very smallest proteins, and it may well number in the thousands or tens of thousands.

A polypeptide of only moderate length may be referred to as a very small protein or as an oligopeptide (this latter term is seldom used), but most frequently these structures are called peptides to distinguish them from proteins. These compounds are in the molecular weight class in the general range from several hundred up to several thousand. Two such compounds of particular interest are oxytocin and vasopressin, which are hormones secreted by the posterior pituitary gland. Oxytocin has the property of causing contraction of smooth muscle and, in particular, of accelerating the uterine contractions leading to childbirth. Vasopressin has the properties of elevating the blood pressure in mammals and of causing antidiuretic effects, that is, decreased urine volume. Each of these hormones has now been completely analyzed and even synthesized to produce active materials. Each of them is an octapeptide containing a cyclic structure. The compositions of the two are quite similar and can be illustrated by Table 5–1, which gives the list of the constituent amino acids. The molecular weights for these compounds are 1025 and 1102. Six of the residues are common to both hormones, but leucine and isoleucine in oxytocin are replaced by arginine and phenylalanine in vasopressin. This detailed information was obtained first for the bovine hormones. The actual structures and sequences

TABLE 5-1

AMINO-ACID CONSTITUENTS OF THE HORMONE PEPTIDES
OF THE BOVINE POSTERIOR PITUITARY

Amino acid	Residues per molecule	
	Oxytocin	Vasopressin
Tyrosine	1	1
Proline	1	1
Glutamic acid	1	1
Aspartic acid	1	1
Glycine	1	1
Cystine	1	1
Leucine	1	0
Isoleucine	1	0
Phenylalanine	0	1
Arginine	0	1
Total	8	8
Ammonia	3	3
Molecular weight (calc.)	1025	1102

for these two compounds are shown in abbreviated form in Fig. 5–6. This disulfide ring structure is of additional interest because a disulfide ring of the same size occurs in the protein insulin, to be discussed further in the next chapter. An interesting comparison of species differences can also be made. Hog oxytocin was found to be identical to the bovine substance, but hog vasopressin was shown to have a single point of difference. The arginine of beef vasopressin is replaced by lysine in the hog molecule. These are now called arginine-vasopressin and lysine-vasopressin. Many

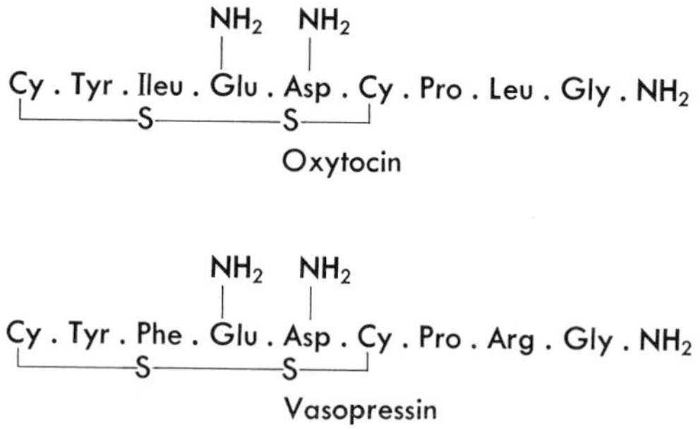

FIG. 5–6. Structural formulas for bovine oxytocin and vasopressin.

studies can be planned concerning the influence on the biological activity of making any substitution or addition to the amino acid constellation in each of these three peptides. A number of studies of this sort have already been reported.

5-5 Conjugated proteins as examples of macromolecular hybrids. The various proteins that have been already considered are simple proteins, which on hydrolysis provide nothing but α-amino acids and ammonia. There also exists a realm of conjugated proteins, which on hydrolysis provide, in addition to α-amino acids, some other group—the conjugated group. Such groups may be quite small or of moderately large size or may even be macromolecules of size comparable to the protein itself, and it then becomes quite arbitrary as to the proper way of naming these compounds.

One type of conjugated protein has been called phosphoprotein. In this type of molecule there is one, or more, phosphate radical attached to the protein. The amino acid that is usually involved is serine, and it is esterified to the phosphate group. Examples are pepsin of the stomach and ovalbumin of egg white. Another type of conjugated protein is lipoprotein. In such molecules various types of lipid units (Chapter 12) are thought to be attached by van der Waals bonds to the hydrocarbon residue of the polypeptide chain. The lipid and peptide portions can also be linked by electrostatic forces and, in some lipoproteins, by covalent links. They vary considerably, from proteins containing only a low percentage of lipid to those containing an amount at least equal to the weight of the polypeptide. Many of them are readily soluble in water, indicating that the lipid is mostly inside the structure, while polypeptide forms most of the outer surface. The reverse can also occur, giving lipoproteins that are only soluble in certain organic solvents. These are more properly termed proteolipids. One of the better-studied lipoproteins is the β_1-lipoprotein of blood plasma. This protein contains approximately 70% of the lipid found in plasma. It is in fact so remarkably rich in lipid content that only 25% of its weight is due to amino acids—the rest is lipid. Another is the α-lipoprotein of plasma; this one is 35% lipid and 65% polypeptide.

There can also be proteins containing carbohydrate units, and these are termed glycoproteins (if the amount of carbohydrate is fairly small, namely, less than 4%) or mucoproteins or mucoids (if the amount of carbohydrate is large, namely, more than 4%). Some of these molecular complexes contain such a high proportion of polysaccharide (Chapter 11) that it is no longer advantageous to refer to them as conjugated proteins, but rather they may be considered as polysaccharides containing variable quantities of polypeptide units. Some typical glycoproteins are serum gamma globulin, a major protein of blood serum, and fibrinogen, the precursor of blood clot formation. Mucoproteins include the seromucoid fraction of serum. While this was originally thought to be a single substance, it was later shown to be a mixture of carbohydrate-containing proteins. The major members are albumin, orosomucoid, 3.5 S α_1-glycoprotein, and haptoglobin. Of these, orosomucoid has been the most thoroughly studied for its carbohydrate content. It contains 41% carbohydrate, made up of hexose, hexosamine, fucose, and sialic acid.

There are also chromoproteins, which include the hemoglobins and other respiratory pigments, that is, transporting agents for oxygen, as well as a variety of other proteins, all having visible color. And there is a large group of metalloproteins which contain one or more atoms of various metals tightly bound to the protein. A protein has been isolated from plasma, which binds iron, apparently for the purpose of transporting it in the blood stream. It has been named *transferrin* or *siderophilin*. It binds two atoms of iron per molecule. A copper-binding protein of plasma has also been isolated. This is called *ceruloplasmin*, and binds eight Cu-atoms per molecule. But certainly the most important of all chromoproteins and metalloproteins is *hemoglobin*—both in its quantity in the body and in the wealth of studies on it. This protein, found in solution within mammalian red cells, contains four iron atoms per molecule of protein. Each of these iron atoms is part of a heme group—a small organic molecular residue. This protein will be further discussed in a later chapter, along with the similarly constructed protein, *myoglobin*.

Finally, one of the most important of the groups of conjugated proteins is the nucleoproteins. These are conjugates of nucleic acid and protein which are strongly bound into a very large unit. These are found in all living cells, both in the nucleus and in the cytoplasm. They are also found to be the essential substance of all viruses. They will be discussed in more detail in later chapters.

REFERENCES

1. A. WHITE, P. HANDLER, E. L. SMITH, and D. STETTEN, *Principles of Biochemistry*, 2nd Ed. McGraw-Hill, New York, 1959.

2. J. S. FRUTON and S. SIMMONDS, *General Biochemistry*, 2nd Ed. Wiley, New York, 1958.

3. E. S. WEST and W. R. TODD, *Textbook of Biochemistry*, 3rd Ed. Macmillan, New York, 1961.

4. V. DU VIGNEAUD, C. RESSLER, and S. TRIPPETT, "The Sequence of Amino Acids in Oxytocin, with a Proposal for the Structure of Oxytocin," *J. Biol. Chem.* **205**, 949 (1953).

5. S. SHULMAN, *The Modeling of Biomolecular Structures*. Ealing Press, Cambridge, Mass., 1963.

CHAPTER 6

PROTEIN STRUCTURE : PRIMARY

CHAPTER 6

PROTEIN STRUCTURE: PRIMARY

6–1 Introduction. The detailed architecture of protein structure is of such tremendous complexity that it has resisted the onslaught of considerable experimental work over many years to the present time. Only recently has it become clear how best to phrase the questions to be answered. The structural details have now been successfully unraveled for one or two proteins, but this does not, by any means, permit us to generalize on the degree of similarity of the principles of construction for proteins as a group of chemical structures. It can be recalled that the protein molecule is fundamentally built as a polypeptide chain, and that this involves covalent linkages of nitrogen and carbon atoms to form a long, threadlike unit. This particular sequence of amino acids is referred to as the primary structure. It may be unbranched and thus have two free or uncombined ends, one of which is the N-terminal amino acid, and the other the C-terminal amino acid; or it may have branch points which would mean that there will be more than one terminal amino acid at either or both ends of the molecule. This threadlike unit is not randomly arranged in space, nor does it vary from moment to moment in its configuration, as would be the case for synthetic high polymers in solution. Instead it is fixed in a very definite and invariant three-dimensional configuration. This is apparently accomplished in many cases by a helical type of winding of the primary chain, and this helix is referred to as the secondary structure of a protein molecule. Finally, this helical coil, where it exists, or the primary chain itself where there is no helix, is wrapped about in a definite but apparently nonregular and meandering fashion to form the overall three-dimensional structure of the molecule. This is referred to as the tertiary structure. Consideration of each of these various levels of structural concept will simplify to some extent our task in elucidating and describing the detailed structure of various proteins.

The concept to be emphasized is that each protein molecule has a very definite and specific structure. It contains an ordered sequence of amino acid units and a definite coiling and configuration, such that particular amino acid side chains at different chain locations will be situated in juxtaposition and can thus form additional chemical links, fixing the total structure more firmly. As a result of these structural details, certain functional groups will be exposed to the environment, while others will be buried within the molecule. The chemical reactions and the biological properties of each

protein must depend primarily on the nature and numbers of these exposed groups, and, in some cases, on their pattern of arrangement on the
molecular surface.

6–2 Amino acid analysis. The first step in studying the structure of a
given protein is, of course, to prepare the protein in highly purified form.
This is no small task in itself, and the degree to which subsequent results
will be unambiguous and meaningful is directly related to the success of
obtaining a homogeneous species of protein molecule.

There are numerous procedures for separating proteins from each other,
and these are based on a variety of fundamental principles. This subject
is, however, beyond the scope of this book. Numerous methods have been
developed for the fractionation of protein mixtures. These include, among
others, salting-out procedures, isoelectric precipitation procedures, cold
ethanol methods, and column chromatography. The first three methods
mentioned involve a sorting out based on differences in solubility of different proteins under varying experimental conditions. These reflect,
therefore, varying degrees of intermolecular forces of attraction between
the identical protein molecules as opposed to the forces of attraction between these molecules and the solvent water molecules. Only when the
former force is greater than the latter will the particles of that type aggregate and precipitate from solution. In the chromatographic procedures,
protein solution is allowed to trickle through a column of ion-exchange
resin using various changes in the pH and/or salt concentration of the solution. At different values of these parameters, different proteins will weaken
sufficiently in force of attraction for the ionized groups of the resin so that
they will be liberated and flow into the liquid dripping from the column.
Here again, then, one has a method which is essentially based on the forces
of attraction exerted by the protein molecules. These chromatographic
methods have become extremely popular in recent years, since they reflect
possibilities for tremendous diversity in applicability. The next stage is the
determination of the correct molecular weight of the protein and the total
analysis of its amino acids. These can then be expressed in terms of residues of amino acid per molecule of protein. Some of the procedures for
molecular weight determination will be described in Chapter 7. The determination of the total amino acid composition involves careful hydrolysis
of the protein, which can be conducted either in strong acid or in strong
alkali at elevated temperature for a period of time. The process of hydrolysis produces cleavage of the peptide links and liberates the amino acid
molecules. Each of the methods has defects deriving generally from the
fact that some destruction of the amino acids will occur during prolonged
treatment. One must therefore perform a number of hydrolyses under
varying conditions. Each such digest is then analyzed according to one of

the numerous methods available for separation and detection of amino acids. The most popular methods at present are based on the techniques of chromatography. Either paper chromatography or column chromatography may be used. By appropriate adjustment of the solvent conditions, the various amino acids can be separated from each other and the quantity of each can be measured. In this way the total number of each type of monomer unit in the molecule can be ascertained.

6–3 Amino acid sequence. The next question that arises is that of the sequence in which the amino acids are linked together in a chain. The number of possible sequential arrangements for a protein of even modest molecular weight is quite enormous. For example, it may be calculated that in a polypeptide containing 20 different amino acids in which each residue occurs only once, the total number of possible sequences is factorial 20, (20!), or approximately 2×10^{18}. All of these have the same empirical formula, that is, the same amino acids in the same proportions. Yet such a polypeptide of 20 amino acids would have a molecular weight of only about 2000.

Until 1945 the determination of amino acid sequence in proteins seemed an insuperable problem, but then methods were developed which made the solution available for at least one protein. The first protein to have its complete amino acid sequence unambiguously determined was insulin. It should be emphasized that this is a protein of very low molecular weight (approximately 6000). Several other proteins have by now been analyzed to the point where the sequence is either completely, or almost completely, known; these are ribonuclease, cytochrome c, tobacco mosaic virus protein, myoglobin, and hemoglogin. Undoubtedly, others will rapidly be added to this list.

The first important method for sequence analysis was introduced and developed by F. Sanger. It consisted of the use of fluorodinitrobenzene as a reagent which would combine with the terminal α-amino groups and not be removed by the subsequent hydrolysis of the protein. The reaction for a typical amino acid is shown in Fig. 6–1, and the resulting derivative is called a dinitrophenyl (DNP) derivative. The DNP-protein is then hydrolyzed and subjected to chromatography on paper or column. Among the separated amino acids, that which contains the label attached to its α-amino group would then be recognized as coming from the N-terminal position of the chain. For a large number of proteins, the N-terminal amino acid has been identified. In a number of instances, partial sequences involving several units in succession at the end of the chain have been established. These might be established by a second method that has been employed for the determination of N-terminal amino acids. This is the method utilizing the enzyme aminopeptidase. This enzyme hydrolyzes

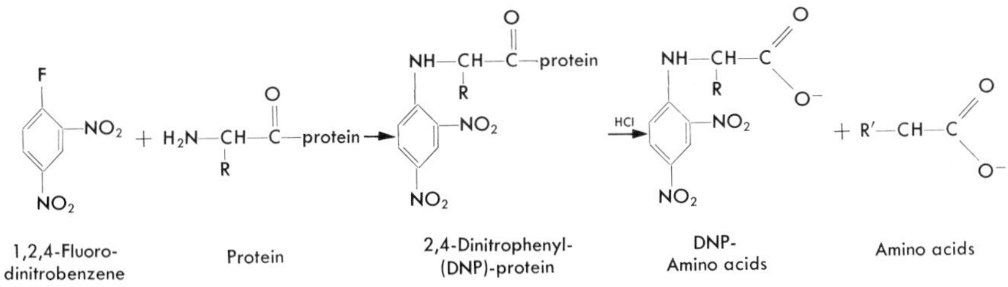

Fig. 6–1. Formation of dinitrophenyl (DNP) derivatives from a protein.

the bond which joins the amino acid containing a free α-amino group to the rest of the chain; it is therefore appropriate for removing the N-terminal unit. Under careful experimental conditions, it may be possible to follow the progressive removal of one amino acid after another for several units along the N-terminal sequence. Another method that has been similarly used is a nonenzymatic one called the phenylhydantoin (PTH) method, or the method of Edman. Here, the protein is treated with phenyl isocyanate. The terminal amino acid is split from the molecule and converted into a derivative which can be readily isolated and identified. The procedure can be repeated several times, again giving the possibility for some degree of sequential analysis. The experimental details and the chemical formulas involved can be studied in the review by Fraenkel-Conrat *et al.* Certain proteins have been analyzed, on the other hand, as to the identity of the amino acid in the C-terminal position. This can be accomplished by a method which involves the enzyme carboxypeptidase. This enzyme is specific for splitting the peptide bond which attaches the amino acid possessing a free carboxyl group to the rest of the chain. It therefore liberates the C-terminal amino acid. Again, by this procedure, one may be able to follow the sequence for several units along the chain from the C-terminus.

Data on the identity of the terminal amino acids of various proteins have provided several types of information. For one thing we now understand that there is apparently no restriction on any amino acid serving in such positions in the appropriate proteins. Secondly, for a particular protein, the number of terminal units indicates the number of polypeptide chains in the molecule. Finally, such information serves as a starting point for determination of the complete chain sequence(s). Some of the results of terminal amino acid identification that have been accumulated are summarized in Table 6–1.

By the use of methods for "tagging" the N-terminal amino acid, and the separation of various short peptide structures as a result of partial hydrolysis and paper chromatography, Sanger and his co-workers were able to deduce the complete amino acid sequence of bovine insulin. The total primary formula for this molecule is given in Fig. 6–2. It should be noted that there are two polypeptide chains linked together by disulfide bridges. The A or glycyl chain has 21 amino acids; the B or phenylalanyl chain has 30 amino acids. This total of 51 amino acids corresponds to a calculated molecular weight of 5733. The insulin molecule has a very great tendency to form molecular aggregates of varying sizes. It is especially apt to form dimers, of approximate molecular weight 12,000, and these often represent the form of the molecule under study. Under other conditions aggregates to form molecular weights of 24,000 or 36,000 can also be encountered. It is of interest to note that there are three disulfide bridges in the monomer protein. Two of these are interchain ($A7$–$B7$ and $A20$–$B19$); the other is intrachain ($A7$–$A11$). It may be of interest to note also a comparative feature shared with the peptides oxytocin and vasopressin. It can be seen that the intrachain disulfide ring is exactly the same size peptide as that found in the pituitary hormones. Comparison may be made with Fig. 5–6. It is not yet clear what significance, if any, this comparison may have in terms of patterns of synthesis and function of biological macromolecules.

Although the sequence was determined originally for *beef* insulin, the analysis of insulin from other species was later carried out; and for hog, sheep, horse, and whale, it was found to be completely identical with that for beef, except for the three amino acids in positions 8, 9, and 10 of the A-chain. This is the triad contained within the intrachain disulfide ring. The comparison of these amino acid triads can be seen in Table 6–2. Presumably, this is the actual chemical basis for the antigenic distinctions that had indeed been found between these

Fig. 6–2.   Structural formula for beef insulin.

TABLE 6-1

N-TERMINAL RESIDUES OF SEVERAL PROTEINS

Protein	Molecular weight	N-terminal amino acid	Number per molecule
Insulin, beef	12,000*	Phe, Gly	2, 2
Ribonuclease, beef	12,600	Lys	1
Myoglobin, whale	17,000	Val	1
Serum albumin, beef	69,000	Asp	1
Gamma globulin, rabbit	160,000	Ala	1
Pepsin	36,400	Leu or Ileu	1
Papain	20,700	Ileu	1

* Molecular weight given for insulin is that for the dimer form of the molecule.

TABLE 6-2

PARTIAL SEQUENCES FROM THE A-CHAIN
OF SEVERAL INSULINS

Species	The A-chain amino acid number		
A	8	9	10
Beef	Ala.	Ser.	Val.
Hog	Thr.	Ser.	Ileu.
Sheep	Ala.	Gly.	Val.
Horse	Thr.	Gly.	Ileu.
Whale	Thr.	Ser.	Ileu.

different types of insulin long before the chemical structures had been elucidated.

In fact several very recent studies have been made on pure insulin from various species. The differing reactivities of antibody to insulin have suggested that the antigenic determinant groups of this molecule are found in the A-chain of the molecule. The specificity may depend on characteristics of structure which involve factors additional to those of the amino acid sequence, since it has also been shown that antibodies may distinguish between two forms of insulin, such as the hog and sperm whale varieties, which have identical amino acid sequences.

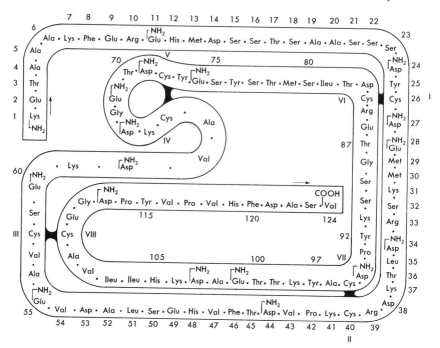

FIG. 6-3. Schematic diagram in two dimensions of bovine pancreatic ribonuclease A, showing the primary sequence and the arrangement of disulfide bonds.
The arrows indicate the direction of the peptide chain, starting from the N-
terminal end. [Reprinted by permission from *J. Biol. Chem.* **235,** 656 (1960)].

In the past seven or eight years a considerable amount of effort has gone
into determination of the sequence for a somewhat larger molecule, namely,
ribonuclease, with a molecular weight of 13,683. This is a molecule which
can catalyze the hydrolysis of ribonucleic acid, one of the two major types
of nucleic acid. It is therefore a *biological catalyst,* or *enzyme.* Ribonuclease
contains 124 amino acids which are arranged in a single chain. This chain
is held into a restricted spatial arrangement by four disulfide bridges.
The primary structure that has been determined is shown in Fig. 6-3. We
will not discuss any further details of this structure except to say that the
true structure in three dimensions must involve many more details than
are shown here. It may be well to emphasize, however, that even the
determination of the primary structure holds unexpected pitfalls and difficulties. For example, the total amino acid sequence of ribonuclease was
published, as a completed work, in 1960. But in 1962 and 1963, several
corrections were published, since one of the methods that had been used
had been found to give rearrangement products with certain amino acids.
The earlier sequence differed in the following portions of the chain: resi-

Val . Leu . Ser . Pro . Ala . Asp . Lys . Thr . Asp . Val . Lys . Ala . Ala . Try . Gly ... Ser . Lys . Tyr . Arg
1 . 2 . 3 . 4 . 5 . 6 . 7 . 8 . 9 . 10 . 11 . 12 . 13 . 14 . 15 ... 138 . 139 . 140 . 141

α-chain

Val . His . Leu . Thr . Pro . Glu . Glu . Lys . Ser . Ala . Val . Thr . Ala . Leu . Try . Gly ... His . Lys . Tyr . His
1 . 2 . 3 . 4 . 5 . 6 . 7 . 8 . 9 . 10 . 11 . 12 . 13 . 14 . 15 . 16 ... 143 . 144 . 145 . 146

β-chain

FIG. 6–4. Partial sequences of the α- and β-chains of hemoglobin A.

dues 11 to 18, 69 to 71, 87 to 89, 95 to 96, and 101 to 103. The pairing of the half-cystine residues has been confirmed as originally elucidated.

Two other illustrations of primary structure will be given. These involve the proteins hemoglobin and myoglobin. Hemoglobin has a molecular weight of about 67,000 and is the important carrier substance for oxygen and carbon dioxide in the blood stream. Four of its 10,000 atoms are iron atoms, which are combined within the 4 heme groups. All the remaining atoms are in 4 polypeptide chains of approximately equal length but differ in amino acid sequence. There are many varieties of the hemoglobin molecule and slight differences in structure. We shall discuss briefly only the human adult form, often called hemoglobin A. This molecule contains a total of 574 amino acids. It consists of two identical pairs of polypeptide chains, which are called the α-chains and the β-chains. The two α-chains have 141 amino acids each, and the two β-chains have 146 residues each. Figure 6–4 shows a portion of each of these chain types. These or similar chains are found in a number of different varieties of human and nonhuman hemoglobins in various combinations. Detailed knowledge of these sequences will permit us to make interesting comparisons along genetic lines, and also to speculate with regard to evolutionary considerations. An additional discussion of the hemoglobins and their structures is given in Section 9–2.

Myoglobin, which is found in muscle tissue, is a protein that is quite similar to hemoglobin except that it is one-fourth the size. Like hemoglobin, it is a red-colored protein, containing iron, combined within a heme group. Unlike hemoglobin, it contains only one of these units. This protein, however, is not simply a quarter-molecule of hemoglobin, but has a structural uniqueness of its own. It will be discussed in greater detail in Chapter 7, but here it should be pointed out that the amino acid sequence has also been worked out for this single polypeptide chain. Figure 6–5 shows a portion of its N-terminal sequence and a short C-terminal sequence.

Val . Ala . Gly . Glu . Try . Ser . Glu . Ileu . Leu . Lys . (?) . Try . (?) ... Gly . Tyr . Gly . Glu
1 . 2 . 3 . 4 . 5 . 6 . 7 . 8 . 9 . 10 . 11 . 12 . 13 ... 150 . 151 . 152 . 153

FIG. 6–5. Partial sequence of the chain of myoglobin.

REFERENCES

1. J. T. EDSALL and J. WYMAN, *Biophysical Chemistry*, Vol. I. Academic Press, New York, 1958.

2. S. W. Fox and J. F. FOSTER, *Introduction to Protein Chemistry*. Wiley, New York, 1957.

3. F. SANGER, "The Arrangement of Amino Acids in Proteins," *Advances in Protein Chemistry*, Vol. VII. Academic Press, New York, 1952.

4. H. FRAENKEL-CONRAT, J. I. HARRIS, and A. L. LEVY, "Recent Developments in Techniques for Terminal and Sequence Studies in Peptides and Proteins," *Methods of Biochemical Analysis*, Vol. II, D. Glick (Ed.). Interscience, New York, 1955.

5. S. A. BERSON and R. S. YALOW, "Antigens in Insulin; Determinants of Specificity of Porcine Insulin in Man." *Science* **139,** 844 (1963).

6. Y. YAGI, P. MAIER, and D. PRESSMAN, "Immunoelectrophoretic Identification of Guinea Pig Anti-Insulin Antibodies," *J. Immunol.* **89,** 736 (1962).

7. D. H. SPACKMAN, W. H. STEIN, and S. MOORE, "The Disulfide Bonds of Ribonuclease," *J. Biol. Chem.* **235,** 648 (1960).

8. D. G. SMYTH, W. H. STEIN, and S. MOORE, "The Sequence of Amino Acid Residues in Bovine Pancreatic Ribonuclease: Revisions and Confirmations," *J. Biol. Chem.* **238,** 227 (1963).

9. G. BRAUNITZER, R. GEHRING-MULLER, N. HILSCHMANN, K. HILSE, G. HOBOM, V. RUDLOFF, and B. WITTMANN-LIEBOLD," Die Konstitution des Normalen Adulten Humanhämoglobins," *Z. Physiol. Chem.* **325,** 283 (1961).

CHAPTER 7

PROTEIN STRUCTURE: SECONDARY AND TERTIARY

CHAPTER 7

PROTEIN STRUCTURE:
SECONDARY AND TERTIARY

7-1 Introduction. It has been demonstrated that the polypeptide back-bone of protein structure is actually a zigzag configuration when fully extended. This is illustrated in Fig. 7-1, where the actual distances between atoms are shown, as well as the bond angles between successive pairs of atoms. This configuration is sometimes called the β-form. The numerical values used in the figure were deduced by Pauling and Corey from a large number of crystallographic studies on simple amino acid derivatives. The extended form is thought to be present only in the insoluble fibrous pro-

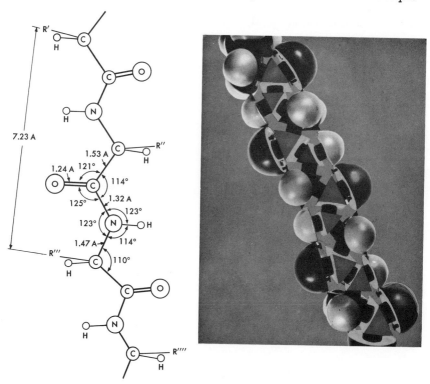

FIG. 7-1. Dimensions and bond angles for a fully extended *trans* polypeptide chain, or β-configuration. [Reprinted by permission from The Royal Society and from Dr. Linus Pauling, *Proc. Roy. Soc.* **B141,** 10 (1953).]

teins, such as keratin, where it corresponds to the so-called β-form of keratin. In many other proteins, it is felt that some sort of helical coiling has taken place so that hydrogen bonds are formed within the molecule between the C=O groups and the N—H groups. The best evidence indicates that among the many helices that have been proposed, the one designated as the α-helix of Pauling and Corey is to be preferred as a probable structural element of many proteins. There is good evidence that the α-helix does exist in a number of synthetic polypeptides, as well as in several purified proteins. Its existence in a number of other proteins is based only on circumstantial evidence and may well turn out later to be an erroneous inference. We must also keep in mind that in certain proteins, such as collagen, a quite different helical arrangement is well established. Even where the α-helix is actually present in a given protein, it should be remembered that only part of the polypeptide is in this form and that undoubtedly some greater or lesser portion of the polypeptide chain is in some other type of configuration.

7–2 Secondary structure: the α-helix. In 1951, Pauling and Corey proposed the α-helix as one possible model for the secondary structure (or coiling) of proteins in general. This suggested form was based upon the assumption that the interatomic distances and bond angles would be identical to the standard distances and angles determined on smaller units, primarily amino acid derivatives and small peptides. Criteria of the following types were therefore established. Each bond distance must be within ±0.02 A of the standard length, and each bond angle must be within ±2° of the standard angle. The selected values are shown in Figure 7–1. A fact of central importance was the realization that the C—N bond, which is the actual link between the residues, has some double-bond character. The C atom bearing the residue group is termed the αC, and the C atom of the carbonyl group is the C′. It can be seen by inspection of Fig. 7–2 that the interatomic distances for αC—N and αC—C′ are essentially identical to the standard lengths for such atom pairs, as illustrated, for example, in Chapter 3. However, the bond length C′—N is 1.32 A, which is a considerable shortening of the 1.47 A that is found in standard compounds. The C′—N bond is not as short as a standard double bond, since this would have a length of 1.26 A. It can be calculated then to involve about 40% double-bond character, as deduced from the actual measured length of the bond. This means then that the peptide group cannot be considered as though the C—N bond were a perfect single bond and the C=O bond were a perfect double bond, but rather that each of these is intermediate in character between single and double bonds. As a result, there is restricted rotation about the C′—N link, and the peptide group is fixed into a planar structure. This is emphasized in Fig. 7–2. In the ex-

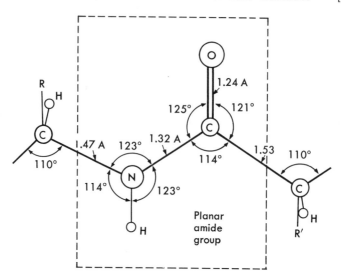

FIG. 7–2. Fundamental dimensions of the peptide group.

tended structure of a polypeptide sequence, the arrangement of side chains is *trans*. This means that the R-groups corresponding to the amino acid residues are alternately on opposite sides of the chain. Finally, it was noted that each nitrogen atom carries a hydrogen atom and can therefore form a hydrogen bond to the oxygen atom of a carbonyl group, a N—H · · · O bond. These bonds should be quite linear in their geometry and should be 2.79 A long.

On the basis of the criteria discussed above, plus the additional assumption that the helix should be constructed in such a way that as many as possible of the N—H and C=O groups would be in position where each could be involved in hydrogen bond formation, only very few structures provided ideal fulfillment. One of these was the α-helix, which is illustrated in Fig. 7–3. Several points should be noted about this structure. First of all, each peptide group is oriented so that it can be considered as a plane, and this plane is tangent to a cylinder around the axis of the helix. The construction of the helix can be thought of as involving a progression from one amino acid residue in the structure to the next, in such a way that there is a rotation around the cylinder of 100° for each such step, and there is a translation along the cylinder of 1.5 A. Each peptide group can be seen to be connected by a hydrogen bond to the third peptide group along the chain in either direction. These hydrogen bonds lie in a direction nearly parallel to the axis of the cylinder, and they serve to hold the turns of the helix together. It should be emphasized that, except for several at the very ends of the helical structure, every CO and every NH is involved in a hydrogen

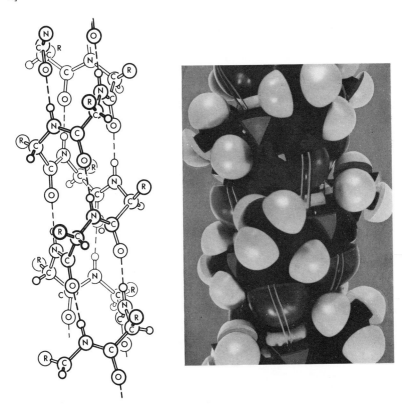

F IG. 7–3. The α-helix of Pauling and Corey shown as a right-handed helix. The amino acid residues have the L-configuration.

bond. There are 3.6 amino acid residues per turn of the helix. In order to obtain an integral number of residues, one must complete five turns, and there will be 18 residues in this unit. Finally, it should be noticed that the helix is packed very tightly; there is no open space in the center, not even enough for water molecules. It might also be mentioned that a helix of this type could be constructed so that it wraps up either like a right-handed or left-handed screw. The helices found in proteins thus far are believed to be right-handed helices.

The prevalence of the α-helix as an actual structure in proteins is a question that is undergoing considerable research at the present time. There is convincing evidence that this structure does occur in some proteins, but it may well be absent from a number of others. Rather than just resting on the belief that it is the most important or even the most common type of configurational arrangement of protein molecules, we find that our interest in this structure is enhanced by the fact that it is a clearly understandable structural unit. The most striking and detailed evidence for the occurrence of the α-helix is for the myoglobin molecule. Its presence here has been proven by means of x-ray diffraction, as will be described in some detail in Section 7–3. There is almost equally strong evidence that it also occurs in hemoglobin, although the details of structure have not been developed quite so far. It very probably occurs also in α-keratin, myosin, epidermin, fibrin, and some other fibrous proteins. These proteins have molecules that are characteristically of very high molecular weight and elongated proportions. Its existence in other proteins has not been firmly established, although many studies have been made attempting to estimate the content of helical or helix-like structure in a variety of proteins. Undoubtedly, some proteins will be proven to contain no α-helix. There is already strong evidence to indicate that certain proteins can be put in this group. Serum γ-globulin is one such example. Furthermore, it should be kept in mind that at least one protein, collagen, is built with a helical structure which is quite different from the α-helix.

7–3 Tertiary structure. There are many indications that proteins contain a complicated, and often irregular, orientation and folding through three dimensions of the primary and/or secondary structure that has been discussed above. This folding is, in general, fixed and highly specific. We may, for example, consider a protein which is very plentiful in bovine blood serum, bovine serum albumin (or BSA). This protein has a molecular weight of 68,000 and contains approximately 590 amino acids. It is known from terminal amino acid analysis that there is only one chain. If the entire molecule were in the form of an α-helix, its length would be $590 \times 1.5 \, A = 885 \, A$, and its thickness would be about 10 A. But it has been well established from physicochemical experiments that the actual dimensions are about 200 A $\times$ 35 A, so there must be folding of the chain unit. The molecule has 17 disulfide links, which also indicates that there is considerable restricted folding.

Many other examples could be provided to indicate that protein molecules in general, and especially those proteins that can exist in solution, consist of specifically folded and twisted chain structures. The elucidation of this detailed meandering of the polypeptide chain to form a bundle with a characteristic shape can be determined best by the method of x-ray diffraction. The fundamental theory, starting with the basic principle of Bragg's law, was discussed in Section 1–2. A crystalline substance will cause a beam of x-rays to be reflected at various discrete and definite angles. The reflection is brought about by the fact that the molecules within the crystal are arranged not at random but in a definite periodicity, i.e., at very definite and regular intervals and distances from each other in all three dimensions, and that in numerous directions one can observe alignments of these molecules into planes. From these various planes, the x-ray beam will be reflected at those particular angles where it receives reinforcement from the reflections from different levels. Many simpler chemicals have been analyzed in detail by this procedure, so that one could calculate the exact location of each atom in the structure. When dealing with proteins, however, the number of reflected spots on the photographic film is so huge, and the resultant number of calculations that must be made have been so formidable, that until recent years little progress was made with regard to the internal structure of a protein molecule. In recent years, however, Kendrew and his group have applied certain new tricks to the technique and have also been aided by the availability of electronic computing machines. The result has been that the internal structural arrangements of one protein were finally revealed in rather full detail. This protein is myoglobin, and a detailed discussion will be given below.

7–4 Structure of myoglobin.   Myoglobin has a molecular weight of about 18,000 and contains 153 residues. These are arranged in a single polypeptide chain, and somewhere in the molecule is attached a heme group. In other words, myoglobin is a conjugated protein; it is, in fact, a chromoprotein, like hemoglobin. The heme group is a flat grouping of atoms with

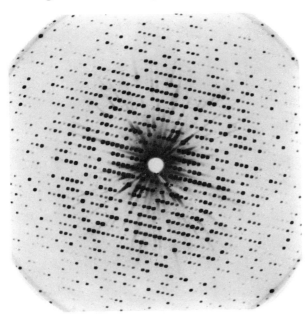

Fig. 7–4.   An x-ray diffraction photograph from myoglobin. [Reprinted by permission from American Physical Society, *Biophysical Science — A Study Program*, J. L. Oncley, ed. (1959). Photograph courtesy of Dr. John Kendrew.]

an iron atom at the center. Its function is to combine in a reversible manner with a molecule of oxygen. The protein is contained within the cells of various tissues, and its probable function is the temporary storage of oxygen brought by the hemoglobin of the blood. The myoglobin molecule itself is very similar to hemoglobin except that it is one-fourth its size. The first step in the analysis of crystals of myoglobin is the collection of x-ray diffraction patterns obtained at various angles of the crystal to the x-ray beam. A typical pattern is shown in Fig. 7–4.

Kendrew and his associates decided, in the first stage of the investigation, to seek a resolution of 6 A. It was felt that this would be adequate for the first period of study, inasmuch as it would allow one to discover such structures as cylinders of α-helix (estimated to be of the order of 9 or 10 A in diameter), and it would at the same time be feasible to accomplish. A higher resolution of 2 A or 1.5 A, which would provide the ultimate in detail, permitting one to see every single atom of the structure as a separate spot of density, would require a much greater amount of measurement and computation. For example, to obtain an analysis at 1.5-A resolution, it would have been necessary to analyze 25,000 x-ray reflections. At 6-A resolution it was necessary to measure 400 reflections. Even then, this work had to be duplicated on a number of different types of protein crystal formed with various metal salts.

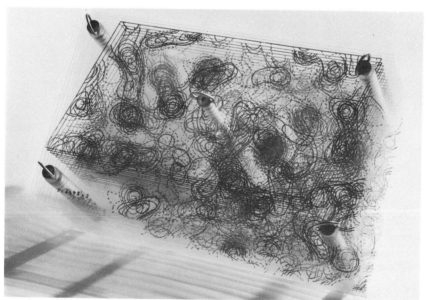

Fig. 7–5. Three-dimensional Fourier synthesis of the myoglobin unit cell. Some of the rod-like polypeptide chains can be seen. [Reprinted by permission from American Physical Society; *Biophysical Science — A Study Program*, J. L. Oncley, ed. (1959). Photograph courtesy of Dr. John Kendrew.]

By appropriate computations, contour maps illustrating the distribution of electron density at any given plane cutting through the crystal could be constructed. This was done for a large number of parallel planes through the crystal, and these contour maps were drawn on transparent plates which were then stacked above each other so that one could reconstruct a three-dimensional view of the molecule. Such an intermediate construction is shown in Fig. 7–5. From inspection of these plates the investigators observed rod-like features having high electron density and penetrating through various regions of the structure of each molecule. It turned out to be possible to follow the path of high electron density, in this way, throughout the molecule. As a result, a model of clay could be constructed, and this is shown in Fig. 7–6. This was the first picture of the actual anatomy of a protein molecule.

As mentioned above, the details shown here were limited to a 6-A scale of resolution. The finest details could not yet be made out, but one could observe several points. The detailed dimensions of the rod arrangement

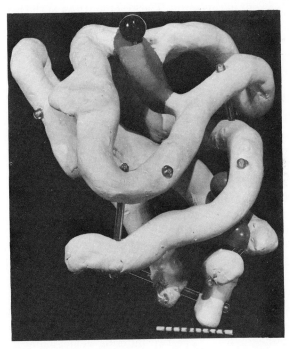

Fig. 7–6. A model of the myoglobin molecule. The gray, disk-like structure represents the porphyrin prosthetic group, and the light and dark colored spheres represent heavy metal derivatives which were attached to the protein to facilitate analysis of the x-ray diffraction data. [Reprinted by permission from American Physical Society, *Biophysical Science — A Study Program*, J. L. Oncley, ed. (1959). Photograph courtesy of Dr. John Kendrew.]

strongly suggested that this rod actually is the α-helix. The adjacent segments of rod are always at least 9 or 10 A apart. The electron density at the rod axis is about 1 electron per A^3. Thus in all respects the rod seems to fulfill the required specifications for an α-helix, and it was postulated that indeed this was its identity. This rod has segments over which it is nearly straight for distances of 20, 30, or even 40 A, but it is twisted in an irregular manner to form a bundle of overall dimension of 45 A by 35 A by 25 A. There is, furthermore, a total lack of symmetry in the molecule. One cannot describe it as a sphere, nor as an ellipsoid, nor any other regular shape. The helix does not really show any lengths that run in parallel. There are regions where this rod is sharply bent, and one cannot follow its path too clearly. An interruption in the dense helical structure would be a suitable explanation for these regions of ambiguity. By assuming that portions of the entire length of the single chain are coiled into an α-helix and that other portions are in some nonhelical form, it could be calculated that about 70% of the protein is in helical form. This means that 30% of the polypeptide chain is not in this form. The exact location of the heme group, and hence the iron atom, can also be described, and one can see just how, and to what extent, the loops of the protein chain fold around this disc-like structure.

In more recent studies carried out at a resolution of 2 A, the interpretation of the rod units as α-helix was definitely confirmed, and, in fact, it was established that the helix was right-handed. Furthermore, a large number of the individual amino acid side-chains could be identified by virtue of the distribution of electron density in each such region of space. Some of these data were summarized in Fig. 6–5.

7–5 The structure of hemoglobin. Hemoglobin is a protein of molecular weight 67,000. Four of its 10,000 atoms are iron atoms, and these are combined within four heme groups. The remaining atoms are in four polypeptide chains, as was described in Chapter 6. The molecule has been subjected to analysis by x-ray diffraction by Perutz and his group in the same way that myoglobin was studied. The analysis was done at a resolution of 5.5 A.

The data showed that the molecule consists of four separate units, occurring in two identical pairs. Figure 7–7 shows one member of each pair together with a model of myoglobin calculated for the same degree of resolution, namely 5.5 A. The two differing hemoglobin units are designated as white and black for the sake of distinctiveness. These two units have also been labeled α and β, respectively. In each of these three unit structures, the chain running through it describes a complicated figure, which can be traced from end to end by following the superimposed ink line. There are several small gaps in the models of the black chain and of

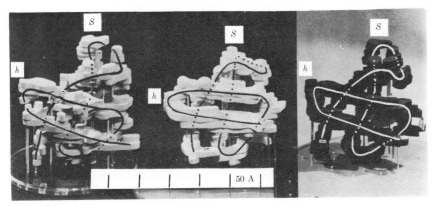

FIG. 7-7. Two different polypeptide chains (black and white) in the asymmetric unit of hemoglobin compared with myoglobin. The heme groups are at the back of the chains. The black chain is also designated as the β-chain, and the white as the α-chain. [Reprinted by permission from Macmillan and Company; *Nature* **185,** 416 (1960). Photograph courtesy of Dr. M. F. Perutz.]

FIG. 7-8. Partially assembled molecule showing two black chains and one white. [Reprinted by permission from Macmillan and Company; *Nature* **185,** 416 (1960). Photograph courtesy of Dr. M. F. Perutz.]

the myoglobin chain. But it is quite certain that there is a continuing polypeptide structure even across these gaps. It was concluded that the four tortuous chain structures in hemoglobin represent the four polypeptide chains. The black and white chains show configurations that are remarkably similar to each other, although not identical. In the black chain, the S-shaped bend at the top is more pronounced, and bend h is sharper, and the heme group is situated lower than in the white chain. Apart from these details of difference, the remarkable finding is the high degree of resemblance, not only between these two units, but also to the unit of myoglobin.

The complete hemoglobin molecule is assembled by fitting together the two black and two white chains. Figure 7–8 shows a partial assembly containing two black chains and one white. Figure 7–9 shows the complete molecule with all four chains. The heme groups are seen to lie in separate pockets on the surface of the molecule. Each of these pockets is formed by the folding in each polypeptide chain, which appears to make contact with the heme group at four different points, at least. Since the

FIG. 7–9. Hemoglobin model. The heme groups are indicated by gray disks. [Reprinted by permission from Macmillan and Company; *Nature* **185,** 416 (1960). Photograph courtesy of Dr. M. F. Perutz.]

function of this molecule is to combine with four molecules of oxygen, and this takes place under specified conditions of oxygen pressure, it would be highly important to attempt to clarify the relation between the structure of the molecule and its function. It is to each heme group that the oxygen molecule is bound—involving, in fact, the iron atom at the center of the heme disk. It is also well known that the union of one heme group with an oxygen molecule has a definite influence on the subsequent union of the next heme group with oxygen, but it is not at all clear how the heme groups interact with each other. Their interaction must indeed occur in a very subtle and indirect manner since they are not located in immediate proximity to each other. Therefore, the postulated interaction may well involve reversible modifications in the tertiary structure of a large part or all of the hemoglobin molecule.

7–6 Intermolecular bonds in tertiary structure. The results presented above concerning the detailed structures of myoglobin and hemoglobin have altered considerably our previous simplified assumptions as to the general shape of proteins. It is now realized that a protein molecule can have a complex, irregular, and highly individual structure. It is of importance to realize that a large number of different types of bonds might be involved in holding the branches and stems of such a structure together. These links might include the disulfide bond between half-cystine units. This would permit the branching of chains and a firm union of parallel chains through covalent links. The forces holding the structure together might also include electrostatic interactions between carboxyl and amino side chains that might be sufficiently close together on different portions of the chain or chains. It could also include hydrogen bonding between side chains, such as might occur between tyrosine groups and carboxyl groups. It might include interactions between nonpolar (hydrophobic) side chains; this involves the mutual repulsion of the aqueous solvent. And it might also include van der Waals forces, which can occur between any atoms that can come sufficiently close to each other, as was described in Chapter 3. Of these various forces that can be contemplated, perhaps the most important is the one that creates the hydrophobic bond—the interaction between nonpolar side chains. Many proteins contain a relatively large number of amino acids with such nonpolar side chains; these include the groups belonging to valine, leucine and isoleucine, and phenylalanine, as well as proline, alanine, and tryptophan. In a large number of proteins, the total for these groups is of the order of 30 to 50 percent. Since these side chains have a low affinity for water, the configurations of the polypeptide chain which are capable of bringing a large number of these groups into contact with each other will be more stable than any alternative configurations, if other factors are the same, since this structural arrangement will tend to remove these groups from the aqueous environment. All of the forces that have been discussed have individual magnitudes within a protein that depend very largely on the geometric details of the coiling and meandering of the polypeptide thread, since this determines the numbers of side-chain atoms that can come close enough at various places in the structure.

7–7 General size and shape of protein molecules. Although in recent years it has been shown that the complete three-dimensional structure of a protein molecule can be determined by x-ray diffraction and probably only by this method, it remains significant that for several decades prior to this time the only ways of obtaining any information concerning the molecular weight and the probable shape of a good many protein molecules were an array of methods based on physicochemical studies. It still remains true that for a very large collection of proteins, and especially for all the proteins of any size appreciably larger than hemoglobin, these other methods will continue to be of great importance. Some of the methods are also of importance for additional reasons, such as the ability to analyze a mixture of proteins to study the proportions of each member of the population. Some of them can also be used in order to follow molecular transformations in a particular type of protein, such as dissociation into subunits or association into aggregated forms. Problems of this type would be far too cumbersome to follow by the complex methods of x-ray diffraction. However, even for the problem of studying the complete three-dimensional structure of a single purified protein, the general physicochemical methods are still important for at least two reasons. For one thing, there are many proteins that do not seem to be crystallizable, or at least, crystallizable in adequate size and regularity. Consequently, x-ray diffraction procedures cannot be used. In other instances, where study by x-ray analysis has been possible, it must be kept in mind that one is studying a highly ordered crystalline arrangement and that the molecules in solution may not necessarily have the same configuration; physicochemical examination is needed therefore in order to demonstrate whether the configuration of the molecule in the crystal is the same as that in solution.

A number of these physicochemical methods are available. They can be described under two main headings: the hydrodynamic or kinetic methods and the thermodynamic or equilibrium methods. In the first group, the hydrodynamic methods, we can include, among others, the techniques of diffusion, sedimentation, and viscosity. In the thermodynamic procedures we have, to name a few, osmotic pressure measurements and light scattering. Some of these phenomena will be discussed in greater detail in later chapters, and others are beyond the scope of this book. However, at this point we shall give some attention to the elementary theory and practice of diffusion, sedimentation, and light scattering. An additional hydrodynamic method of considerable importance is that of electrophoresis, and more will be said about this, later.

The methods of sedimentation are based on the use of the ultracentrifuge. This machine will rotate a solution at very high speeds, *and* will also permit direct optical observation through the solution at the same time. In addition to providing data for the determination of molecular weight, the ultracentrifuge is often used to study the heterogeneity of the macromolecular preparation, i.e., to describe its purity. Another use of the instrument is the sedimentation of particles of very small size for the purpose of clarification of a solution. There are actually two types of ultracentrifugal study insofar as molecular parameters are concerned. These can be described as follows:

(a) *Equilibrium ultracentrifuge.* This involves the use of the instrument at moderately low speeds, 10,000 to 15,000 rpm, giving accelerations equal to about 15,000 times the earth's gravity. Under these conditions the macromolecules being sedimented toward the periphery of the rotor develop a tendency to diffuse in the opposite direction. These two forces acquire the same magnitude in time, and there is established a gradient of concentration throughout the solution which no longer changes with time.

(b) *Velocity ultracentrifuge.* At quite high speeds the tendency toward back diffusion is completely overcome by the enormous acceleration, and the molecules sediment continuously to the periphery. This generally requires a speed of the order of 40,000–60,000 rpm. At the highest speed and at the radius that is used, one has an acceleration of approximately 260,000 times gravity.

Protein molecules in a solution in the ordinary gravitational field of the earth are subject to some degree of settling out. This tendency, however, is overcome by Brownian motion, that is, the random buffeting by the small molecules of solvent because of their kinetic energy, and by convection currents due to thermal gradients throughout the solution. By means of rotation of the solution, an increased force directed toward the periphery can be produced. In accordance with Newton's second law of motion, this force is expressed as follows:

$$\text{Force} = ma = \frac{mv^2}{x} = m\omega^2 x, \qquad (7\text{-}1)$$

where m is the mass of the particle, x is its distance from the axis of rotation, v is the linear velocity around the circumference of motion (in cm/sec), and ω is the angular velocity (in rad/sec). Figure 7–10 illustrates the rotor and cells as used in the Spinco ultracentrifuge. By means of an appropriate optical system, usually a schlieren system, based on refractive index gradients, the migration of the protein molecules with time can be

Fig. 7–10. A rotor and cell as used in the Spinco ultracentrifuge. The counter-balance cell is also shown, along with a cell centerpiece and sector cups holding quartz windows. [Reprinted by permission from Spinco Division, Beckman Instruments, Inc.]

followed. The sedimentation coefficient, s, has been defined by Svedberg, who first developed and applied the ultracentrifugal techniques, as

$$s = \frac{dx/dt}{\omega^2 x}, \tag{7-2}$$

where dx/dt is the speed of sedimentation of the protein molecules, and $\omega^2 x$ is the angular acceleration. The sedimentation coefficient is usually expressed in Svedberg units, with one Svedberg unit $= 1 \times 10^{-13}$ sec. The sedimentation coefficient is obtained then from a run in the ultracentrifuge. The measured sedimentation coefficient is corrected to the value it would have in a solvent whose viscosity and density is that of water at 20°C. By this means, experiments performed in different solutions and at different temperatures can be made comparable. The sedimentation coefficient, when further corrected for any effects of protein concentration, is a characteristic parameter of the particular protein, and is very useful in identifying the protein as well as in helping to determine its molecular weight.

In order to calculate the molecular weight from such ultracentrifugal data, one must employ a combination of two hydrodynamic methods.

These can be either ultracentrifugal sedimentation plus the measurement of diffusion, or sedimentation plus measurements of viscosity. The latter is seldom used. In order to derive an equation for the molecular weight, we must begin by understanding that when the ultracentrifuge has arrived at constant speed, one has the condition of terminal velocity; that is, the sedimenting proteins are moving at a constant speed throughout the solution. Under these conditions, centrifugal force = frictional force. Therefore,

$$m_e\omega^2 x = f\,\frac{dx}{dt}\,; \qquad (7\text{-}3)$$

and substituting the actual mass for the equivalent mass by the relation

$$m_e = m(1 - \bar{v}\rho), \qquad (7\text{-}4)$$

we have

$$m(1 - \bar{v}\rho)\omega^2 x = f\,\frac{dx}{dt}, \qquad (7\text{-}5)$$

where f is the coefficient of friction, and dx/dt is the speed of the molecule, m is the mass of a molecule, m_e is the equivalent mass (as affected by the buoyancy due to the solvent), $\bar{v}$ is the partial specific volume of the protein, and ρ is the density of the solution. The coefficient of friction of a moving particle is the proportionality constant between the frictional force resisting the motion and the speed of motion. The partial specific volume can properly be defined only by thermodynamic reasoning; but in a rough way, it can be thought of as the reciprocal of the density of the dry protein molecule. Now, this equation has two unknowns, m and f. To eliminate one of these, we make the assumption that the coefficient of friction in the sedimentation process is identical to the coefficient of friction in the diffusion of this protein. In other words,

$$f_s = f_D. \qquad (7\text{-}6)$$

This turns out to be a valid assumption, since molecular weights determined in this way agree well with other methods of determination. From the theory of the diffusion process, it is known that

$$f_D = \frac{kT}{D}, \qquad (7\text{-}7)$$

where k is a universal constant (the Boltzmann constant), T is the absolute temperature, and D is the diffusion coefficient. The meaning of D will be defined and discussed in greater detail in Chapter 19, but for now we can recognize it as a characteristic parameter for the particular macromolecule, describing its rate of diffusion as a function of the gradient of concentration. Like the sedimentation coefficient, it is corrected to standard conditions of solvent and temperature.

Substituting this value of f_D, one derives

$$m(1 - \bar{v}\rho)\omega^2 x = \frac{kT}{D} \frac{dx}{dt}. \tag{7-8}$$

Multiplying by N, the Avogadro number, one obtains

$$M(1 - \bar{v}\rho)\omega^2 x = \frac{RT}{D} \frac{dx}{dt}, \tag{7-9}$$

since $mN = M$, the molecular weight, and $kN = R$, the gas constant, which is another universal constant, to be discussed in detail in later chapters.

Then, rearranging, we have

$$M = \frac{RT}{D(1 - \bar{v}\rho)} \frac{dx}{dt} \frac{1}{\omega^2 x}; \tag{7-10}$$

and recognizing that

$$s = \frac{dx}{dt} \frac{1}{\omega^2 x}, \tag{7-12}$$

by definition of the sedimentation coefficient, we arrive finally at

$$M = \frac{RTs}{D(1 - \bar{v}\rho)}. \tag{7-11}$$

This is the Svedberg equation of the ultracentrifuge and has been the basis for the determination of many molecular weight values.

Diffusion coefficients are determined by carefully layering a salt solution above a solution containing the protein in a solution of the same salt composition. Starting with an initially very sharp boundary, the gradual migration of protein molecules into the layer above can be followed by optical means, and a diffusion coefficient can be measured. This parameter will be described in Chapter 19. It should be noted here that its magnitude depends on both the size and shape of the protein molecule.

The procedure of electrophoresis is used for the analysis of proteins and their transformation. It does not provide any information concerning the molecular weight of proteins, but it is extremely useful for studying composition of mixtures of proteins. This technique is based on the fact that proteins are usually charged ionic molecules and will therefore migrate in an electric field. The direction and speed of the migration will depend on the pH of the solution and on the properties of the particular protein. Various proteins will have different magnitudes of charge at a given pH, as a result of the numbers and proportions of those side chains which can be ionized to give a charged group. Therefore, different proteins will generally migrate at different rates. Again, optical methods may be used to follow the migration, and most commonly the schlieren optical system is used, whereby a number of peaks can be visualized, each peak representing a particular protein or family of proteins having the same electrophoretic mobility. The mobility is defined as the speed of migration of the molecule divided by the electric field strength. The field strength is the electric potential applied across the solution, divided by the length of the migration path. The rate of migration of a protein molecule in an electric field is dependent primarily on the net charge of the protein. It also has some dependence on the molecular size and shape. The pH at which there is no migration in either direction is known as the isoelectric point. At a lower pH, a protein will migrate as a cation; at a higher pH, it will migrate as an anion. The mobility at various pH levels can be plotted against pH, and such a graph is quite similar to the titration curve of the protein (see Chapter 17 for more detailed discussion of protein titration curves).

The definition of isoelectric point that has been given is an operational definition and is therefore unambiguous. It could also be defined in a theoretical sense as the pH at which the net charge of each protein molecule, or the average of the net charges for all the protein molecules, is zero. In either case, it is important to keep in mind that the charged groups on a protein molecule arise from two sources, which include not only the ionization of protons from the various dissociable groups but also the binding of other ions from the salts and buffers in solution. The isoelectric point therefore varies not only from protein to protein, but is in addition dependent on the exact composition of the solvent medium. A similar, but not identical, concept is that of the isoionic point. This has been defined in slightly different ways but for the present purpose it can be defined in an operational sense as the pH of a solution of isoionic protein in water or in a salt solution of a salt which does not produce hydrogen or hydroxyl ions when dissolved in water itself; by isoionic protein is meant a preparation from

TABLE 7–1

ELECTROPHORETIC ANALYSIS AND MOBILITIES FOR NORMAL
HUMAN PLASMA IN 0.10 IONIC STRENGTH DIETHYLBARBITURATE
BUFFER AT pH 8.6

Component	Concentration, gm/100 ml	Percent of total protein	Mobility, $cm^2 \cdot volt^{-1} \cdot sec^{-1}$
Albumin	4.04	60.3	-5.9×10^{-5}
α_1-Globulin	0.31	4.6	-5.1
α_2-Globulin	0.48	7.2	-4.1
β-Globulin	0.81	12.1	-2.8
Fibrinogen	0.34	5.1	-2.1
γ-Globulin	0.74	11.0	-1.0

TABLE 7-2

STRUCTURAL PARAMETERS OF SEVERAL PROTEINS

Protein	Knowledge of primary structure	s, sec	D, $cm^2 \cdot sec^{-1}$	Molecular weight	Total number of amino acids	Number of N-terminals	Content of α-helix
Insulin	Complete	1.2×10^{-13}	16×10^{-7}	5,734	51	2	Apparently some
Ribonuclease	Complete	1.8	13.6	13,684	124	1	Apparently some
Myoglobin	Complete	2.0	11.3	18,000	153	1	Approx. 70%
Hemoglobin, human adult	Complete	4.5	6.9	67,000	574	4	Approx. 70%
Serum albumin	Unknown	4.3	6.1	68,000	590	1	Approx. 50%
γ-globulin	Partial	7.0	4.1	160,000		1	Apparently none
Fibrinogen	Unknown	7.8	2.0	330,000	Approx. 1500	4	?
Thyroglobulin	Unknown	18.7	2.6	660,000	Approx. 2800	?	?

which all ions, other than hydrogen or hydroxyl, have been removed by extensive treatment, either by dialysis or by chromatography. If the protein, when dissolved in a particular buffer solution, fails to bind ions other than hydrogen ions, the isoelectric and isoionic points coincide.

The plasma proteins constitute a group of special interest with regard to the technique of electrophoresis. If blood plasma, that is, blood minus the cells, is examined by this means, then one can observe six major components. These are named in decreasing order of migration rate at pH values between 8 and 9, as albumin, α_1-globulin, α_2-globulin, β-globulin, ϕ (fibrinogen), and γ-globulin. Table 7–1 gives the rate of migration (mobility) and the relative quantity of each of these components in a normal human plasma.

In conclusion, many proteins have been studied by these physicochemical methods, and considerable information has been accumulated on molecular size and structure. The extent of information differs for various proteins. Unfortunately, the interpretation of much of the data is clouded by the presence of some residual impurities in the particular preparation that was studied. For this reason, and also, at times, because of varying experimental error in different laboratories, the facts on each protein sometimes show considerable variation in different reports. For the better characterized proteins, however, we can have some confidence in the information accumulated. It may be of interest to summarize the information available for a number of important proteins. This is tabulated in Table 7–2.

REFERENCES

1. J. T. Edsall and J. Wyman, *Biophysical Chemistry*, Vol. I. Academic Press, New York, 1958.
2. S. W. Fox and J. F. Foster, *Introduction to Protein Chemistry*. Wiley, New York, 1957.
3. F. W. Putnam (Ed.), *The Plasma Proteins*, Vol. I. Academic Press, New York, 1960.
4. R. B. Corey and L. Pauling, "Fundamental Dimensions of Polypeptide Chains," *Proc. Roy. Soc.* **B141,** 10 (1953).
5. L. Pauling and R. B. Corey, "Stable Configurations of Polypeptide Chains," *Proc. Roy. Soc.* **B141,** 21 (1953).
6. J. C. Kendrew, "The Three-Dimensional Structure of a Protein Molecule," *Scientific American*, December, 1961.
7. A. F. Cullis, H. Muirhead, M. F. Perutz, M. G. Rossmann, and A. C. T. North, "The Structure of Hemoglobin," *Proc. Roy. Soc.* **A265,** 161 (1962).
8. A. B. Edmundson, C. H. W. Hirs, J. C. Kendrew, H. C. Watson, B. E. Strandberg, R. E. Dickerson, D. C. Phillips, and V. C. Shore, "The Amino-Acid Sequence of Sperm Whale Myoglobin," *Nature* **190,** 663 (1961).

9. S. SHULMAN, "The Size and Shape of Bovine Fibrinogen; Studies of Sedimentation, Diffusion, and Viscosity," *J. Am. Chem. Soc.* **75,** 5846 (1953).

10. W. KAUZMANN, "Some Factors in the Interpretation of Protein Denaturation," *Advances Prot. Chem.* **14,** 1 (1959).

11. R. AUDUBERT and S. DE MENDE, *The Principles of Electrophoresis.* Macmillan, New York, 1960.

12. M. BIER (Ed.), *Electrophoresis; Theory, Methods, and Applications.* Academic Press, New York, 1959.

13. H. NEURATH (Ed.), *The Proteins,* Vols. I–II. Academic Press, New York, 1963 (Vol. I), 1964 (Vol. II).

14. H. A. SCHERAGA, *Protein Structure.* Academic Press, New York, 1961.

15. V. M. INGRAM, *The Hemoglobins in Genetics and Evolution.* Columbia University Press, New York, 1963.

16. S. SHULMAN, N. ALKJAERSIG, and S. SHERRY, "Physicochemical Studies on Human Plasminogen (Profibrinolysin) and Plasmin (Fibrinolysin)," *J. Biol. Chem.* **233,** 91 (1958).

CHAPTER 8

THE NUCLEIC ACIDS

CHAPTER 8

THE NUCLEIC ACIDS

8-1 Introduction. The nucleic acids constitute another type of biological macromolecule which is found in all living cells, and also in all viruses. There are two major types which must be differentiated. These are ribose nucleic acid (RNA) and deoxyribose nucleic acid (DNA). Actually, there are four kinds of RNA, differing in anatomic localization, molecular size, and biochemical function. Each of these five nucleic acids is a family of closely related but not identical molecular entities. However, the members within each family have not yet been separated from each other and individually characterized, although many studies are currently in progress for the successful achievement of this goal. For this and other reasons, we will continue most often to discuss nucleic acids under the two major headings of DNA and RNA.

In the cell, DNA is located within the nucleus, and it is restricted to this region of the cell. On the other hand, RNA is found predominantly in the cytoplasm, although a small amount is also found in the nucleus, where it is primarily located in the nucleolus. Nucleic acids can be isolated from preparations of nucleoprotein, which is the form in which they usually occur. These can be either nucleoprotamines, as have been most frequently studied in the sperm of certain fish, or they may be nucleohistones, such as the type that has been extensively studied from the thymus gland. Or one may investigate the nucleoproteins of bacteria or viruses. After purifying the nucleoprotein itself, the nucleic acid is isolated by means of denaturation of the protein component. The nucleic acid can be readily precipitated with ethanol and redissolved in water. This procedure can be repeated several times, and in this way DNA or RNA can be obtained quite free of other components.

8-2 Polynucleotide structure. The unit structure of each type of nucleic acid is the nucleotide. This monomeric unit can be expressed in abbreviated form as

$$\text{phosphate—sugar—base}$$

In this construction the base is either a purine molecule or a pyrimidine molecule. The pyrimidines include cytosine, uracil, and thymine. The purines include adenine and guanine.

All these structures are illustrated in Fig. 8-1. This figure also shows the steric arrangements of these structures, using the atomic models. It

110

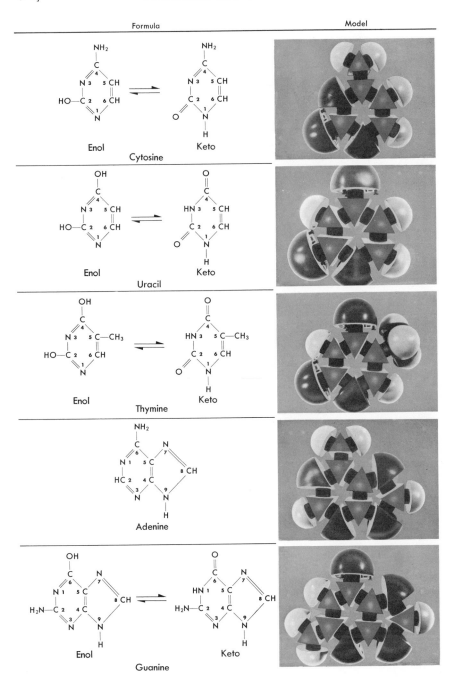

FIG. 8–1. Structures of the nucleic acid purines and pyrimidines.

D-ribose

2-deoxy-D-ribose

FIG. 8–2. Structure of the nucleic acid pentoses.

Adenosine

(9-β-D-ribofuranosyladenine)

Cytidine

(1-β-D-ribofuranosylcytosine)

FIG. 8–3. Typical nucleoside formulas.

TABLE 8–1

COMPONENTS OF THE NUCLEIC ACIDS

DNA	RNA
Adenine, A	Adenine, A
Thymine, T	Uracil, U
Guanine, G	Guanine, G
Cytosine, C	Cytosine, C
2-deoxy-D-ribose	D-ribose
Phosphate	Phosphate

should be emphasized that guanine and all of the pyrimidines can exist in tautomeric forms.. There can, in some cases, be even more than two of these forms for a substance. The predominant forms are shown here. Actually, the equilibrium that is indicated is believed, from evidence collected on crystalline preparations, to favor considerably the keto forms. But the preferred form *in solution* is still not clear. Nonetheless, only the keto form will adapt itself to the accepted structure of nucleic acid itself, as will be further described below.

The sugar is either D-ribose or 2-deoxy-D-ribose. These structures are illustrated in Fig. 8–2. The phosphate group is the conventional acid phosphate radical, insofar as its ionization properties are concerned. Actually, the linkage between sugar and phosphate is an ester linkage, while the base is connected to the sugar by a glycoside linkage. (The glycoside linkage is discussed in Chapter 11.)

It has been pointed out that the nucleic acids occur in two major families, which differ in the content of the constituents described above. This is tabulated for convenience in Table 8–1. DNA or deoxyribose nucleic acid contains 2-deoxy-D-ribose as the sugar component and cytosine and thymine as the pyrimidines. RNA or ribose nucleic acid contains D-ribose as the sugar component and cytosine and uracil as the pyrimidine components. In both types of nucleic acid, adenine and guanine are the purine components. It should also be pointed out that while the above constituents are found in the great majority of DNA or RNA preparations, there are occasional alternative purines or pyrimidines that are found in only certain types of cells or viruses.

Partial hydrolysis of nucleic acids gives nucleosides, which are units containing in each a sugar and a base. Examples in Table 8–2 illustrate the usual naming system as well as the compositions. Typical formulas of some nucleosides are shown in Fig. 8–3. The nucleotides are phosphoric esters of the nucleosides and are strong acids, since the phosphate groups

TABLE 8-2

COMPOSITION OF THE USUAL NUCLEOSIDES AND
NUCLEOTIDES OF NUCLEIC ACIDS

Nucleoside	Sugar unit	Base unit	Nucleotide
Adenosine	Ribose	Adenine	Adenylic acid
Guanosine	Ribose	Guanine	Guanylic acid
Cytidine	Ribose	Cytosine	Cytidylic acid
Uridine	Ribose	Uracil	Uridylic acid
Deoxyadenosine	Deoxyribose	Adenine	Deoxyadenylic acid
Deoxyguanosine	Deoxyribose	Guanine	Deoxyguanylic acid
Deoxycytidine	Deoxyribose	Cytosine	Deoxycytidylic acid
Thymidine	Deoxyribose	Thymine	Thymidylic acid

still contain in ionizable form two of the
original three —OH acid groups. The
nucleotides are also shown in Table 8-2.
The formula for deoxyadenylic acid is
shown in Fig. 8-4 as a typical nucleotide.
This would be a component of DNA. The
corresponding molecule that would be
found in RNA, namely, adenosinemono-
phosphate (AMP) or adenylic acid, is illustrated in Fig. 8-5. It should be noted
that the purine is attached to the sugar
through position 9 of the purine and position 1' of the ribose (the carbons in the
sugar ring are given prime numbers in
order to avoid confusion with the num-
bering of the base). It is important to
note that the base is essentially a flat
planar structure, and the sugar ring, while
not perfectly planar, is quite close to being
a flat structure. One can then consider the
orientation between these two planes.

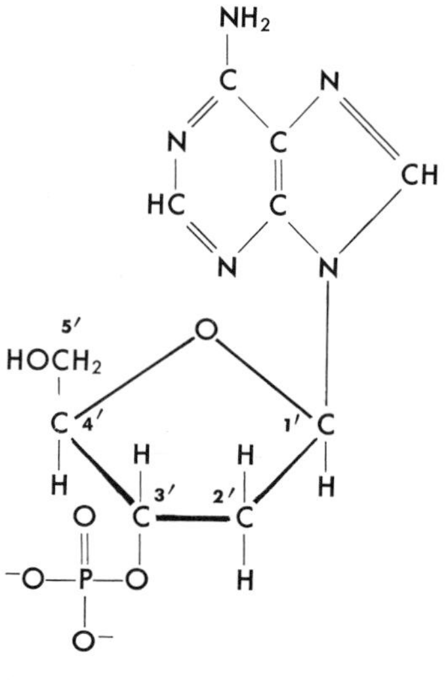

Deoxy-3'-adenylic acid
(deoxyadenosine-3'-phosphate)

FIG. 8-4. Formula for a typical nucleotide of DNA.

They have been found to be at an angle of
about 70° to 75° to each other, and this fact will be of great importance in
considering the structure of the nucleic acid molecule. The phosphate in
this structure has been shown as being attached to the 5' position. It could
equally well be attached to the 3' position (or the 2' position). Similarly,

Fig. 8–5. Formula for a typical nucleotide of RNA.

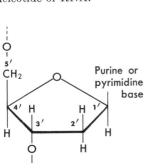

5'-adenylic acid
(adenosine-5'-phosphate)

Fig. 8–6. Structure of DNA. The individual nucleotides are linked through the 3'- and 5'-phosphate diester bridges.

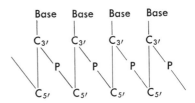

Fig. 8–7. Simplified scheme depicting the structure of a nucleic acid.

in deoxyadenylic acid (Fig. 8–4), there can be either the 3'- or 5'-phosphate derivative. There are therefore several nucleotides for each base-sugar combination. In forming the polynucleotide, these phosphate units are attached on either side, alternatively, to 3'- and 5'-positions of ribose or deoxyribose units. We essentially have a structure which can be written as

—sugar—phosphate—sugar—phosphate—sugar—phosphate—

| | | |

   base   base   base

The actual covalent structure can be pictured as in Fig. 8–6. This can be alternatively written in a simple line drawing as shown in Fig. 8–7.

In the past decade or so, it has become evident that the different bases do not occur in equal numbers nor therefore in perfectly regular or periodic sequence; and the remaining problems for the establishment of the structure of a nucleic acid are:

(1) The relative numbers of the bases;

(2) The sequential arrangement of the bases.

Studies on the proportions of the bases (the base ratios) have been made on many preparations of DNA, and certain generalizations have appeared for this type of nucleic acid. The following statements have been found to be true for all preparations of DNA that have been studied (with the single exception of one very unusual virus DNA). This has been true for preparations from various tissues and from various species of plants and animals.

(1) The molar ratio of A/T = 1.

(2) The molar ratio of G/C = 1.

It follows that the sum of the purine nucleotides equals the sum of the pyrimidine nucleotides. It also follows that

$$A + C = G + T.$$

However, if one compares the (A + T)-sum with the (G + C)-sum, it is found that DNA's do come in two groups:

(1) The "AT type." In these preparations of DNA, adenine and thymine predominate over the other bases. These are found in the higher animals. The ratio of (A + T)/(G + C) can be as high as 1.9.

(2) The "GC type." In these preparations, guanine and cytosine predominate. These are generally found in microorganisms. The (A + T)/ (G + C) ratio can vary from 1 down to 0.4.

Although it has been found that this base ratio is different in different species of plants and animals, it is remarkably constant in various tissues of the same animal or plant.

It must be kept in mind that the sequence of the bases is still to be elucidated by future research, although many recent studies have given some preliminary notion of partial sequences. This sequence must eventually be correlated with the specific properties of the nucleic acid molecule. The number of theoretically possible sequences is seen to be quite enormous when one considers that a DNA of 6.0×10^6 molecular weight contains approximately 20,000 nucleotide units, and it is quite possible to have DNA preparations with molecular weight as high as 130×10^6.

It is an interesting (and very useful) feature of nucleic acid to absorb light very strongly in the ultraviolet. A maximum for absorbency (or optical density) occurs at or very close to 260 mμ. All the purines and pyrimidines participate in this absorption. It would be expected that the total absorption for the nucleic acid preparation would equal the summation of the contributions of the individual bases. This, however, is not the case. The polynucleotide itself shows a decreased absorbency by as much as 40%. This effect is called *hypochromism*, and its exact magnitude depends on the solvent and on the previous treatment of the nucleic acid. One can readily demonstrate this phenomenon by subjecting a sample of DNA or RNA to hydrolysis, and by measuring the light absorption, before and after this reaction. It will be found that the absorbency increases; this may be called a *hyperchromic* effect.

It will be later seen that these absorbency measurements can be used to follow various structural changes in the molecule of nucleic acid.

8–3 Structure of DNA: the Watson-Crick helix. In 1953, a helical structure for DNA was proposed by Watson and Crick. This was based on the experimental data from x-ray diffraction studies (which showed DNA to contain a helical structure) of Wilkins and his group, and also on the chemical analysis of base ratios, and especially on the fact that A = T and G = C, implying some type of complementarity in structure.

The Watson-Crick formulation proposed:

(a) There are two parallel helical chains attached to each other through numerous hydrogen bonds.

(b) Each chain contains a sequence of alternate phosphate and sugar groups with the attached bases extending inward toward the central axis of the helix.

(c) These bases could always be linked to each other if they were paired in a specific manner. Opposite A would always be located T, and opposite G would always be located C. The way in which these pairs of units would fit just right is shown in Fig. 8–8. It can be seen that two hydrogen bonds can form in the AT pair, and that three can form in the GC pair.

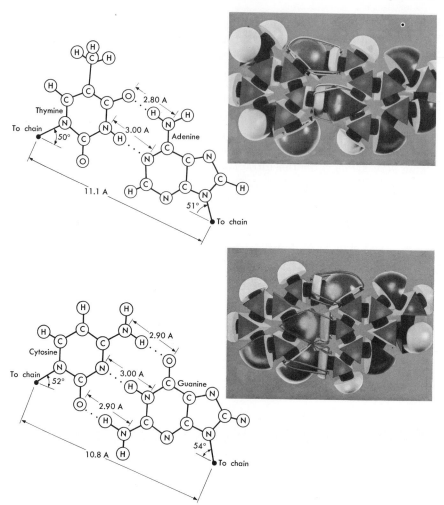

FIG. 8–8. Pairing of thymine and adenine and of cytosine and guanine by means of hydrogen bonds. [Reprinted by permission from Academic Press; *Arch. Biochem. Biophys.* **65,** 164 (1956).]

Therefore, the two chains are deemed complementary in that the sequence of one chain completely determines the other. This base pairing fits the analytical data and also is possible sterically, as detailed pictures show. The proposed structure of the helix is illustrated in Figs. 8–9 and 8–10.

There are very important implications for genetic replication and genetic control in these considerations of structure. For one thing, if the chains could separate from each other, each could then serve as a mold

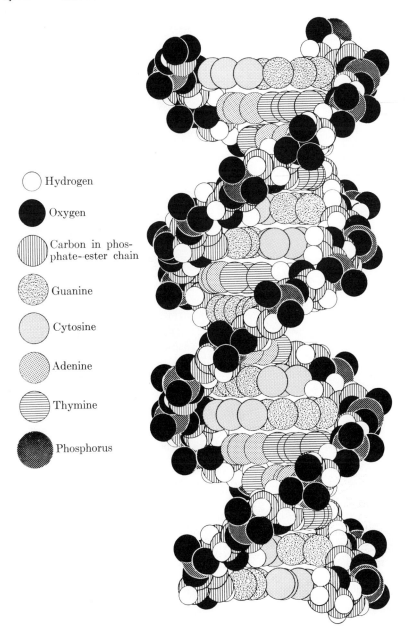

○ Hydrogen

● Oxygen

Carbon in phosphate-ester chain

Guanine

Cytosine

Adenine

Thymine

Phosphorus

FIG. 8–9. Schematic model of the structure of deoxyribonucleic acid. The horizontal atoms of carbon and nitrogen of the purine-pyrimidine pairs are shown in the lighter shades. [Reprinted by permission from American Cancer Society and Dr. L. D. Hamilton; *CA, A Bulletin of Cancer Progress* **5,** 163 (1955)].

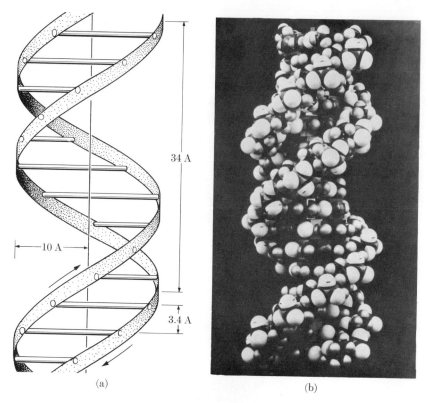

(a)   (b)

FIG. 8–10. (a) Schematic drawing of the two-stranded structure of deoxy-ribonucleic acid. (b) Photograph of a molecular model, built with Courtauld units, of deoxyribonucleic acid. [Photograph courtesy of Dr. M. H. F. Wilkins.]

or template on which could be laid down the corresponding nucleotides, which, when condensed together, would be an exact copy of the previous partner. In this way the two separate chains could each direct the synthesis of a new chain, and the resultant pair of double helices would be two exact copies of the original helix. For this and other reasons the Watson-Crick model has received considerable acceptance and has stimulated a tremendous body of theoretical speculation and experimental activity. For example, the DNA helix would have a narrow groove and a wide groove, and it was early pointed out that this wide groove could conceivably be the temporary location of a polypeptide chain built under the template guidance of the DNA nucleotide sequence or simply wrapped around peripherally to the DNA helix. The actual mechanism is now known to be more complex than this. It has, nonetheless, been proposed in a number of speculative hypotheses that the DNA serves indirectly as a template for protein synthesis. This also has been a reason for the considerable excitement over the discussions of the DNA structure. The genetic considerations will be given further attention in the next chapter.

It may be noted at this point that the phenomenon of hypochromism can be interpreted on the basis of this molecular structure. It is felt that hypochromism results from the stacking of the bases in an array of parallel planes. This geometry causes an interaction between the electrons in neighboring bases, and a consequent alteration in their interaction with light. Hypochromism can therefore serve as a measure of the extent of the existence of an ordered structure. A different example of ordered structures can be seen in the study of mixtures of certain synthetic polynucleotides. The best-known example is that of polyriboadenylic acid (poly A) and polyribouridylic acid (poly U). Each of these is a long-chain molecule consisting of a single type of monomer unit. Neither one is in a continuous helical form, nor double-stranded, but a body of evidence indicates that in each the molecule is in the form of a randomly arranged coil. Poly U is a completely random coil, while poly A does apparently have some short

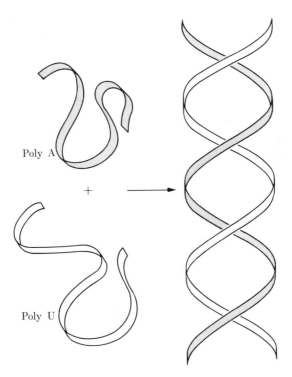

Poly A

+

Poly U

Fig. 8–11. Schematic version of the combination of poly A and poly U to form poly (A + U), a double-stranded helix.

regions of helical ordering, presumably due to hydrogen bonded adenine-adenine pairs.

When poly A and poly U are mixed, they interact to form molecular complexes. One striking indication of this was the observation that the absorbency did not correspond to the expected sum for the separate polymers. This absorbency was in fact a function of the proportions that were mixed, being clearly a minimum for an equimolar ratio of adenine and uracil. A hypochromatic effect of 25% was found for such mixtures, suggesting an extensive degree of orderly structure. Confirmation of this interpretation has been obtained from many other studies. One example was ultracentrifugal analysis. If a poly A sample and a poly U sample, with sedimentation coefficients of 5.3 S and 2.2 S, respectively, were mixed in optimal proportions, then one observes only a single peak, and this has a sedimentation coefficient of 9.9 S.

Because of the close chemical similarity of uracil to thymine, it has been proposed that the equimolar complex of poly A and poly U has a double-stranded helical structure, analogous to that of DNA. Here, the helix is stabilized by adenine-uracil bonding, in a manner similar to the adenine-thymine bonding in DNA. The transformation is illustrated in Fig. 8-11. Considerable evidence has now been accumulated to substantiate this interpretation. Other examples of molecular complex formation from synthetic polynucleotides have been discovered and studied.

8–4 Strand separation and recombination in DNA. An important and much studied property of DNA is the ability to undergo *denaturation*, named by analogy to the alterability of ordered structure in protein molecules. This process can be brought about by extremes of pH, by very low ionic strength, or by high temperature. Heat is generally the most convenient to use, because it can be applied and terminated quickly and without altering the composition of the sample. It is found that there is a decrease in hypochromism; i.e., the asorbency rises. Other observations indicate that the molecules assume a more compact form. Generally, there is no drop in molecular weight, and it is believed that the process is one of strand separation. Thus, this represents the destruction of the secondary structure of the DNA molecule, a transformation also referred to as a helix-coil transition. The transition is remarkably sharp, usually going to completion over a range of 5°. It is quite analogous to a phase change and corresponds to the melting of a one-dimensional crystal. The midpoint of the thermal transition is known as the melting temperature, T_m. This value, for a given DNA, depends on the ionic strength. For example, the T_m for DNA from *Diplococcus pneumoniae* in 0.01 M KCl is 68°, whereas it is 90° in 0.6M KCl. The melting temperature for different preparations of DNA depends on the base composition, that is, on the relative amounts

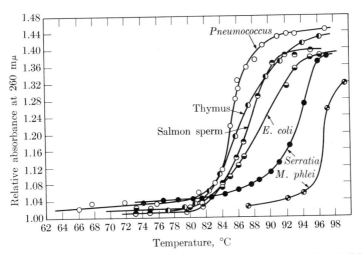

FIG. 8–12. Absorbancy-temperature curves for various samples of DNA.

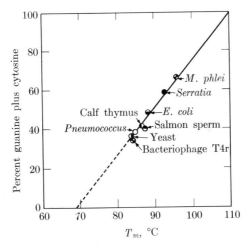

FIG. 8–13. Dependence of the melting temperature, T_m, on the guanine-cytosine content of various samples of DNA.

of G-C and of A-T pairs. This is clearly seen in Fig. 8–12. The T_m-values from these data range from 84° to 96° at an ionic strength of 0.2 and neutral pH. They are plotted against the mole percent of G-C in Fig. 8–13, and one sees a linear dependence.

If the solution is cooled, two alternative results may occur, depending on the speed of cooling. If it is cooled rapidly, substantial irreversible changes are found. Most or all of the product is in the form of random coils formed from the individual single strands. If, however, the cooling is slow, there will be a kind of "annealing" process, and the separated strands can recombine to form the Watson-Crick helix again. This has been referred to as *renatured* DNA. There are variations, however, in the degree of renaturation, depending on the source and treatment of the DNA.

One interesting application of the renaturation phenomenon is its application to the estimation of the degree of homology between different related species of plant or animal. For example, if two bacteria have some genetic relationship, a part of their DNA may be identical. The portion that is common should readily undergo formation of hybrid helices in addition to formation of double-stranded forms of the original DNA molecules. It was found, in fact, that a hybrid DNA was formed from *Escherichia coli* and *Shigella dysenteriae* when the mixture of DNA samples was heated and slowly cooled. These two bacteria are closely related organisms. On the other hand, a similar experiment with *Diplococcus pneumoniae* and *Serratia marcescens*, two quite unrelated bacteria, failed to give any hybrid molecule.

8–5 Structure of RNA. No regular molecular helical configuration for RNA, similar to that for DNA, has been proposed as a general form. Presumably the RNA molecule is built in a considerably more flexible manner. The RNA molecule is believed to be single-stranded in general, rather than double-stranded, and to follow some coiling, but not any regular or systematic molecular arrangement. Base ratios have been studied and do not demonstrate the same regularity that has been found for DNA. There is no base pairing for the whole molecule at any rate; this is an important feature distinguishing it from DNA. This feature results from the single-stranded nature of this type of nucleic acid. It is thought that base pairing might occur over limited regions of the molecule, forming some local loops or helices. A schematic picture that has been proposed for RNA is shown in Fig. 8–14. Since the ribose unit contains three hydroxyl groups rather than two as in deoxyribose, it is not impossible that branched-chain segments may occur in RNA; this type of branching would be impossible for DNA. However, the evidence for branching in RNA is by no means conclusive. The additional hydroxyl group does apparently add to the lability of the molecule, and it is indeed true that RNA preparations are more easily degraded than are preparations of DNA.

It has been shown that RNA is also of genetic significance. It may function in a direct sense, as in certain viruses, where it is the only type of nucleic acid present. This is further discussed in Chapter 10. More commonly, however, it functions in several ways to transmit the genetic information stored in DNA to those cytoplasmic centers where protein synthesis takes place, and it participates actively in this synthetic mechanism. This will be discussed at greater length in Chapter 9.

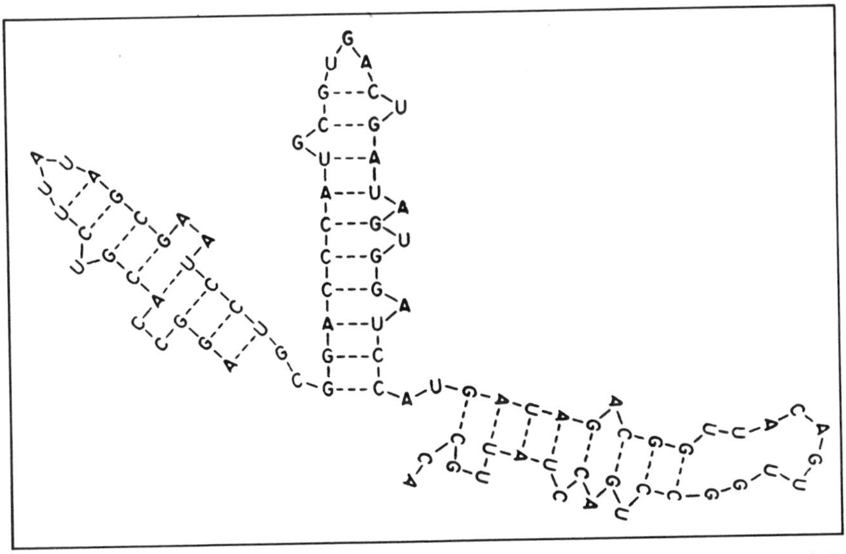

Fig. 8–14. A probable arrangement for a hypothetical chain of ribonucleic acid. Each letter represents the corresponding nucleotide. The dashed lines represent base pairing through hydrogen bonds. [Reprinted by permission from Macmillan and Company and from Dr. Paul Doty; *Nature* **188,** 98 (1960)].

It should also be kept in mind that there are several varieties of RNA, performing different functions in various cells and viruses. Four distinctive types have thus far been defined and studied. The general statements given above may well become modified as these different RNA molecules are better separated and more intimately investigated.

REFERENCES

1. E. CHARGAFF and J. N. DAVIDSON (Eds.), *The Nucleic Acids: Chemistry and Biology*, Vols. I and II, 1955, Vol. III, 1960. Academic Press, New York.

2. J. D. WATSON and F. H. C. CRICK, "Molecular Structure of Nucleic Acids: A Structure for Deoxyribose Nucleic Acid," *Nature* **171**, 737 (1953).

3. F. H. C. CRICK and J. D. WATSON, "The Complementary Structure of Deoxyribonucleic Acid," *Proc. Roy. Soc.* **A223**, 80 (1954).

4. R. LANGRIDGE, H. R. WILSON, C. W. HOOPER, M. H. F. WILKINS, and L. D. HAMILTON, "The Molecular Configuration of Deoxyribonucleic Acid. I. X-Ray Diffraction Study of a Crystalline Form of the Lithium Salt," *J. Mol. Biol.* **2**, 19 (1960).

5. R. LANGRIDGE, D. A. MARVIN, W. E. SEEDS, H. R. WILSON, C. W. HOOPER, M. H. F. WILKINS, and L. D. HAMILTON, "The Molecular Configuration of Deoxyribonucleic Acid. II. Molecular Models and Their Fourier Transforms," *J. Mol. Biol.* **2**, 38 (1960).

6. J. MARMUR and P. DOTY, "Thermal Renaturation of Deoxyribonucleic Acids," *J. Mol. Biol.* **3**, 585 (1961).

7. I. RUBENSTEIN, C. A. THOMAS, and A. D. HERSHEY, "The Molecular Weights of T2 Bacteriophage DNA and Its First and Second Breakage Products," *Proc. Nat. Acad. Sci.* **47**, 1113 (1961).

8. S. KATZ, "Low-Angle Light Scattering and the Molecular Weight of Deoxyribonucleic Acid," *Nature* **191**, 280 (1961).

9. J. R. FRESCO, B. M. ALBERTS, and P. DOTY, "Some Molecular Details of the Secondary Structure of Ribonucleic Acid," *Nature* **188**, 98 (1960).

10. R. F. STEINER and R. F. BEERS, JR., *Polynucleotides: Natural and Synthetic Nucleic Acids*. Elsevier, Amsterdam, 1961.

11. M. H. F. WILKINS, "Molecular Configuration of Nucleic Acids," *Science* **140**, 941 (1963).

12. G. ZUBAY, "The Isolation and Fractionation of Soluble Ribonucleic Acid," *J. Mol. Biol.* **4**, 347 (1962).

13. J. MARMUR and P. DOTY, "Determination of the Base Composition of Deoxyribonucleic Acid from its Thermal Denaturation Temperature," *J. Mol. Biol.* **5**, 109 (1962).

CHAPTER 9

MECHANISMS OF GENETIC CONTROL

CHAPTER 9

MECHANISMS OF GENETIC CONTROL

9–1 Introduction. There are a number of reasons for considering DNA to be of central significance in the mechanism by which genetic control is exercised in all cells and organisms. Some of the more cogent arguments can be listed as follows:

(a) *Chromosome analysis.* It is well established that chromosomes contain DNA as well as protein. By means of special microscopic procedures, one can actually measure the content of DNA in each individual cell nucleus. Alternatively, by careful analysis of extracts from homogenized tissues, one can measure the average content of DNA in the cells of that particular tissue. By both procedures it has been shown that diploid cells in a given organism all contain the same mass of DNA and furthermore that haploid cells contain just exactly one-half this quantity. This would fit well with the fact that haploid cells contain half as many chromosomes as do diploid cells. The DNA content of cell nuclei is rather large. It falls within the range of 15 to 40% of the nuclear dry weight for most types of cells. In the heads of fish sperm cells, the DNA accounts for almost 50% of the dry weight. This clearly indicates that the genetic mass, as indicated by ploidy, is closely related to the mass of DNA. In itself it does not, of course, prove that DNA has exclusive responsibility for genetic significance.

(b) *Transformation of bacteria.* There are many strains of pneumococci which can be distinguished from one another by means of tests with particular antiserum preparations. A given antiserum will agglutinate or clump one strain of pneumococcal organisms, while it will not show any reaction with other strains of pneumococcal organisms. Each such type of organism breeds true in that its continuing offspring react with the same antiserum as did the parental organisms. The reason for this specific reaction is to be traced to the outer capsule material of the bacterial cell. This capsule is made of polysaccharide (Chapter 11), and it represents another example of specificity of macromolecular structure. For each characteristic strain of pneumococci, there is a different characteristic polysaccharide substance. It has been found that a preparation of highly purified DNA can be obtained from any one particular type of pneumococci, and that when pneumococcal organisms of a second type are cultured under suitable conditions in the presence of this DNA preparation, they are transformed into organisms which are of the type that originally provided the DNA preparation. This, then, corresponds to a change in the synthesis of the capsule polysaccharide, and this change is a heritable one which is reproduced in the progeny organisms. This is a clear-cut example of the fact that DNA, by itself, can transmit genetic regulation into other cells. In other words, it can carry instructions for the synthesis of a particular substance that had not previously been synthesized by the cell. Other microorganisms have also been shown to produce DNA material which will cause transformation of certain properties that differentiate one strain of the organism from another. These properties may relate to nutritional requirements or to antibiotic sensitivities. In these situations the synthesis of specific proteins is altered in some fashion.

(c) *Infection by bacteriophage.* Certain viruses that infect bacterial cells have been extensively studied with regard to the mechanism of infection. The virus structure itself (as will be further discussed in the next chapter) consists of DNA and protein. It has been shown that the attachment of the virus particle to the bacterial cell is followed by penetration of the cell by the DNA portion of the virus, with no more than approximately 3% of the viral protein entering the cell. Essentially, all of the protein is, therefore, discarded. The subsequent chain of events consists of a drastic alteration of the metabolism within the cell, leading up to the synthesis of several hundred new virus particles which are then liberated by rupture of the cell. Here again, one can see that genetic information is quite unequivocally carried by DNA.

It is perfectly possible that some function for protein in genetic regulation is still to be elucidated. But the fact that DNA does have a commanding role in the mechanism can no longer be doubted.

It may be well to point out the significance of RNA in genetic mechanisms. It is clear that in cells of all types, whether the single cells of bacteria or those of the very complicated groupings of metazoan organisms, the DNA preserves and transmits from one cell generation to the next the bulk, if not all, of the genetic information. RNA apparently serves as an intermediate material which transfers the information from the DNA, and implements the actual synthesis of the various proteins in accordance with the blueprints that have been preserved in the DNA molecule. In certain viruses, however, RNA must be the sole carrier of genetic information. For example, the plant viruses, such as Tobacco Mosaic Virus, contain only RNA and protein. No DNA whatsoever is present. This is also true of a number of viruses that infect animals. In these instances, RNA must carry the genetic information, and experimental studies confirm this point quite adequately.

9–2 The template concept. In addition to synthesizing new supplies of DNA for the chromosomal apparatus of the subsequent daughter cells, each individual cell must synthesize a large number and variety of proteins.

Certain cells must also synthesize specialized proteins, for example, the various digestive enzymes that are secreted from certain tissues, and the antibodies that are manufactured by specialized cells. The detailed mechanism controlling the specific synthesis of each individual protein has been a tantalizing problem for many years. In early speculations, two schools of thought developed. On the one hand, it was proposed that proteins were synthesized by attaching one amino acid after another to a growing polypeptide chain and that the appropriate choice of each amino acid to be added at any time was a matter of enzyme specificity, since there would be a different enzyme to catalyze the condensation of each of the amino acids to the chain. This hypothesis has been abandoned, partly because it created the additional dilemma that the preformed enzymes, which themselves were proteins, required specific synthesis.

The alternative picture was the template idea. It was proposed that one particular macromolecule could serve as a mold or template against which the constituent monomers for the formation of another macromolecule would be arranged in proper sequence, and that subsequently these would be condensed to each other to form the chain. The crucial step of the process, of course, is the placement of the new monomer units in the correct sequence. In the earliest speculations there were conflicting proposals that protein might serve as a template for other protein or that protein might even serve as a template for nucleic acid. In more recent years, however, this picture has become much clearer and more consistent. It is now commonly felt that the fundamental template is DNA, and that this material, according to the Watson-Crick picture, can carry out the two essential functions of a genetic substance. It can duplicate itself to produce additional copies for continued preservation of the "master plan," and it can also control the synthesis of the appropriate polypeptide chains for the enzymes, structural units, and other proteins that the cell must manufacture.

Each cell nucleus contains a large number of DNA molecules, and it may be proposed that each of these has a different sequence of bases. Each such sequence of bases can be considered to be a code for a corresponding sequence of amino acids in a particular polypeptide chain. There has, therefore, been a large amount of speculation in recent years concerning the precise way in which the genetic "blueprint" (or information, as it is frequently referred to) can be transmitted from the DNA to the machinery of protein synthesis. Actually, protein synthesis occurs primarily in the ribosomes (or microsomes). These and other structures of the living cell will be discussed in detail in Chapter 13, but we must introduce the ribosome at this point. Studies with the electron microscope have shown that the cytoplasm of many cells contains an intricate and extensive arrangement of membranes and tiny particulates. The cytoplasm actually contains a network of canals which are lined with small dense particles called ribosomes. These units contain approximately 50% RNA and 50% protein. Some 80% of the RNA of the cell is contained in the ribosomes. These units not only synthesize the protein in the living cell but also can synthesize protein *in vitro* if they are supplied with the appropriate enzymes and energy sources from within the cell. Being located in the cytoplasm, these particles are at some distance from the DNA itself. It is, therefore, felt that the genetic information in DNA is first translated into a corresponding sequence of nucleotides in new RNA moelcules and that these are then transferred to the cytoplasmic sites of synthesis. Here, in some direct or indirect manner, the RNA controls the alignment of amino acids for polypeptide synthesis.

The apparent difficulty, however, is that we have only four kinds of nucleotides in DNA (*or* RNA), while we have approximately twenty kinds of amino acids whose sequence must be determined in the proteins that are formed. There must be a code, therefore, which will permit translation of a sequence of four types of nucleotide into an unambiguous corresponding sequence of approximately twenty types of amino acids. A large number of mathematical speculations have arisen to suggest how to fulfill this requirement. In most cases, the number of amino acids has been assumed to be exactly twenty. Unfortunately, experimental details are sparse, and therefore the various theories cannot be confirmed or ruled out conclusively insofar as actual proteins or natural peptides are concerned. There is by now, however, a large body of data on synthetic systems. This will be discussed below.

It would be of the utmost value for experimental study of these concepts to be able to establish the complete amino acid sequence in a particular protein whose corresponding DNA could be identified and, in addition, could have its complete nucleotide sequence established. We would then presumably be in a position to have an unequivocal determination of the mechanism of genetic coding. Several partial successes along these lines have been attained, but much remains to be clarified in the near future.

9–3 Mechanism of protein biosynthesis. We have seen above that the master plan for the construction of all macromolecular substances of a particular organism is contained in the genes, that is, in the DNA within the nucleus. We must now consider the details of the mechanism whereby the code contained in the DNA is actually implemented into the finished product of the various protein molecules. The assembly site in which protein is formed is the ribosome, within the cytoplasm.

The question remaining is two-fold. One part involves the manner in which each amino acid is identified correctly by an appropriate triplet (see Section 9–4) of nucleotides in the structure of DNA, and the other involves the means whereby the DNA information becomes transmitted to the ribosome factory. In recent years it was discovered that in fact amino acids are attached to RNA before they are assembled to form a protein and that an intermediate complex of RNA and amino acid must be formed for each amino acid before it is incorporated into a protein. It turned out, however, that the type of RNA to which amino acids are bound is not the plentiful supply of material in the ribosomes, but instead is a minor constituent of the soluble portion of the cytoplasm. This RNA was named "soluble RNA" or "S-RNA," and was found to consist of relatively small RNA molecules. It is also named "transfer RNA" because of its role in transferring the amino acids to the ribosome template. This type of RNA has a molecular weight of about 15,000–30,000 and has 50 to 100 nucleotides. It was learned that each amino acid attaches to a specific location on a different soluble RNA molecule. This reaction can take place *in vitro* quite independently of ribosomes themselves. It requires an enzyme and it requires a supply of energy. The sequence of events whereby the monomers of protein are combined is now partially understood. An amino acid must first be "activated" by reacting with adenosinetriphosphate, or ATP. The formula for this "energy-rich" molecule is shown in Fig. 9–1. This very important nucleotide has a role in many biochemical reactions within the cell. The coupling that occurs here is catalyzed by a specific enzyme,

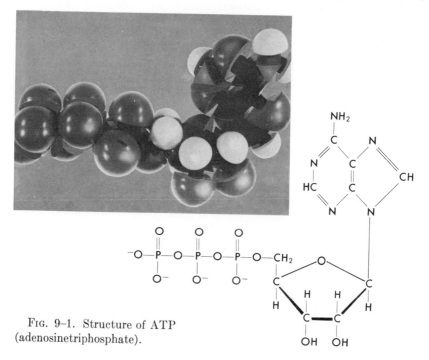

FIG. 9–1. Structure of ATP (adenosinetriphosphate).

and it is accompanied by the release of two of the phosphate groups, resulting in a conjugate of the amino acid and AMP, called an amino acidadenylate. The amino acid is now said to be "activated." The activated amino acid is then joined to a molecule of transfer RNA, being released from the AMP unit. Each amino acid is "recognized" by a different transfer RNA. The transfer RNA's carry the amino acids to the ribosomes, where they are joined in proper sequence to form a polypeptide chain. The transfer RNA's are then released intact to pick up more amino acid molecules.

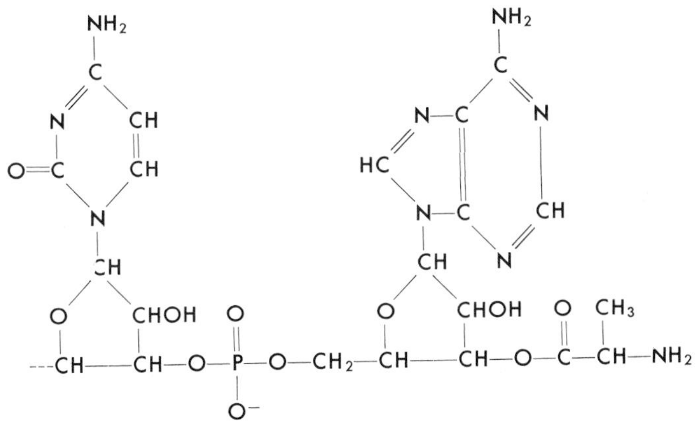

Fig. 9–2. The terminal two nucleotides and the alanine residue of Alanyl-s-RNA.

The mode of attachment of an amino acid to the end of a soluble RNA molecule is shown in Fig. 9–2. Each amino acid when attached to its corresponding transfer RNA receives an identity which can be recognized by the RNA templates in the ribosomes. This probably results from the fact that a few nucleotides in the transfer molecule are in a complementary arrangement to a corresponding group of nucleotides on the RNA template. The actual process whereby the amino acid replaces the two outer phosphate groups of transfer RNA to form an adenylic-acid-amino-acid complex is mediated by a specific enzyme. There are 20 different enzymes, each shaped to accommodate a specific amino acid. The enzyme permits the substances to be brought close together in the proper steric relationship and then to be joined.

This reaction is followed by another, in which the amino acid is transferred to its own appropriate transfer RNA. The same enzyme directs and controls this transformation. In the final form, the amino acid is attached to an adenine residue at the chain end of the transfer RNA. In fact, all of the types of transfer RNA terminate in adenylic acid, and the two subterminal units are cytidylic acid. It is presumably significant that

ATP and the end unit of transfer RNA contain the same base unit. The enzyme apparently must be assumed to contain a section that is shaped to fit this unit so that the adenylic acid of the activated amino acid complex can be readily replaced by the adenylic acid which terminates the transfer RNA. The enzyme must also be assumed to contain a steric portion which is adapted to the specific groups of nucleotides located somewhere else in the transfer RNA structure and which identifies this particular transfer RNA and therefore connects it to the correct (activated) amino acid. Some other triplet of nucleotides in the structure then locates itself on the complementary group in the ribosomal RNA. In the process of attachment the terminal group of the transfer RNA presumably bends at some angle forming an extension arm that permits the amino acids to have free access to each other along the surface of the template RNA. The final step is a condensation of the amino acid groupings to form a polypeptide chain and the splitting off of the various transfer RNA units to recycle through the cell.

It has been proposed, in very recent studies of Wilkins and his group, that transfer RNA does, in fact, have a helical structure. A schematic diagram, showing such a helix and illustrating the packing of a group of molecules into a crystalline lattice, is shown in Fig. 9–3. Each molecule is about 100 A long and has approximately $3\frac{1}{2}$ helix turns. The unpaired

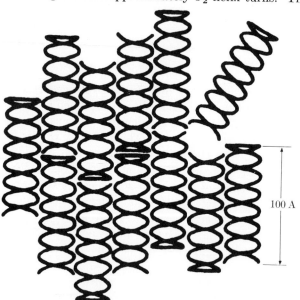

Fig. 9–3. Diagram of the arrangement of double-helical transfer RNA molecules in a crystalline array. The lines represent polynucleotide chains. A single molecule is shown at top right. Reprinted by permission from Macmillan and Company [*Nature* **194,** 1014 (1962)].

portion at the fold at the end of the molecule would seem to contain just three nucleotides. This would fit in very well with current theories that a triplet sequence of nucleotides in this molecule is responsible for the correct selection of a transfer RNA-amino acid complex against the RNA template.

It is of additional importance to understand the mechanism whereby a suitable template exists in the ribosome, so that the appropriate *S*-RNA's can be properly located. It has been discovered that cells contain a mechanism for the synthesis of a type of RNA whose specific sequence is directed by a corresponding portion of DNA, and therefore has a sequence of bases which is complementary to that in the DNA, with the substitution of uracil for thymine. This type of RNA has been termed "messenger RNA," for it is now understood that it carries the message of the information code from the DNA structure in the nucleus out to the cytoplasm and to the sites of protein synthesis in the various ribosome structures. It is now understood that this messenger RNA (*or* mRNA) attaches itself to the ribosomes; and it is this structure to which the molecules of transfer RNA attach by a complementary fit of base sequences. The ribosome by itself is inert and quite nonspecific. Ribosomes, in other words, are "for hire." They are structures which synthesize protein, but only when they are provided with appropriate instructions. The same ribosome apparently can receive instructions from any DNA source (*via* mRNA) and will then form the appropriate protein material. It is not clear how much of the RNA in a given preparation of isolated ribosomes is mRNA. The generalized scheme for the interaction of these various molecular units is shown diagrammatically in Fig. 9–4.

Quite recently, it has become clear that the *active* particle in protein synthesis is an aggregate of ribosomal particles. This cluster has been called "ergosome" by some investigators and "polyribosome", or for short, "polysome" by others. These aggregates have been seen very clearly in the electron microscope. It is felt that the individual ribosomal particles are held together by a strand of messenger RNA, since a connecting thin strand can be seen in the pictures; and it is also found that treatment with ribonuclease breaks down the aggregates, so that only single particles are then seen. Most studies of mammalian cells have been made on reticulocytes, thus involving the synthesis of hemoglobin. Polysomes from these cells usually contain five ribosome units. In contrast, polysomes from muscle have been studied more recently, and these seem to be much longer, containing 60–100 ribosome units.

It has been proposed, from the reticulocyte studies, that each individual ribosome first becomes attached to one end of a strand of mRNA, and begins to synthesize a polypeptide chain, as a consequence of the selection of amino-acyl-sRNA units. It has even been determined that each ribosome unit has two sites for the attachment of the sRNA complexes. In

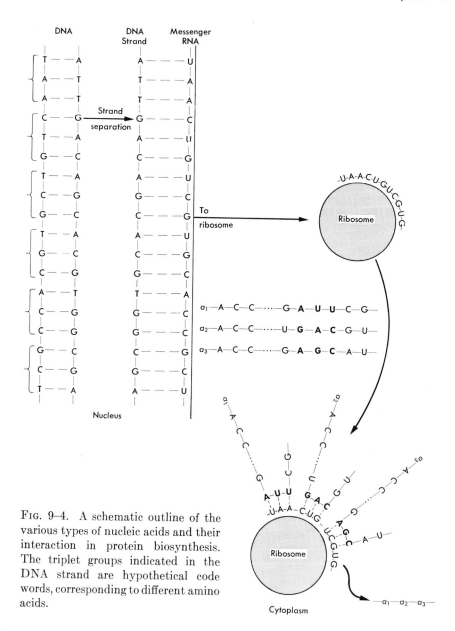

FIG. 9-4. A schematic outline of the various types of nucleic acids and their interaction in protein biosynthesis. The triplet groups indicated in the DNA strand are hypothetical code words, corresponding to different amino acids.

order that the mRNA can continue to govern the selection of these units, at the ribosomal surface, the mRNA is thought to move relative to the ribosome. After some movement of this first unit along the strand, a new ribosome particle attaches to the strand end. By the time that several, perhaps five, particles are attached at different places, the first one is at the far end, with its growth of polypeptide chain completed. It then releases both the mRNA and the polypeptide and becomes an inactive particle once more. A polysome structure therefore represents several connected ribosomes, on each of which a copy of the same polypeptide has been synthesized to a different stage of completion.

9–4 The transfer of information; the question of coding. The role of deoxyribose nucleic acid as the "blueprint" for genetic mechanisms involves at least two distinctive functions, as we have already indicated. One of these is the formation of new DNA (in other words, the replication of itself), so that this blueprint will be preserved through various generations of daughter cells and also through generations of the living organisms in an evolutionary sense. The other function is the control of protein synthesis. There are certainly activities of importance related to the synthesis of certain polysaccharides, but these will not be considered because the significance is considerably less than that of protein construction. Furthermore, it is very likely that the fundamental mechanisms that occur with proteins will explain much about the methods of polysaccharide formation. The other macromolecule is RNA, and it seems clear now that this substance is not so much formed for its own sake but primarily is involved in the formation of protein; it will, therefore, be considered in that light.

The self-replication of DNA will be considered only briefly. The suggestion that was first made by Watson and Crick with regard to the replication of DNA was the rather attractive possibility that the two chains unwrap, either partially or completely, while deoxyribose nucleotides were laid down on each of them as a template, by means of hydrogen bond formation involving specific base pairing, and that subsequently these free nucleotides were linked to each other to form complete new strands. Such a mechanism faces considerable difficulty because of the mechanical problems of the unwinding process. The untwisting of several hundred turns would seem to require a considerable supply of energy and might also encounter the hazard of tangling. Because of this dilemma several other schemes have been proposed, involving processes of breakage of covalent links along the backbone at various turns of the helix during replication, but these schemes introduce additional difficulties in themselves. Actually, the energy requirement of unwinding the helix is fairly small if the helix is restricted to rotating about its own axis. It has been shown that under these conditions there is a minimal chance of tangling and that the energy required per turn of the helix is smaller than the energy of formation of the phosphate-diester linkage. The transfer of information from parental DNA to new DNA seems then quite likely to involve unwinding at various stages.

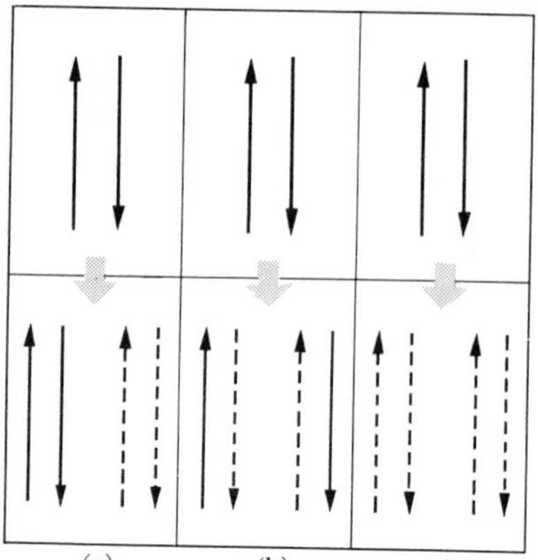

FIG. 9–5. A schematic outline of three modes of DNA replication. Each double arrow represents a double stranded DNA molecule. The mechanisms illustrated are (a) conservative, (b) semi-conservative, (c) dispersive.

Schemes of replication can be distinguished from one another in terms of the fate of the original DNA. If it remains completely intact during the replication process, so that the new collection of DNA contains all of the original parental material in one of the two daughter double helixes and none of it in the other, then a *conservative* system is said to exist. If the two individual DNA chains of the original helix remain undamaged, but are physically separated from each other so that each has a new chain partner, then a *semiconservative* system is said to exist. The original Watson-Crick scheme of replication was a semiconservative one. Finally, if the various nucleotides of the parental DNA are scattered among all the various daughter DNA molecules, such that within each chain there is a mixture of parental and new DNA material, a *dispersive* mechanism is said to exist. Considerable experimental evidence suggests that a semiconservation mechanism is the correct one for DNA replication in cellular division. The exact details of the strand separation mechanism remain to be completely elucidated. The three mechanisms are illustrated schematically in Fig. 9–5.

Our major discussion, however, has dealt with the process of synthesis of protein as directed by the information encoded in the DNA structure. One speaks of the information content of the DNA or the code for genetic information, meaning that there is a specific set of directions available in the structure of the DNA molecules which specifies the precise primary structure of every protein synthesized by the particular cell involved. It is currently believed that a given region or length of a DNA strand is responsible for the formation of a specific polypeptide chain in a protein molecule. This particular length of DNA structure is called a *cistron*, and for each of the polypeptide chains in all the protein molecules synthesized within a given cell, there must be a corresponding cistron in a DNA molecule in the nucleus. It is also assumed that the genetic information in DNA specifies only the primary structure of the protein and that the actual secondary and tertiary coilings are the direct consequence of the primary structure. It is thus believed that the information concerning the formation of various secondary bonds and the additional covalent bonds, such as disulfide links, in the formation of the higher orders of protein configuration, is all contained within the primary sequence of amino acids itself. It may well be that this occurs correctly only when the polypeptide chain is peeled off the template in the proper manner. There must also be some exceptional cases, such as the formation of antibody molecules, in which the three-dimensional structure has a specific configuration which is complementary to a particular external material, called the antigen. In this type of situation, there may well be some additional mechanism for arranging the proper tertiary configuration.

The transfer of information from DNA into protein must involve the monomer units as the units of the code. There are only 4 different kinds of bases in the DNA molecule, and yet this sequence must uniquely determine the sequence of approximately 20 amino acids along the polypeptide chain. It has been emphasized by Crick that in fact there are *precisely* 20 amino acids of interest. Almost all of them occur in every protein, although some proteins are deficient in several. For example, tryptophan does not occur in insulin. Some proteins contain amino acids other than the "magic 20," but it is generally believed that these amino acids are actually produced in the final polypeptide chain by a modification of another amino acid that was first incorporated. An example is hydroxyproline in collagen (also discussed in Chapter 13). Another example is thyroxine in thyroglobulin. These units result, in all probability, from alteration of, respectively, proline and tyrosine, which had already been assembled into the polypeptide chain. It can also be reasoned that cystine is not incorporated as such and does not need to be coded, since its existence in the protein surely results from the oxidation of a pair of cysteine residues. Experimental proof of these contentions is not yet available. Table 9–1 shows a list of the 20 amino acids that would definitely necessitate coding.

It would require at least three bases to select a unique member from among the 20 amino acids, since 4^2 is only 16, but 4^3 is 64. In other words, 4 bases taken 2 at a time would give 4^2 arrangements while 4 bases taken 3 at a time would give 4^3 arrangements. From this reasoning, the concept for a *triplet* of bases developed, as a minimum equivalent to a single amino acid. The geometry of a direct transfer of information from the DNA molecule to a polypeptide molecule created some difficulty, however, in the early theories. The distance required for three nucleotide pairs along the DNA molecule is about 10 A (3 × 3.4 A), while the distance between amino acids in an extended polypeptide chain is only about 3.7 A. The first mechanism for a code under these conditions was suggested by Gamow.

TABLE 9–1

TRIPLET CODE UNITS FOR AMINO ACIDS AS DEDUCED
FROM THE FIRST GROUP OF STUDIES*

Amino acid	Nucleotide code	Amino acid	Nucleotide code
Alanine	UCG	Leucine	UUA UUC UUG
Arginine	UCG	Lysine	UAA
Asparagine	UAA UAC	Methionine	UAG
Aspartic acid	UAG	Phenylalanine	UUU
Cysteine	UUG	Proline	UCC
Glutamic acid	UAG	Serine	UUC
Glutamine	UCG	Threonine	UAC
Glycine	UGG	Tryptophan	UGG
Histidine	UAC	Tyrosine	UUA
Isoleucine	UUA	Valine	UUG

* The sequence of nucleotides within each code word is unknown.

He suggested an overlapping scheme in which N amino acids would be determined by a sequence involving $(N + 2)$ bases. This might be diagrammed as ATATTCAG . . ., where A, T, C, and G, represent the four different nucleotides that are to be involved; and we further assume that ATA is the code for one amino acid, TAT is the code for the next amino acid, ATT is the code for the third amino acid, etc. This type of overlapping code has two consequences. For one thing, it should be possible to find proteins of very similar nature but only slightly different structure, possibly those occurring as the corresponding proteins in different species of organisms or occurring as mutations that accidentally are formed with time in a given type of organism. In such alternative proteins, two or even three amino acids in sequence should differ. No mutations or comparisons of this type have been observed. Secondly, many pairs of amino acids would be restricted; that is, not all amino acid sequences could be possible. Analysis of known sequences of amino acids in proteins has shown that an overlapping code of this or any other sort is extremely improbable, since sequences have indeed been found which would not be possible under these conditions.

Crick and his co-workers later suggested the alternative mechanism that when DNA acts as a template for the formation of protein the amino acids themselves do not actually fit on the DNA template. They assumed that instead there is some type of adapter molecule which would attach to three nucleotides of DNA, and also that at the other end of the adapter molecule, the one specific amino acid would be attached. This particular theoretical approach was very nicely confirmed by the subsequent discovery of transfer RNA. This removed the spatial dilemma, and as such one had to consider the problem only from the viewpoint of coding. Crick and his colleagues suggested that a nonoverlapping code could be formed by proposing that various triplets of bases would specify the individual amino acids. It was also suggested that the code was comma-less. In other words, it should be unambiguous as to where the reading of each triplet is to begin. There should also be starting and stopping commands to signify which is the beginning base for the triplet sequence, and which is the final triplet for a particular polypeptide chain. One assumed that certain triplets (called sense triplets) do correspond to certain amino acids and that other triplets (called non-sense triplets) do not. A group of speculations was evolved in this way, centering largely around the questions, whether a coded sequence was comma-less, whether only one triplet could code for each amino acid, whether there really were non-sense triplets, and so forth. For example, one kind of coding philosophy assumed that triplets should be chosen in such a way that two sense triplets adjacent to each other must not contain any sense triplets among the overlap units. For example, the sequence

$$\text{ATACGTTCAACC}$$

contains four successive sense triplets, if one has agreed in advance that such triplets as TAC, ACG, GTT, etc., are non-sense triplets. In other words, the meaningful triplets are picked out uniquely if commas are inserted, that is, ATA, CGT, TCA, ACC. It was known that schemes could be devised whereby, out of 64 possible arrangements of four units, precisely 20 were needed to be sense triplets and the remaining 44 were non-sense triplets. Thus, it is possible to deduce the number 20 in a completely natural way from the number 4. The scheme of Crick and his co-workers was worked out by arranging the 4 units in the following manner:

$$AT_T^A \qquad {}_T^A CT_C^A \qquad {}^A_C TG{}^T_G^{\,A}{}_{C}, $$

where

$$AT_T^A$$

means that two of the permitted triplets are ATA and ATT, etc. The number of permitted triplets that comes from this scheme is exactly 20. Several other codes of this type have been proposed, and it has in fact been shown that there are 5, and only 5, codes of this sort which satisfy the comma-free condition and contain 20 units. It should be clearly understood, however, that the types of code pattern discussed above have not yet been proven but were proposed as reasonable speculations.

In the past year or two, however, considerable activity has gone into the question of discovering the actual codes that specify each of the 20 amino acids. While this field of research is in considerable flux at the moment, some preliminary discoveries may be mentioned. It was shown, for example, in 1961, by Nirenberg and Matthaei, that if a synthetic "RNA" molecule consisting of only uridine (poly U) is introduced to an appropriate collection of ribosomes, obtained from *E. coli*, then a small amount of peptide will be formed consisting of only phenylalanine. From this it was suggested that the code for phenylalanine is UUU. This in itself would be the transcription of an AAA sequence of DNA. This first discovery, soon confirmed by Ochoa and his co-workers, of a nucleotide triplet corresponding to an amino acid initiated a tremendous surge of both experimental activity and consequent theoretical speculation. It should be noted that the polyuridylic acid, in these first experiments, served as an artificial messenger, and that the appropriate corresponding amino acid was discovered by testing each amino acid separately for its incorporation into an acid-insoluble product. Such a product indicated that polypeptide formation had occurred, and the incorporation was proven by using a radioactivity-labeled amino acid in each case. Only phenylalanine was incorporated. The next logical step was to try various polynucleotides containing several bases, randomly ordered, as coding assemblies. Polymers with different ratios of two or three bases did in fact cause significant incorporation of different amino acids. For each preparation, the probability of any particular sequence of three nucleotides can be calculated. A series of such studies was soon reported from Nirenberg's laboratory at the National Institutes of Health in Bethesda and from Ochoa's laboratory at New York University, and as a result, 22 triplet combinations, all containing U, were proposed as codes for 19 amino acids, together with an inferred code of U, C, and G for glutamine. The list of these triplets is shown in Table 9–1. It should be emphasized that the sequence of bases within each triplet was quite unknown, and that this was an arbitrary parameter at that time. This may be said to have ended the first era of protein cryptography.

Several points had become apparent by this time. One was that each amino acid was coded by a single triplet, except for leucine and asparagine. A degenerate code is defined as one in which two or more different coding units can direct the incorporation of the same amino acid into protein. It was seen that the code was degenerate for these two amino acids, but there was uncertainty as to the generality of this situation. Part of the confusion may have arisen from the views then widely current that essentially all but 20 of the possible triplets should be non-sense units. A more serious dilemma arose from the rather startling fact that these triplets contained a great preponderance of uracil. The average composition of uracil was, in fact, 48 percent. This was much higher than the approximately 30-percent level of uracil found in various samples of natural messenger RNA. It was suspected that perhaps U-containing units had been selected by the methods of study, but this could not be readily proven until later, when the techniques were improved so that polymers that did not contain U were successful as templates. As it turned out, this problem and the one about degeneracy were solved as simultaneous developments. There were also some doubts expressed by some workers that the code words must be triplets. It was argued that a doublet code could also explain most of the data.

During the next year, developments reported from Nirenberg's and Ochoa's laboratories showed that polyribonucleotides not containing U could be used to stimulate amino acid incorporation. It was thus discovered that a reasonable number of non-U triplets did occur. At the same time, the total numbers of coding triplets was so increased that at least half the amino acids had more than one code word. The tabulated results from these two groups are shown in Table 9–2. Of the 49 different triplets, there are only a few uncertainties. It seems likely that every amino acid will be found to have several code words and that all the possible triplets are really code words. The converse, fortunately, is not true, even according to these more extensive data; each triplet codes uniquely for a particular amino acid. Only one exception is known, and this is UUU, which codes not only for phenylalanine, but also, less effectively, for leucine. This might be an artifact of the experimental situation or it may have some fundamental significance. These various findings probably end the second era of protein cryptography.

In recent reports, a totally new approach has been applied to the determination of nucleotide code words, and this method gives promise of determining the actual sequences, at last. In this procedure, ribosomes are incubated with various oligonucleotides and then tested with various radiolabeled amino-acid-sRNA complexes. With the correct choice of constituents, the C^{14}-amino-acyl-sRNA is bound to the ribosomes; otherwise, it is not. Positive results can be quickly and easily discovered by washing the suspension on a plastic filter sheet, which retains the ribosomes, and then determining whether this filter is radioactive. In this way, it was found that trinucleotides were effective and specific in corresponding to an amino acid. For example, UUU, AAA, and CCC were found to direct the binding of phenylalanine-, lysine-, and proline-sRNA, respectively. This added *direct* proof that triplets probably function as the code words. It was also shown that the dinucleotide, UU, was very poor, and that the tetra-, penta-, and hexanucleotide forms were no more active than the trinucleotide.

Additional structural details of code words could be studied. Triplets with 5′-terminal phosphate were more active as templates than those without terminal phosphate. Triplets with 3′-terminal phosphate were markedly less active as templates. Most exciting of all, it was now possible

TABLE 9–2

AMINO ACID CODE AS DETERMINED AT THE NATIONAL
INSTITUTES OF HEALTH AND AT NEW YORK UNIVERSITY*

Amino acid	Nucleotide code	
	NIH	NYU
Alanine	CCG	CUG CAG CCG
Arginine	CGC	GUC GAA GCC
Asparagine	ACA	UAA CUA CAA
Aspartic acid	—	GUA GCA
Cysteine	UUG or UGG	GUU
Glutamic acid	ACA AGA AUG	AAG AUG
Glutamine	ACA	AGG ACA
Glycine	UGG	GUG GAG GCG
Histidine	ACC	AUC ACC
Isoleucine	UUA	UUA AAU
Leucine	GUU CUU AUU (UUU)	UAU UUC UGU
Lysine	AAA AAC AAG AAU	AUA AAA
Methionine	UGA	UGA
Phenylalanine	UUU	UUU UUC
Proline	CCC CCU CCA CCG	CUC CCC CAC
Serine	UCG UUC UCC	CUU CCU ACG
Threonine	CAC CAA	UCA ACA CGC
Tryptophan	UGG	UGG
Tyrosine	UAU	AUU
Valine	UGU	UUG

* The sequence of nucleotides within each code word is unknown.

to determine actual sequences. For valine, it was learned that the effective triplet was GUU; the sequence isomers, UGU and UUG, were not active. Furthermore, GUU had no effect on the complexes that corresponded to the other amino acids. It was therefore proposed as a specific codeword in messenger RNA. It may be anticipated that all the triplet sequence codes will now be quickly discovered. Among other questions, it will then be necessary to learn which ones are actually utilized in natural RNA, whether nonsense words are employed, and whether there are preferences in the utilization of synonym alternatives for a particular amino acid.

9–5 Molecular disease—sickle-cell anemia. The mechanisms that regulate the synthesis of protein can occasionally produce errors. For example, the chemical structure of a single base might be altered by the chance impact of an x-ray beam or cosmic ray in the immediate vicinity of this unit. As a result, a different amino acid might be selected for the corresponding point in the protein molecule. Or possibly, several bases may be altered, and then a quite different protein may be produced, or perhaps no protein at all—a protein defect. Such alterations are generally observed as mutations in the organism. Mutations can be elicited by the introduction into the organism of certain chemical substances, as well as by radiation, or they can arise spontaneously; but all the agents are believed to operate by alteration of one or more bases. Through study of various groups of mutations in certain organisms, it could be reasonably inferred that whenever one particular enzyme is missing in a mutant (a protein defect), then a corresponding gene (or, as we might now say, a cistron) is missing, or is at least inoperative. Based on numerous studies, the concept developed that for every enzyme (and, by extension, for every protein) there exists a corresponding gene, and this was called the "one-gene-one-enzyme" hypothesis. There are many examples of protein defect or modification that have been studied, but here we shall consider only one of them. This is the basis for a human disease, involving the hemoglobin molecule in its slightly different molecular forms.

The red blood cells of certain individuals show a reversible change in shape in response to changes in oxygen concentration. In the venous circulation, these cells may be distorted into a crescent sickle-like shape. In some of the affected individuals, the condition is so severe that there is an extensive destruction of the red cells with a resultant chronic anemia, which has been called "sickle-cell anemia." The explanation for this condition of the red cells can be found in the nature of the hemoglobin contained within the cells. It has been found that actually a different type of hemoglobin is present and can be distinguished electrophoretically. In other words, in an electrostatic field at a certain pH, this form of hemoglobin could be seen to migrate at a slightly different rate from the rate of hemoglobin from normal individuals. We can therefore distinguish normal adult hemoglobin, called hemoglobin A, and sickle-cell hemoglobin, called hemoglobin S.

This disease is transmitted under genetic control. We may have individuals who are homozygous for either the normal or the sickle-cell condition, or heterozygous for the combination. In the latter case, the condition is very much milder and is called "sickle-cell trait." If there are offspring from two people with sickle-cell trait, the distribution among the children is that of normal sickle-cell trait and sickle-cell anemia, in the Mendelian ratio of 1 : 2 : 1. Sickle-cell trait can be detected from the fact that these red cells will sickle if the oxygen pressure is reduced sufficiently, i.e., well below the value needed to affect the cells from a person with sickle-cell anemia. In the chromosomes of the normal adult, there are present the genes for the synthesis of hemoglobin A, and there is a complete absence of sickle-cell gene. Correspondingly, the red cells of this individual contain 100 percent hemoglobin A. This hemoglobin, then, is the phenotypic manifestation of the particular gene. In the somatic cells of individuals with sickle-cell anemia, on the other hand, there are two sickle-cell genes and a complete absence of the normal allele. Correspondingly, there is in the red cells 100 percent of hemoglobin S. In the intermediate condition of sickle-cell trait, there is, in the genetic apparatus, one gene for sickle cell and one normal gene; and correspondingly in the red cells, there are approximately equal amounts of hemoglobin A and hemoglobin S.

This disorder, sickle-cell anemia, has been termed a *molecular disease*, because its characteristic symptoms can be explained entirely on the basis of a different structure of one particular macromolecule. There are many hemoglobins other than A and S, even if we restrict ourselves just to the human varieties. For one thing, there is one other principal normal form of hemoglobin. This, called hemoglobin F, because it is found during fetal life, normally disappears by the end of the first year of postnatal life. There are also several minor components in normal individuals. However, with regard to abnormal hemoglobin, a long and constantly growing list can be described. The next most important one after hemoglobin S is hemoglobin C. This species of molecule may also be responsible for a particular type of disease. It shows an electrophoretic migration rate which is different from both A and S. There are also hemoglobins D, E, G, H, I, J, and others.

The differences between hemoglobin S and hemoglobin A in electrophoretic migration rate provide a clue to the nature of the chemical differences between these two macromolecules. It has been found that at alkaline pH values, a molecule of hemoglobin A contains two more negative charges (or two fewer positive charges) than does a molecule of hemoglobin S.

The amino acid sequence for hemoglobin A has been worked out in very recent studies; but even the partial sequences that had been elucidated a few years ago were sufficient to explain the difference between hemoglobin A and hemoglobin S. This comparison is shown in Fig. 9–6. The corresponding information for hemoglobin C is also given. This nonapeptide is

HbA   ...$^+$His . Val . Leu . Leu . Thr . Pro . Glu$^-$. Glu$^-$. Lys$^+$ . ...

HbS   ...$^+$His . Val . Leu . Leu . Thr . Pro . Val . Glu$^-$. Lys$^+$ . ...

HbC   ...$^+$His . Val . Leu . Leu . Thr . Pro . Lys$^+$. Glu$^-$. Lys$^+$ . ...

FIG. 9–6. Amino acid sequences in the *distinguishing* peptide from hemoglobulins A, S, and C. The arrows indicate the points of attack by trypsin, which liberated this peptide.

among the fragments obtained by partial digestion of hemoglobin with the enzyme trypsin, and only this peptide in the digest mixture differs between the different hemoglobins. A residue of glutamic acid in hemoglobin A is replaced by a residue of valine in hemoglobin S. As a result, the negative electric charge is decreased by one unit. Since each molecule is made of two identical half-molecules, this corresponds to a change of two electrical units of charge per molecule, which explains quantitatively the observed difference in electrophoretic mobility. In hemoglobin C, this is carried one step further. This very subtle distinction must also be represented in some minute change in the corresponding nucleotide sequence of the DNA portion that serves as a template for hemoglobin synthesis. It has been known for some time that when hemoglobin is placed in an acid medium, the molecule splits into two dissimilar subunits. Each of these contains two polypeptide chains, which in hemoglobin A are designated α and β, or white and black, as was discussed in Chapter 6. When the solution is neutralized, the two halves of the molecule recombine to form the complete hemoglobin structure. In the total molecule of molecular weight 67,000, there are two identical α-chains and two identical β-chains. Hemoglobin A is then designated as $\alpha_2^A \beta_2^A$, which means that there are two α-chains of the type first found in hemoglobin A and similarly two β-chains. This is also true of the abnormal hemoglobins, but in them there is an alteration in the amino acid sequence of either both α-chains or both β-chains. For example, hemoglobin S contains the same α-chains as hemoglobin A but a slightly different β-chain, termed a β^S-chain. Hence, this molecule can be written as $\alpha_2^A \beta_2^S$. As yet, no hemoglobins have been found to have alterations in both their α-chains and β-chains. Apparently, a separate gene or cistron controls the synthesis of each pair of chains. After the two pairs are synthesized separately, they join together to form the complete protein molecule.

References

1. W. D. McElroy and B. Glass (Eds.), *A Symposium on the Chemical Basis of Heredity.* Johns Hopkins Press, Baltimore, 1957.

2. R. B. Drysdale and A. R. Peacocke, "The Molecular Basis of Heredity," *Biol. Rev.* **36,** 537 (1961).

3. M. B. Hoagland, "Nucleic Acids and Proteins," *Scientific American,* December, 1959.

4. F. H. C. Crick, "On Protein Synthesis," *The Biological Replication of Macromolecules,* in *Symp. Soc. Exptl. Biol.* **12,** 138 (1958).

5. C. Levinthal, "Coding Aspects of Protein Synthesis," *Biophysical Science—A Study Program.* Wiley, New York, 1959.

6. J. Hurwitz and J. J. Furth, "Messenger RNA," *Scientific American,* February, 1962.

7. M. SPENCER, W. FULLER, M. H. F. WILKINS, and G. L. BROWN, "Determination of the Helical Configuration of Ribonucleic Acid Molecules by X-ray Diffraction Study of Crystalline Amino-Acid Transfer Ribonucleic Acid," *Nature* **194**, 1014 (1962).

8. M. W. NIRENBERG and J. H. MATTHAEI, "The Dependence of Cell-Free Protein Synthesis in *E. coli* upon Naturally Occurring or Synthetic Polyribonucleotides," *Proc. Natl. Acad. Sci. U. S.* **47**, 1588 (1961).

9. P. LENGYEL, J. F. SPEYER, and S. OCHOA, "Synthetic Polynucleotides and the Amino Acid Code," *Proc. Natl. Acad. Sci. U. S.* **47**, 1936 (1961).

10. M. W. NIRENBERG, "The Genetic Code, II," *Scientific American*, March, 1963.

11. R. V. ECK, "Genetic Code: Emergence of a Symmetrical Pattern," *Science* **140**, 477 (1963).

12. V. M. INGRAM, *The Hemoglobins in Genetics and Evolution*. Columbia University Press, New York, 1963.

13. P. F. DAVISON, D. FREIFELDER, and B. W. HOLLOWAY, "Interruptions in the Polynucleotide Strands in Bacteriophage DNA," *J. Mol. Biol.* **8**, 1(1964).

14. M. MESELSON and F. W. STAHL, "The Replication of DNA in *Escherichia coli*," *Proc. Nat. Acad. Sci.* **44**, 671 (1958).

15. J. R. WARNER, A. RICH, and C. E. HALL, "Electron Microscope Studies of Ribosomal Clusters Synthesizing Hemoglobin," *Science* **138**, 1399 (1962).

16. C. LEVINTHAL, A. KEYNAN, and A. HIGA, "Messenger RNA Turnover and Protein Synthesis in *B. subtilis* Inhibited by Actinomycin D," *Proc. Nat. Acad. Sci.* **48**, 1631 (1962).

17. J. D. WATSON, "Involvement of RNA in the Synthesis of Proteins," *Science* **140**, 17 (1963).

18. T. STAEHELIN, F. O. WETTSTEIN, and H. NOLL, "Breakdown of Rat-Liver Ergosomes *in vivo* after Actinomycin Inhibition of Messenger RNA Synthesis," *Science* **140**, 180 (1963).

19. A. RICH, S. PENMAN, Y. BECKER, J. DARNELL, and C. HALL, "Polyribosomes: Size in Normal and Polio-Infected HeLa Cells," *Science* **142**, 1658 (1963).

20. J. R. WARNER, P. M. KNOPF, and A. RICH, "A Multiple Ribosomal Structure in Protein Synthesis," *Proc. Nat. Acad. Sci.* **49**, 122 (1963).

21. G. ZUBAY, "Molecular Model for Protein Synthesis," *Science* **140**, 1092 (1963).

22. W. GILBERT, "Polypeptide Synthesis in *Escherichia coli*. II. The Polypeptide Chain and S-RNA," *J. Mol. Biol.* **6**, 389 (1963).

23. J. R. WARNER and A. RICH, "The Number of Soluble RNA Molecules on Reticulocyte Polyribosomes," *Proc. Nat. Acad. Sci.* **51**, 1134 (1964).

24. P. LEDER and M. NIRENBERG, "RNA Codewords and Protein Synthesis. II. Nucleotide Sequence of a Valine RNA Codeword," *Proc. Nat. Acad. Sci.* **52**, 420 (1964).

25. M. NIRENBERG and P. LEDER, "RNA Codewords and Protein Synthesis. The Effect of Trinucleotides upon the Binding of sRNA to Ribosomes," *Science* **145**, 1399 (1964).

26. C. R. WOESE, "Universality in the Genetic Code," *Science* **144**, 1030 (1964).

27. H. E. UMBARGER, "Intracellular Regulatory Mechanisms," *Science* **145**, 674 (1964).

CHAPTER 10

VIRUSES

CHAPTER 10

VIRUSES

10–1 Introduction. It is well known that viruses are agents which are responsible for a large number of diseases in plants and animals and also in bacteria. While it will be helpful to attempt a definition for this entity, it should be kept in mind that no definition will perfectly satisfy all the experimental results, nor will it give fully satisfying comparisons in concept with regard to other types of structure. It has been much debated as to whether viruses should be considered as molecules or organisms, but this distinction should really be seen as a semantic trap, covering our deep ignorance of the essential characteristics which underlie the phenomena that differentiate living systems from nonliving. Some of the important characteristics of viruses are that they are submicroscopic entities (with a maximum dimension smaller than about 2000 A) which are capable of being introduced into specific living cells. Unless they enter such host cells, viruses do not replicate; they cannot be cultivated, or grown or reproduced on artificial media in the way that, for example, bacterial organisms can be cultured. The cells that can act as host cells are narrowly defined for each particular virus, and this specificity between virus and host cells is of some importance in understanding the nature of the interaction. Finally, viruses reproduce or replicate themselves inside such cells, leading generally to a liberation of a large number of virus units in place of the single unit that had originally infected the cell. A recent definition (Luria, 1959) for these entities states that "Viruses are elements of cellular genetic material that can determine, in the cells where they multiply, the biosynthesis of a specific apparatus for their own transfer to other cells." This concept emphasizes the genetic aspect of viruses, since after entering the cell, they wrest control of the metabolic machinery from the DNA of the host cell and subvert the biosynthetic process for the purpose of manufacturing the enzymes and other proteins, as well as nucleic acids, which will be used for the virus itself.

Viruses are of particular interest to biophysicists, because they represent macromolecular structures which are very complex compared with molecules and yet are quite simple compared with whole cells in composition and organization. Thus, the virus entity carries a set of genetic instructions which, with some aid from a host cell, can direct the synthesis of additional virus particles and also of the related intermediate macromolecules. It involves the same type of biosynthetic process—of fabrica-

150

tion of complicated protein and nucleic acid molecules—as occurs ordinarily in the life of every normal cell. But the virus represents a substantial portion of the genetic machinery that can be isolated from all the rest of the cell and subjected to detailed analysis. Such analyses would include data on the nucleotide and amino acid sequences, as well as on matters of structural symmetry, subunits of organization, and general principles of size and shape. This eventual fund of knowledge should help very considerably in formulating a better comprehension of the analogous mechanisms within cells.

10–2 Types of viruses. There are a very large number of viruses, and they differ considerably in size, shape, and other parameters. One can make a classification in terms of the type of host that is involved. We can, therefore, consider the following four groups:

(1) *Plant viruses.* These infect only angiosperms. Examples are TMV (Tobacco Mosaic Virus), BSV (Bushy Stunt Virus), TYMV (Turnip Yellow Mosaic Virus), and SBMV (Southern Bean Mosaic Virus).

(2) *Animal viruses.* These infect mammals and birds, and possibly amphibia. Examples are vaccinia virus, influenza virus, rabbit papilloma virus, and poliovirus.

(3) *Insect viruses.* These cause diseases in certain types of insect larvae.

(4) *Bacterium viruses or bacteriophages.* Many types of bacteria can be infected by virus, and possibly every bacterium will be found to have its viral parasites. The most famous and most extensively studied group are the coliphages, or T-phages, which infect *Escherichia coli* organisms. However, there are many other examples.

Viruses also differ in their morphologic appearance, and this can also be used as a basis for classification:

(1) Some have a breadloaf appearance. An example is vaccinia, which has dimensions of 2700 × 2300 × 2300 A. This is a very large and complex structure. It even has a limiting membrane.

(2) Some are linear in form, including most of the insect viruses and several of the plant viruses. The outstanding example is tobacco mosaic virus, which is shaped in the form of a stiff rod with dimensions of 150 × 3000 A.

(3) Many viruses seem to have a perfectly spherical shape. When this matter is examined more closely, however, it is found that these are actually polyhedra, and most commonly the shape is that of an icosahedron (a regular polyhedron with 20 faces). A number of plant viruses, such as TYMV, SBMV, and BSV, are in this group. All of these are about the same size (namely, approximately 300 A in diameter) and do not have any limiting membrane. The spheroidal group also includes a number of animal viruses, such as poliovirus, influenza virus, rabbit papilloma virus,

mumps virus, and others. These have various sizes ranging from 400 Å to 4500 Å in diameter.

(4) The additional shape that is sometimes found is that of a head and tail, or tadpole-like arrangement, and this has been found only among certain bacteriophages. The best known examples are the *E. coli* agents which have been named T1, T2, . . ., T7.

In very recent years, there has been a growing interest in virus structures, as examples of symmetric assemblies of subunit particles. The small and the medium-sized virus particles can be well described by such an analysis. According to current concepts, the infective virus particle or *virion* consists essentially of a core made of a single kind of nucleic acid and surrounded by a protein shell or *capsid*. The capsid is constructed from a number of structural subunits called *capsomeres*. These have been defined *and counted* in high magnification electron microscope pictures. They, therefore, constitute structural units that are discernible morphologically. They have been found to come in different numbers for different virus groups. The existence of structural subunits has also been inferred in many instances from x-ray crystallographic studies, as interpreted by certain symmetry considerations. The numbers of such units are not necessarily the same as for the capsomeres. A third type of unit is the chemical subunit, actually separable into the form of a purified protein, which is generally smaller than the capsomere unit. The larger and more complicated virions may also have additional structures, such as an *envelope* surrounding the capsid, or a tail structure.

These considerations have also been used to provide a newer scheme for the classification of viruses. This is illustrated in Table 10–1. The cubic symmetry refers to the spheroidal particles mentioned previously. They have all been found to be icosahedra. The helical symmetry is either that of a stiff rod, as in tobacco mosaic virus, or as in the other examples, that of a flexible, highly bent, and coiled rod, wrapped up inside an envelope. The complex symmetry involves particles that cannot really be analyzed by any single system of symmetry.

10–3 Chemical nature of viruses. The most important concept in describing the chemistry of viruses is that of nucleoprotein. All viruses contain nucleoprotein, and some viruses are nothing but nucleoprotein. This can be outlined as follows:

(1) *Plant viruses.* All plant viruses contain RNA and protein. RNA is the only nucleic acid to be found in these entities.

(2) *Bacteriophages.* These viruses (with very few exceptions) contain DNA plus protein. The quantity of DNA per particle is very large, sometimes thought to be a single molecule or only two or three molecules, and it has formed the subject for considerable correlation of genetic mecha-

TABLE 10–1

VIRUS CLASSIFICATION ACCORDING TO TYPE OF
SYMMETRY AND CAPSOMERE NUMBER*

Type of symmetry	Virus	Number of capsomeres	Dimensions of capsid	Nucleic acid
Cubic	Tipula iridescent	812	130 mμ	DNA
	Adenovirus	252	70	DNA
	Herpes simplex	162	100	DNA
	Polyoma	42	45	DNA
	Warts	42	50	?
	Turnip yellow mosaic	32	28	RNA
	φX174	12	25	DNA
Helical	Tobacco mosaic	2130	300 × 15	RNA
	Mumps	—	17	RNA
	Influenza	—	10	RNA
Complex	T-even bacteriophage	—	100 × 70, head	DNA
	Vaccinia	—	300 × 240	DNA

* Only a selected number of examples are listed.

nisms with DNA structure. In early studies it was felt that RNA was also present, but this was eventually completely ruled out. It is now known, however, that there are one or two bacterial viruses that are made of RNA + protein, and these are, therefore, very similar to the plant viruses. These rare exceptions need not concern us here.

(3) *Insect viruses.* Some of these contain DNA and some contain RNA, but apparently none contains both.

(4) *Animal viruses.* These may be either RNA or DNA viruses (apparently the mixture of nucleic acids does not occur, although there is no conclusive evidence concerning the larger units). Examples of an RNA virus are poliovirus and influenza virus, and examples of a DNA virus are vaccinia virus and rabbit papilloma virus.

As mentioned above, it has been found that the protein forms the outer surface of the virus and that the nucleic acid is located either in the center or, at any rate, below the surface of the structure. One may think of a virus, therefore, as a system for safe transport, by means of a protein protective shell, of a unit of DNA or RNA for the purpose of transmitting genetic information from one host cell to another. Some of the large viruses contain additional constituents, such as enzymes, lipids, and polysaccharides. We shall now proceed to consider only two examples in some greater detail.

10–4 The tobacco mosaic virus molecule. This virus was the first one to be discovered, and it initiated the discipline of virology. It causes a mottling disease of tobacco plants showing discolored spots on the leaves, as the general indication. These lesions constitute the mosaic pattern of injury sites. Some variants or strains of the virus are more destructive than others and may kill the plant. But, generally, the disease is fairly mild and is localized in the leaves that have been infected. It was also the first virus to be purified. In 1935 it was found that this infectious activity could be purified and even crystallized and stored for an indefinite period of time in this completely inert state, showing the properties of a nonliving chemical substance. Chemical analysis showed it to be a nucleoprotein. However, it could at any subsequent time be redissolved and rubbed onto tobacco plant leaves, whereupon an infection would follow and a large quantity of new virus would be formed. It is also perhaps the most thoroughly studied virus. By direct visualization in the electron microscope, it is seen to be a stiff rod with dimensions of 150 × 3000 A. Pictures are shown in Fig. 10–1, and a schematic diagram is given in Fig. 10–2.

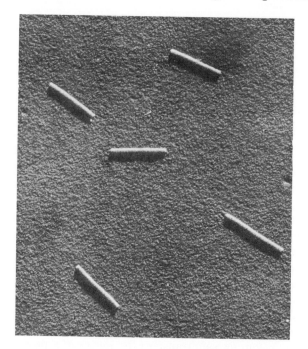

Fig. 10–1. Electron micrograph of tobacco mosaic virus. The rod-shaped forms can be seen in this shadowed preparation. [Reprinted by permission from American Chemical Society and from Dr. Wendell M. Stanley. Photograph courtesy of Dr. W. M. Stanley.]

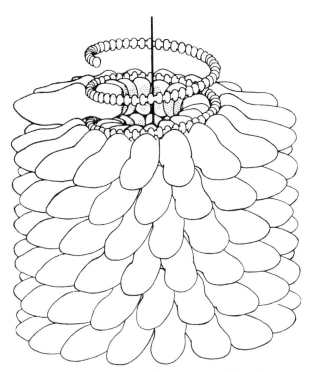

Fig. 10-2. A schematic diagram for the structure of the tobacco mosaic virus rod. The internal helix is the RNA and the external bodies are the protein subunits. This picture shows about $\frac{1}{20}$ of the total length. The entire rod has 2130 protein subunits in 130 turns of the helix. Reprinted by permission from American Chemical Society and from Dr. Wendell M. Stanley.

The cross-section of this rod seems to be hexagonal, and there is apparently a spiral or helix of RNA which is held stiffly in place by the layers of protein material. The molecular weight of this molecule is 40,000,000. This molecular weight has been determined by a large number of procedures which, in general, give good agreement. The information from the ultracentrifuge and diffusion method can, for example, be employed. The sedimentation coefficient was found to be 185 S, when suitably extrapolated. The diffusion coefficient is 0.53×10^{-7} cm^2/sec. The RNA of this virus particle has a molecular weight of 2.4×10^6, if it is taken as a single molecule of nucleic acid.

In recent years it has been found possible to isolate the RNA and the protein separately and in a sufficiently gentle manner, so that each could be tested for infectivity as a virus entity by itself. While the RNA was definitely infectious, the protein material had no activity whatever; and while its infectivity was less than that of the original total virus, it was

higher than could be accounted for by any trace contamination by residual
whole virus. It was also discovered that the RNA and the protein could be
combined again and that virus particles showing both the original infectivity and the original morphological appearance could be reconstituted.
The discovery that nucleic acid by itself could be infectious has opened
the door to a wide range of exploratory investigations, and infectious RNA
has now been prepared from a fairly large number of viruses, illustrating
the general principle that nucleic acid (in this case, ribose nucleic acid)
is significant in the transfer of genetic information. This RNA seems to
be analogous to messenger RNA in the biosynthetic mechanisms within
the normal cells. It differs, obviously, in its site of origin and, perhaps, in
the mechanism for its synthesis. It will be an interesting question for future
research to determine the full extent of these analogies.

The function then of the protein "overcoat," as it is termed, is primarily
twofold. For one thing, it protects the genetic carrier from destructive
influences and thus stabilizes it. Particularly, it prevents attack by ribonuclease (or in the case of the DNA viruses, by deoxyribonuclease) as well
as the harmful influence of temperature and other factors. Secondly, it
determines the specificity as to which type of host cells will be infected and
which will remain unattacked. This presumably involves an organized
configuration in the tertiary structure of some portion, at least, of the protein coat, which has an arrangement complementary to some structures
on the surface of the cell that is infected.

The isolated protein of tobacco mosaic virus has been found to be made of
subunits of molecular weight about 18,000. This repeating subunit contains
158 amino acids, and its complete amino acid sequence has been determined. It was the third such sequence to be elucidated, coming after insulin and ribonuclease. There is now considerable hope for extensive
correlation of structure and function, as well as further elucidation of the
details of genetic mechanism, by relating the nucleotide sequence in the
RNA of tobacco mosaic virus to the amino acid sequence of its protein.
Unfortunately, the nucleotide sequence is not yet known, but progress
along this front should produce the desired correlation.

10–5 The T2 coliphage molecular complex. This is one of the viruses
which attack certain strains of *E. coli*. Electron microscope pictures show
it to have a "head" which is an elongated hexagon with dimensions of
about 650 × 950 A, and attached to it is a "tail" which is 250 × 1000 A
(Fig. 10–3). Actually, the structure is much more complex than this. The
DNA is coiled up inside the head unit, and the outer material is protein,
as is also the material of the tail. The tail protein is demonstrably different
from the head protein. The tail is not hollow but contains a core of protein
surrounded by a contractile substance which forms a sheath. There are

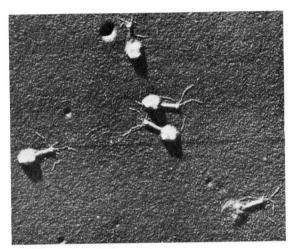

FIG. 10–3. Electron micrograph of bacteriophage T2. The tail fibers are clearly visible. [Reprinted by permission from Academic Press [*Virology* **2,** 296 (1956)] and from Dr. Robley C. Williams. Photograph courtesy of Dr. Williams.]

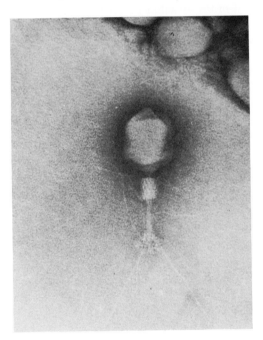

FIG. 10–4. Electron micrograph of bacteriophage T2, showing the filled head, contracted sheath, core, and tail fibers. [Reprinted by permission from Academic Press (*J. Mol. Biol.* **1,** 281 (1959); Plate IV) and from Dr. R. W. Horne. Photograph courtesy of Dr. Horne.]

also some tail fibers attached at the tip which again are presumably of a different type of material. This also is well illustrated in Fig. 10–3. By certain treatments, the tail sheath can be shown in contracted form (shortened and thickened), revealing the core (Fig. 10–4).

When this virus attacks a bacterial cell, attachment is made first by the tip of the tail, and through some mechanism the core in the tail disappears so that the DNA can penetrate into the bacterium. The hollow head and its connected tail are then discarded and have no further function. The extruded DNA, however, proceeds to displace the bacterial DNA in regulating the synthetic machinery of the cell, and in approximately twenty minutes the cell ruptures, liberating about 100 new coliphage units.

The initial attachment involves a high degree of specificity, since the bacteriophage will infect only certain host cells. Since it is known that the tip of the tail, rather than the head, is involved in this attachment, it must be that some specific structural arrangement of the protein of the tail is characteristic for each different type of bacteriophage, and that there must be a specific and corresponding arrangement at the receptor site on the membrane of the host cell. It is also thought that the tail fibers are somehow involved in the attachment mechanism. The receptor site on the bacterium is thought to involve polysaccharide structure in addition to polypeptide material, and it is of interest that the bacteriophage unit contains lysozyme, which is an enzyme capable of degrading certain polysaccharides. Presumably through the attack of this enzyme, a hole is formed in the cell membrane and the next step can proceed. This is the process of dissociation, whereby the viral DNA separates from the protein of the head and enters the cell body, leaving the protein on the outside.

The remaining events can be summarized under the heading of replication. There is a period of time, approximately 20 to 30 minutes for the various T-phages, during which no phage organisms are liberated as progeny. This is called the latent period. At the end of this time, there is a burst, and each cell is dissolved with the consequent liberation of about 100 new bacteriophage particles, each of which can then infect a new host cell. A latent period then is indicative of a type of reproduction process quite different from the mitosis or the binary fission of replicating cells. The latent period may be divided into two approximate halves. The first half is called the "eclipse," because it is found that if the cell is burst open by artificial means, no virus particles or activity of virus can be discovered—not even the original single unit that infected the cell. This could be explained by the fact that the protein to be assembled into virus particles is being synthesized as such and that the appropriate DNA is also being replicated as such, but these two synthetic mechanisms are distinct from each other. During the second half of the latent period, there begins to be a gradual appearance of bacteriophage particles, and their numbers increase with time, although it is still necessary to rupture the cell artificially to discover that they exist. When this process has run long enough the cell wall is dissolved by an unknown mechanism, possibly because of the accumulation of the sufficiently massive quantity of lysozyme in the form of numerous bacteriophage tail organs.

The process whereby DNA and protein are assembled to give bacteriophage units is called maturation. The final process in the mechanism is called release, whereby infective phage is liberated.

It should be pointed out that while some of the mechanisms of infection and replication that have been developed for tobacco mosaic virus and for bacteriophage may very well be common to the behavior of other types of viruses, it is unlikely that all the details are the same. The viruses constitute an enormous group of nucleic acid-protein patterns of structure, and we must expect great variation in their mechanisms of physical and chemical interactions with cells. For instance, it is clear that absorption involves a high degree of specificity in all viruses, and presumably there must be architectural details on some portion of the virus surface, which match in some manner the surface distribution of charged groups, hydrogen-bonding groups, or other bond-forming units on the surface of the host cell. While the process of penetration by bacteriophage makes use of the tip of the tail, other viruses which lack tails clearly must operate through some other mechanisms. It is not clear whether an organized structure is involved or whether the total surface of, for example, a spheroidal virus is covered with specific units for this purpose. It is quite possible that the surface protein consists of a large number of identical subunits, and that each of these is capable of interacting in a similar way with the cell surface. During the eclipse phase, which is a phase that is observed for all viruses, the tiny bit of DNA or RNA that has been introduced is a source of information for the mechanism of protein biosynthesis that then occurs. But not all cells are eventually ruptured by virus infection. Instead, in certain systems, virus is shed continuously from a permanently infected cell, and it must be assumed then that a more limited degree of control over the genetic mechanisms has been imposed by the invading DNA. This is characteristic, for example, of cells that have been infected by influenza virus or poliovirus. In the maturation process, at any rate, the protein, and sometimes lipoprotein, structures have been formed to serve as vehicles for the DNA (or in some cases RNA), which can then be safely liberated to the extracellular world, and which provide mechanisms for re-entry into new host cells. This process of release can vary both quantitatively and qualitatively for different viruses. But again one wonders how a cell can extrude such a large particle as a virus and apparently not suffer any mortal damage in the process.

REFERENCES

1. S. E. LURIA, *General Virology*. Wiley, New York, 1953.

2. S. E. LURIA, "Virus Growth and Variation," *Symp. Soc. Gen. Micro. Biol.* **9**, 4 (1959).

3. C. B. ANFINSEN, "The Substructure of Genes," *Molecular Basis of Evolution*, Chapter 4. Wiley, New York, 1959.

4. H. SCHUSTER, G. SCHRAMM, and W. ZILLIG, "Die Struktur der Ribonucleinsäure aus Tabakmosaikvirus," *Z. Naturforsch* **6**, 339 (1956).

5. H. FRAENKEL-CONRAT, B. SINGER, and R. C. WILLIAMS, "Infectivity of Viral Nucleic Acid," *Biochim. Biophys. Acta* **25**, 57 (1957).

6. R. G. HART, "The Nucleic Acid Fiber of the Tobacco Mosaic Virus Particle," *Biochim. Biophys. Acta.* **28**, 457 (1958).

7. S. BRENNER, G. STREISINGER, R. W. HORNE, S. P. CHAMPE, L. BARNETT, S. BENZER, and M. W. REES, "Structural Components of Bacteriophage," *J. Mol. Biol.* **1**, 281 (1959).

8. A. TSUGITA, D. T. GISH, J. YOUNG, H. FRAENKEL-CONRAT, C. A. KNIGHT, and W. M. STANLEY, "The Complete Amino Acid Sequence of the Protein of Tobacco Mosaic Virus," *Proc. Nat. Acad. Sci.* **46**, 1463 (1960).

9. R. W. HORNE and P. WILDY, "Symmetry in Virus Architecture," *Virology* **15**, 348 (1961).

10. "Basic Mechanisms in Animal Virus Biology," *Cold Spring Harbor Symposia on Quantitative Biology* **27**, (1962).

11. H. FRAENKEL-CONRAT, *Design and Function at the Threshold of Life: The Viruses*. Academic Press, New York, 1962.

12. I. J. BENDET, "Biophysical Characterization of Bacteriophage Nucleic Acid," *Advances in Virus Research* **10**, 65 (1963).

13. R. W. HORNE and P. WILDY, "Virus Structure Revealed by Negative Staining," *Advances in Virus Research* **10**, 102 (1963).

14. G. S. STENT, *Molecular Biology of Bacterial Viruses*. W. H. Freeman, San Francisco, 1963.

15. D. FREIFELDER, A. K. KLEINSCHMIDT, and R. L. SINSHEIMER, "Electron Microscopy of Single-Stranded DNA: Circularity of DNA of Bacteriophage ØX174," *Science* **146**, 254 (1964).

CHAPTER 11

POLYSACCHARIDES

CHAPTER 11

POLYSACCHARIDES

11-1 Introduction. The biologic organism is composed of 20% solids. The commonest organic components are lipids, amino acids, and carbohydrates. These substances exist not only as simple units, but also as polymers and complex aggregates. Such larger molecules have importance in both the structural characterization of the organism and in its function. In the following chapters we will concentrate on the physical properties of these molecules and their biologic significance. To make the discussion more meaningful for the beginning student, some elementary biochemical considerations are interwoven.

The word *polysaccharide* implies a polymer formed from simpler units termed saccharides (simple carbohydrates). The varieties of structural "building blocks" (monosaccharides of simple or complex structure) are numerous, perhaps even more numerous than the 20 amino acids commonly found in polypeptide chains. Striking differences will shortly become clear between polysaccharides and polypeptides. First, while the long polypeptide and protein molecules contain many (perhaps all 20) amino acids in definite arrangement, most polysaccharides are built from but one (homopolymer) or a few (heteropolymer) monosaccharides. Second, while polysaccharide chains can be as long as, or longer than, most proteins and polynucleotides, they usually do not form hydrogen bonds within the polymer and hence their structure is more random in solution than hydrogen-bonded chains.

Our attention is focused on polysaccharides because of their wide distribution in plants and animals and their multiple functions. Many polysaccharides occur free, as for example cellulose (a structural component of plants), chitin (a major component of the exoskeleton of insects), amylose and amylopectin (starches produced by plants, and hence a major component of the human diet), and glycogen (a storage form of carbohydrate in animals). In addition, polysaccharides are also found in chemical combination or association with other molecules, as for example in connective tissue where polysaccharides and proteins form an intercellular mesh. Other examples of polysaccharides in combined form are the glycoproteins and mucoproteins (although these are complex and may be instead protein-monosaccharide units). Nucleic acids can also be viewed as a type of polysaccharide because of the repeating ribose or deoxyribose molecules. Other less well characterized polysaccharides include antigenic materials from bacteria.

To understand this great array of biologically distributed polysaccharides, we will first point out the structure and characteristics of the monosaccharides, which are the component units. We will discuss the linkage of monosaccharides into longer units and finally the properties and role of the polysaccharides themselves.

11–2 The monosaccharides. The commonest monomers which go into the production of polysaccharides contain 5 (pentose) or 6 (hexose) carbon atoms. Structurally they can be represented as shown in Fig. 11–1. The monosaccharides can be seen to be

$$\text{aldehyde} \quad (R{-}\overset{\displaystyle \overset{O}{\|}}{C}{-}H) \quad \text{or} \quad \text{ketone} \quad (R_1{-}\overset{\displaystyle \overset{O}{\|}}{C}{-}R_2)$$

derivatives of polyhydroxy (—OH) straight chain carbon compounds. Since the aldehyde, ketone, and hydroxy groupings are hydrophilic (water loving), we can expect the monosaccharides to be water soluble. This is indeed the case, and the monosaccharides usually have solubilities greater than the amino acids (and certainly greater than the nearly insoluble lipids discussed in the following chapter).

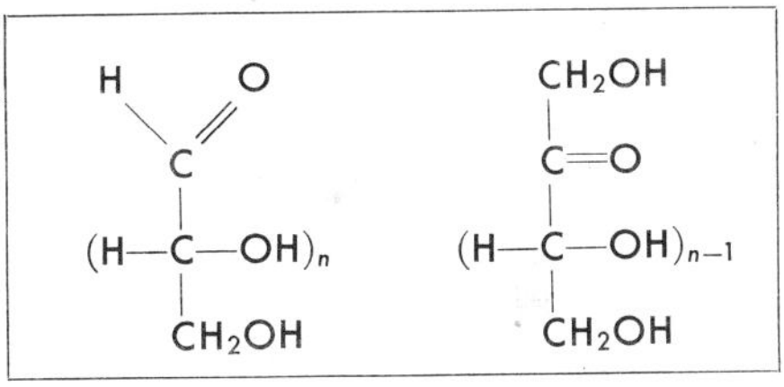

Fig. 11–1.   Structure of an aldose (left) and a ketose.

If a beam of polarized light is passed through an aqueous solution of most monosaccharides, the plane of light is observed to be rotated clockwise (dextrorotary) or counterclockwise (levorotary), when viewed by an appropriate instrument termed a polarimeter. This phenomenon is termed optical rotation and its study dates back to Biot in the nineteenth century. To quantitate optical rotation, a solution containing a known amount of the monosaccharide is placed in the analyzing instrument (at a fixed temperature), a monochromatic beam of polarized light is passed through the solution, and the rotation is noted. Specific rotation is then defined as follows:

$$[\alpha]_D^{20} = \frac{100A}{CL}. \tag{11–1}$$

Here α is the specific rotation in degrees measured at 20°C, employing the

D line of the sodium spectrum (589 mμ wavelength), A is the observed rotation in degrees ($+$ or $-$), C is the concentration of the solution in gm/100 ml solution, and L is the length of the optical path of the solution (measured in decimeters).

Substances which rotate a beam of polarized light, as do the monosaccharides in solution, are termed optically active. The reason for optical activity was first discerned by Pasteur, who suggested that the compound must possess molecular asymmetry. The insight to a rational description of the structural arrangement was provided in 1874 by van't Hoff and Le Bel. These investigators independently pointed out that the valence bonds of tetravalent carbon were arranged at the apices of an equilateral tetrahedron (see Chapter 2). Hence when a carbon atom had four *different* substituents at the apices of the tetrahedron, two different nonsuperimposable arrangements could be formed. Thus the simplest monosaccharide, glyceraldehyde, can be represented in either of two configurations (Fig. 11–2). These are specific examples of two mirror-image but nonsuperimposable configurations predicted by the tetrahedral theory of carbon valence. All carbohydrates can be described as having a structural arrangement similar to L-glyceraldehyde or to D-glyceraldehyde. The compound is named D or L according to the arrangement about the asymmetric carbon atom most remote from the aldehydic or ketonic end of the molecule (the glyceraldehydes were designated arbitrarily as D and L). It must be emphasized that D and L are structural designations and have no relationship to the sign of the optical activity.

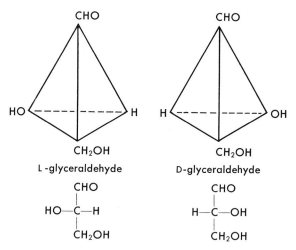

Fig. 11–2.   Configurational relationships of L-glyceraldehyde (left) and D-glyceraldehyde (right). The central carbon atom is not shown. The planar formulae are written below the tetrahedral representations.

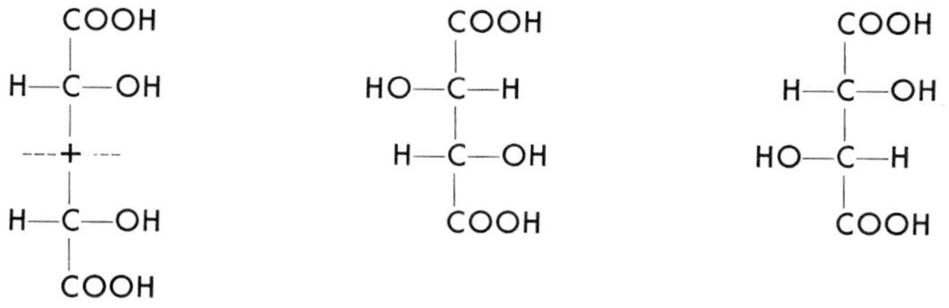

```
        COOH                    COOH                    COOH
         |                       |                       |
    H—C—OH                  HO—C—H                  H—C—OH
         |                       |                       |
    ---+---                 H—C—OH                  HO—C—H
         |                       |                       |
    H—C—OH                    COOH                    COOH
         |
        COOH
```

| "Meso" tartaric acid | D-tartaric acid | L-tartaric acid |
| internally compensated | optically active | optically active |

Fig. 11–3. Forms of tartaric acid. Observe the plane of symmetry in the "meso" form.

It can be appreciated that the two different isomers will react differently with polarized light. One configuration would interact with electromagnetic energy of the light beam to cause rotation in the clockwise direction (called d or $+$). The opposite configuration would result in counterclockwise rotation (called l or $-$). Each monosaccharide has in its name an indication of its structural relationship to glyceraldehyde (D or L) and the direction of rotation of polarized light ($+$ or $-$). Thus the glucose commonly encountered is D($+$)glucose. Both designations are important; one tells us of structure, the other of the rotation of light.

Since optical activity results from asymmetry about a single carbon atom, it can be conceived that some compounds will contain more than one asymmetric carbon atom and hence more than one distinct pair of optically active isomers. This is indeed the case. The number of possible optically active isomers is $2n$, where n is the number of asymmetric carbon atoms. Occasionally substances are found which contain a plane of symmetry. This means that the portion of the molecule above the plane will rotate polarized light in one direction, and the portion of the molecule below the plane will rotate the light in the opposite direction. The result is no net rotation, and the molecule is said to be internally compensated. The classical example is mesotartaric acid, one of the compounds originally studied by Pasteur (Fig. 11–3). It can be mentioned in passing that synthetically prepared organic compounds are often equal mixtures of the d- and l-forms, and show "external compensation" and hence no net rotation of polarized light. Such mixtures are referred to as "racemic." Biologic systems however show great specificity in their syntheses, producing either the d- or l-forms, but not both.

An understanding of these principles is essential in following carbohydrate nomenclature. There is, however, a deeper meaning that should always be kept in mind. Biologic systems often are stereospecific in their reactions. That is, they will react with one of the steric isomers, but they

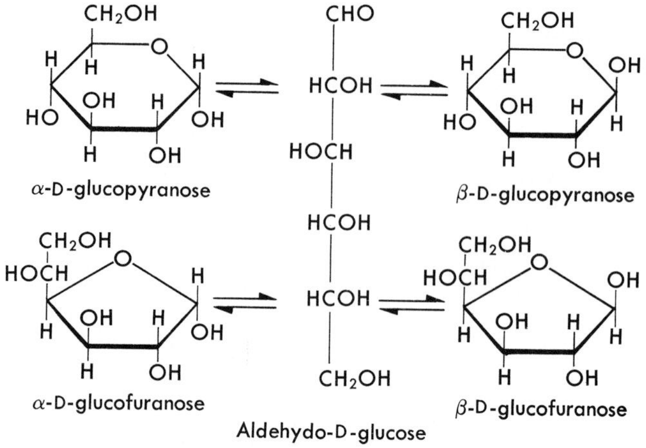

α-D-glucopyranose

β-D-glucopyranose

Aldehydo-D-glucose

α-D-glucofuranose

β-D-glucofuranose

FIG. 11–4. Structural representations of glucose. The significance of the α- and β-configurations of the hydroxyl group at C_1 is discussed in the text.

will react at a reduced rate or not at all with the opposite isomer. For example, L-amino acids (their structure is similar to L-glyceraldehyde) are transported by the small intestine against a concentration gradient (see Chapter 21). The D-amino acids are transported at a slow rate or not at all. It is a property of most forms of what we term life that steric differences can be readily detected. Indeed, the ability of microorganisms to utilize one stereoisomer but not the other was originally used by Pasteur to separate the components of racemic mixtures (racemic means equal mixtures of l- and d-forms, and is therefore optically inactive).

Physicochemical studies indicate that in the pentoses and hexoses, the first and last carbon atoms are in reality close together. That is, the molecule is arranged not linearly, but as though it were a cyclic structure. The cyclic, or Haworth, formulas are used in this chapter since they more nearly represent the true structure of carbohydrates than do linear formulas. The darker markings on the rings indicate the position of the molecules closest to the reader. While the formula is written as though it were planar, there is in reality deviation from this arrangement. Carbohydrates with 6-membered rings are termed pyranoses (after pyran, a simple organic compound with this structure). Similarly, carbohydrates containing 5-membered rings are called furanoses, after the compound furan. The structure of glucose in the pyranose and furanose forms is shown in Fig. 11–4.

11–3 Glycoside bonds. The monosaccharides are joined into long chain polymers (oligosaccharides and polysaccharides) by means of glycosidic bonds. This bond, like the peptide linkage, can be viewed as an "anhydro"

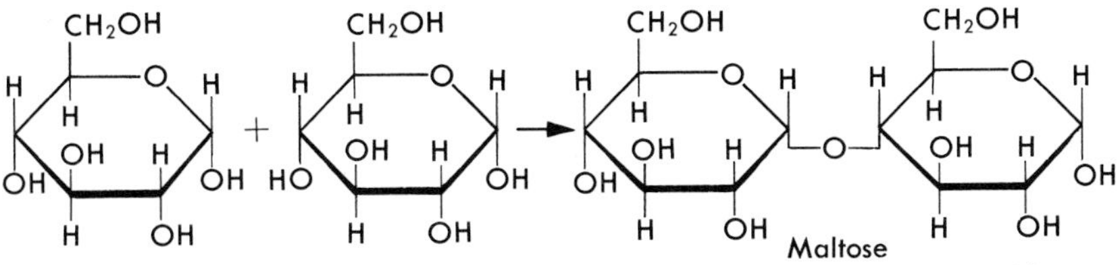

CH$_2$OH   CH$_2$OH   CH$_2$OH   CH$_2$OH

α-D-glucose α-D-glucose   4-D-glucose-α-D-glucopyranoside

Maltose

FIG. 11–5. Formation of maltose from two glucose molecules.

linkage in which water is split off between two molecules. This analogy is
illustrated below.

$$
\begin{matrix}
\text{H} \\
| \\
\text{—N·H}
\end{matrix}
+ \; \text{HO—}\overset{\displaystyle O}{\underset{\displaystyle \|}{\text{C}}}\text{—} \;\to\;
\begin{matrix}
\text{H} \\
| \\
\text{—N}
\end{matrix}\overset{\displaystyle O}{\underset{\displaystyle \|}{\text{—C}}}\text{—} + \text{H}_2\text{O} \qquad \text{peptide bond}
$$

$$\text{—OH} \quad + \text{HO—} \qquad \to \text{—O—} \qquad + \text{H}_2\text{O} \qquad \text{glycoside bond}$$

Let us look at a model reaction (Fig. 11–5). The hydroxyl (at C_1) reacts
with an alcoholic hydroxyl (in this case at C_4). Water is split off, and a
glycosidic bond is formed. The resulting compound is a disaccharide (in
this instance, maltose). The disaccharides are named according to whether
the glycosidic linkage is α or β. To understand what is meant by α and β,
we will refer to Fig. 11–4. In the previous section it was pointed out that
the monosaccharides in solution exist primarily as ring structures with a
bond joining, in the case of glucose, the first and fifth carbon atoms through
oxygen. When such a bond is formed it can be seen that the hydroxyl
group at C_1 can have either of two arrangements. In other words, by clos-
ing the ring we have created another asymmetric carbon atom. One of
the arrangements around the asymmetric C_1 is termed α, and the other β.
This is of crucial importance, for what might seem to be a trivial detail
largely determines whether the compound can be utilized by an organism.
The glycosidic linkage is also named for the carbon atoms involved. Thus
maltose is an α-1,4 disaccharide. In cellobiose we have an example of
a β-glycoside (Fig. 11–6). Indeed, cellobiose is identical to maltose, except
that the glycosidic linkage is β (cellobiose is thus 4-D-glucose-β-D-glucopy-
ranoside). The cellobiose type of repeating unit (glucose linked to glucose

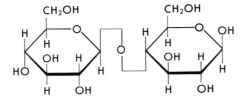

FIG. 11–6. Structure of Cellobiose.

by means of β-glycosidic linkages) is found in cellulose. The difference between α- and β-glycosidic linkages is of more than academic interest. Man and most other animals do not possess enzymes capable of hydrolyzing the β-1,4 glycosidic linkages found in cellulose. Hence cellulose, although composed of glucose, is useless as food material for most animals. The cow overcomes this by having an enlarged gastrointestinal tract populated by bacteria which can split the β-glycosidic linkage of cellulose. In addition to certain bacteria, some insects and earthworms contain cellulases (enzymes capable of cleaving the β-1,4 glycosidic linkage).

The commonest disaccharides are maltose (glucose-glucose), sucrose (glucose-fructose), and lactose (galactose-glucose). These disaccharides are models of polysaccharides, in that they indicate the union of monosaccharides to form more complex units. It is interesting to note that man possesses specific disaccharases (enzymes for splitting disaccharides into the monosaccharides). Thus the enzymes maltase, sucrase, and lactase have all been identified. Further, human beings have an α-amylase, also capable of cleaving α-1,4 glycoside linkages. This latter enzyme degrades α-1,4 linkages of polysaccharide chains.

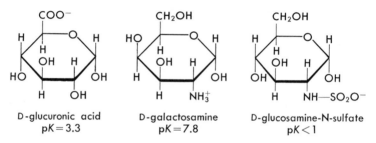

D-glucuronic acid   D-galactosamine   D-glucosamine-N-sulfate
pK = 3.3   pK = 7.8   pK < 1

FIG. 11–7. Structures and pK values for 3 monosaccharide derivatives.

While the simple monosaccharides are the commonest building blocks of polysaccharides, there are other derivatives which are of importance, since they also are involved in polymer formation. Some examples are shown in Fig. 11–7. Such compounds are of special interest since they are electrically charged (ionized) at biological pH values. The pk_a, a measure of the point at which the charged group is one-half ionized (cf. Section 4–5), is given below each compound.

11–4 Polysaccharides. The polysaccharides most frequently encountered in biological systems are outlined is Table 11–1. It can be seen from the table that the most common linkages are α and β from carbon 1 of one monosaccharide to carbon 4 of the next monosaccharide (or monosaccharide derivative). Of the polysaccharides listed, five are composed of but one type of monomer unit in each. In the others, more than one type

TABLE 11–1   DATA ON THE PRINCIPAL POLYSACCHARIDES

Polysaccharide	Subunits	Linkages	Biological properties
Agar	D-galactose, L-galactose, H_2SO_4	?	Extracted from certain seaweed used in culturing bacteria; marked swelling on exposure to moisture.
Amylopectin	Glucose	96% α-1,4 4% α-1,6	A plant starch; major dietary component.
Amylose	Glucose	α-1,4	Similar to amylopectin.
Pneumococcal (Type III)	Glucose and glucuronic acid	?	Certain types have antigenic properties; and the end groups may differ from the main polymer.
Cellulose	Glucose	β-1,4	Structural constituent of plants.
Chitin	N-acetyl-D-glucosamine	β-1,4	Principal component of insect exoskeletons.
Chondroitin sulfate	N-acetylglucosamine-6-sulfate and glucuronic acid	β-1,4 (?)	Connective tissue component.
Glycogen	Glucose	91% α-1,4 9% α-1,6	A storage form of carbohydrate in animals; liver and muscle are principal storage sites.
Heparin	D-glucosamine-N-sulfate and glucuronic acid	α-1,4 (?)	Prevents clotting of blood; found in liver.
Hyaluronic acid	N-acetylglucosamine and glucuronic acid	β-1,4 (?)	Component of connective tissue.
Pectins	Galacturonic acid	?	Found in fruits; used as jelling agents in canning.

of monomer (usually two) are involved. It is uncertain whether the latter polysaccharides can be represented as A_1-A_2-A_1-A_2-A_1-A_2 . . . (the monomeric units alternating in orderly fashion) or are arranged randomly. All of the polysaccharides listed, with the exception of amylopectin and glycogen, are straight chain polymers. In amylopectin and glycogen, side branchings occur to produce a complex network. This is accomplished

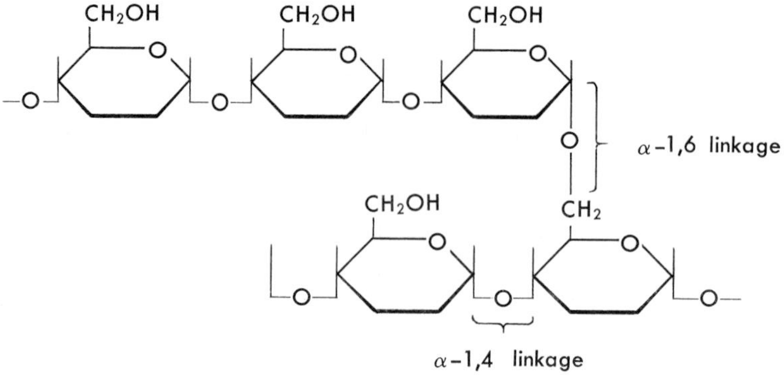

Fig. 11–8. Illustration of the α-1, 4 and α-1, 6 linkage in a branched polymer of glucose.

by having α-1,6 linkages in addition to the usual α-1,4 type. At "branch points" in the molecule, the arrangement is as shown in Fig. 11–8. The common mammalian amylases hydrolyze only the α-1,4 linkage. The α-1,6 bonds are cleaved by a distinct enzyme (oligo-1,6-glucosidase) found in the intestine and liver. The chain is cleaved by the amylases until an α-1,6 bond is reached. This is broken through the action of oligo-1,6-glucosidase, and amylase action once again continues on the α-1,4 bonds.

It is a fair generalization that the β-1,4 glycosidic linkage in a polymer produces limited solubility in water (cellulose, chitin). The α-1,4 bond, however, produces a spiraling of the polysaccharide and greater solubility in water (amylopectin, amylase, glycogen). The number of monomers in a polysaccharide molecule is large. For cellulose there are 300 to 2500 glucose molecules per chain. Amylose likely contains about 1800, and glycogen from 1700 to 22,000 (depending on the method of preparation or purification).

The multiple actions of forming, extending, and degrading the polysaccharide chains do not always proceed without error. There are a series of human diseases, actually genetically determined inborn errors of metabolism, characterized by defects of one or more of the enzymes involved in glycogen metabolism. The resultant glycogens have an abnormal composition and are not as readily cleaved to glucose as the normal polymer. These "glycogen storage diseases" form an interesting chapter in the study of carbohydrate metabolism, which the student may wish to pursue further.

The importance of glycogen as a storage form of carbohydrate can be seen in the following example. Cells must maintain a certain osmotic pressure (π) in order to retain a semblance of shape. Too great an osmotic pressure will result in an influx of solvent, while too low an osmotic pressure will be followed by efflux of solvent from the cell. The osmotic pressure is given approximately by van't Hoff's law (see Chapter 18) as

$$\pi = RTc, \qquad (11\text{–}2)$$

where c is the concentration measure of the number of molecules present, R is the gas constant, and T is temperature. Hence the number of particles within the cell determines the osmotic pressure. To store 10,000 glucose molecules singly in a cell would contribute 10,000 particles toward the osmotic pressure. When the 10,000 glucose molecules are combined into a single glycogen polymer, only one particle is present in the cell. It will be pointed out in Chapter 13 that animal cells are bounded by a membrane of lipid and protein which has little resistance to pressure changes. Plant cell walls, however, are composed of cellulose and offer greater rigidity and resistance to pressure.

11–5 Physical properties of polysaccharides. Cellulose, chitin, and other insoluble linear polysaccharides are not cross-linked structures. Their filaments are, however, interlaced effectively forming three-dimensional structures. To extract the polysaccharides, the three-dimensional structure is broken by chemical treatment, and derivatives (such as cellulose nitrate) of different chain length are obtained. These are said to be polydisperse (a broad molecular weight distribution is present). A cellulose nitrate chain of 1400 glucose units would have a length of about 7000 A if fully extended. The effective end-to-end distance is actually only 1500 A. Thus there is coiling. This is because the bonds between the monomers are not entirely rigid but allow a degree of rotation and hence a degree of chain shortening. In the ultimate case, as is true of some synthetic polymers, a "random coil" is formed, which undergoes thermally induced gyrations in solution. To appreciate this phenomenon, we have only to compare the behavior of the polysaccharide chain with that of protein or DNA chains. In the latter there is hydrogen bonding which restricts movement, as well as possible disulfide linkage and other bonds between protein chains. No such restrictions are present in the polysaccharides and there is almost random motion in solution. Hence the terms secondary and tertiary structure, which can be applied to proteins and DNA, have no significance for the uncharged polysaccharides. Polysaccharides composed of charged monosaccharides likely have electrostatic interactions which restrict free motion of the chain; and there may be a secondary structure, although there is little definitive evidence.

Viscosity was mentioned in Chapter 4 and will be brought up again in connection with the equations of transport. The coefficient of viscosity η (or viscosity for short) can be measured by a number of experimental techniques such as the rate of flow of a liquid under standard conditions.

The unit of viscosity is the poise, named after Poiseuille, an early investigator in the field. For water at 20° C, η is 0.01 poise. At this temperature, glycerol has a viscosity of 8.3 poise. Solutions of certain charged polysaccharides, such as hyaluronic acid (found in connective tissue), are exceedingly viscous. As the molecule is degraded (by an enzyme termed hyaluronidase) the viscosity falls. It is likely that the charges make the molecule more stable and less yielding than uncharged polysaccharides. There is a good correlation, in the case of hyaluronic acid, between the viscosity and the degree of intactness of the molecules. As the polysaccharide chains are broken, the viscosity falls.

Polysaccharides containing charged monomers (such as galactosamine, and various sulfated monosaccharides) have the ability to attract small charged molecules to their vicinity. These polysaccharides are more difficult to study since reagents which degrade them often split off the charged groupings. The charged monosaccharide derivatives are often found associated with proteins. The two groups that have been distinguished (see Chapter 5) are called glycoproteins and mucoproteins (although this classification is not used in all texts).

There are some data that the carbohydrates may be attached to a relatively small fragment of the peptide chain, although the point of linkage is uncertain. In some cases it is conceivable that the linkage is between the carboxyl group of the acid and the —NH$_2$ of the protein's terminal amino acid residue. Neuraminic acid, a condensation product between mannosamine and pyruvic acid, is present on certain bacterial cell walls and in this locale is necessary for the attachment of various particles to the bacteria.

REFERENCES

1. A. Gottschalk, W. H. Murphy, and E. R. B. Graham, "Carbohydrate-Peptide Linkages in Glycoproteins and Methods for their Elucidation," *Nature* **194**, 1051–1053 (1962).

2. M. Stacey and S. A. Barker, *Polysaccharides of Micro-organisms*. Oxford University Press, 1960.

3. D. J. Bell, *The Structure and Biosynthesis of Macromolecules*. Cambridge University Press, 1962.

4. G. Natta, "Precisely Constructed Polymers," *Scientific American* **205**, 33–41 (1961).

CHAPTER 12

LIPIDS AND ARTIFICIAL MEMBRANES

CHAPTER 12

LIPIDS AND ARTIFICIAL MEMBRANES

12-1 Introduction. In previous chapters we have considered monomeric units which were polymerized to form macromolecules. Thus the nucleic acids, proteins, and polysaccharides were well defined, usually water-soluble, molecules. We now turn our attention to a new class of materials, perhaps of no less importance, for which few of the previous generalizations hold. These substances are the lipids. We give the lipids not a precise chemical definition, but rather an operational one. If a biologic system is extracted with ether, chloroform, carbon disulfide, or benzene, certain of its components dissolve. These materials are termed lipids, and the organic solvents are designated as lipid solvents or fat solvents. Because of such a functional definition, it can be expected that multiple structural types will fall under this heading. We will discuss only the major types of lipids occurring in nature, but the principles outlined can be extended to other members of the group as they are encountered.

Standing in marked contrast to most other molecules of biologic interest, the lipids have but limited solubility in water. The consequences of this fact will appear again and again in the following discussion. Despite this limited solubility, lipids occur in all living forms. Indeed, various lipids are dietary essentials for most species (that is, various types cannot be synthesized but must be supplied in the diet; certain insects, for example, must have cholesterol in their diet, while man requires one or two unsaturated fatty acids in his food). The best known biologic deposits of lipids are the adipose cells or fat cells of mammals. These serve as storage areas for fats which can be mobilized by the body. Large quantities of lipids also occur in the nervous system, appearing to act as insulation for certain nerve trunks (this insulating sheath, myelin, is discussed further in the following chapter). Less apparent, but perhaps of even greater importance are lipids of the pericellular membranes; it will be pointed out in Chapter 13 that the lipid composition of membranes helps explain their properties and function. In the following sections we will note the structure of various classes of lipids and attempt to relate this to their biologic role.

12-2 Fatty acids. These compounds correspond to the general formula $H-(CH_2)_n-COOH$, where n is an integer ≥ 0. The structure of a fatty acid is shown in Fig. 12-1. The term fatty acid itself is almost a contradiction of terms; fatty denotes water insoluble, while the acid function (the carboxyl group —COOH) is water soluble. A fatty acid thus has two distinct "ends" to the molecule, a hydrocarbon "tail" of limited water solubility, and a carboxyl "head" that is water soluble. The biologic properties of fatty acids follow from this unusual composition. The first members ($n = 0$ to 6) of the fatty acid series are water soluble. When $n > 7$, water solubility of the free fatty acids is negligible. One might immediately expect different biologic handling of fatty acids with more than 8 carbon atoms than those with less than 8 carbon atoms. An example of this is found in the intestinal absorption of fatty acids. The lower members of the homologous fatty acid series, which are water soluble, pass through the gut wall into the blood stream. The less soluble fatty acids enter the lymphatic vessels and are held as complexes, with other molecules, rather than in solution.

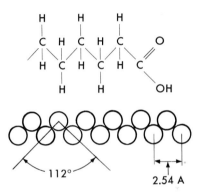

Fɪɢ. 12–1. Structural formula of a fatty acid. Observe the carboxyl end of the molecule and the hydrocarbon "tail." The lower diagram shows the dimensions of the chain in side view.

Among the commonest fatty acids in mammals are those containing 12 to 18 carbon atoms. It is apparent that in high concentration they cannot exist free in the aqueous phase. In living organisms, fatty acids occur largely in the form of esters (that is, in linkage to an alcohol). A model reaction is as follows:

$$H \cdot (CH_2)_n \cdot C\overset{O}{\diagup}\!\!\!-OH + R \cdot OH \rightleftarrows H \cdot (CH_2)_n \cdot C\overset{O}{\diagup}\!\!\!-OR + H_2O, \quad (12\text{–}1)$$

where R is the hydrocarbon portion of the alcohol. This ester linkage can be viewed as another bond formed by the loss of water, similar to the peptide and glycoside bonds. To form this bond, one molecule of water is split out as two molecules are joined. The principal alcohol involved in ester linkage, with fatty acids, is the trihydroxy compound glycerol (and the resulting compound is called a fat). In the presence of the enzyme lipase (present in alimentary tissue and most cells), water is added across the ester bond, which is then hydrolyzed, reforming the fatty acid and the alcohol. The ester bond can also be hydrolyzed by strong alkali. When the process is carried out in alkaline solution, the alkaline salt of the fatty acid is produced; this product is called a soap, and the overall process is referred to as saponification. It should be recognized that the fatty acids have true acid properties and can form ionizable salts with alkali metal ions. The acidic character

$$R—(CH_2)_n—C\diagup_{\diagdown OH}^O \;\leftrightarrows\; R—(CH_2)_n—C\diagup_{\diagdown O^-}^O \;+\; H^+ \qquad (12\text{-}2)$$

is often not appreciated because of the limited solubility of the fatty acids. The acids are half dissociated at pH $= 4.7$ (that is, $pK = 4.7$; see Chapter 17 for a discussion). At pH 7.4 (that of the blood), the fatty acids are principally in the ionized form.

The sodium and potassium salts of the fatty acids are water soluble. As the familiar soaps, the salts find widespread use in evoking the mixing of water and oil (forming an emulsion). To appreciate this action, consider the situation when many small oil droplets are dispersed in water. Brownian movement will bring numbers of the droplets into contact with each other, and in the course of these collisions, some droplets may coalesce. The force which largely determines the degree of occurrence of coalescence is surface tension. It can be visualized that all molecules of a single component liquid are attracted by other molecules of the same species in its neighborhood by secondary intermolecular bonds. The only exceptions are molecules at the surface of the liquid (Fig. 12–2). These are not surrounded by molecules of their own kind at the surface. The net asymmetric effect is that the surface molecules tend to be pulled inward. The resulting surface tension can be viewed as a tendency to reduce the surface area.

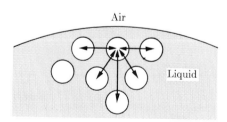

Fig. 12–2. Schematic diagram of the asymmetric attraction for a molecule at the surface of a liquid. The double headed arrows indicate van der Waals attractions between the molecule and its neighbors.

Operationally, surface tension (γ) is commonly measured by means of the relationship

$$\gamma = \frac{F}{2L},\tag{12–3}$$

where F is the force (as in dynes) required to raise a loop of length L (usually measured in centimeters) from the surface of the liquid; the factor 2 is present since there is liquid surface on either side of the loop, tending to retard its movement. As measured in this manner, the surface tension is obtained at a fluid-air surface. More germane to biologic systems is the surface tension between two immiscible liquids. We will show below how this can be calculated once the value of γ for each of the liquid-air interfaces has been determined. The surface tensions of some liquid-air interfaces are given in Table 12–1; additional values were presented in Chapter 4.

TABLE 12–1

SURFACE TENSION OF THE LIQUID-AIR INTERFACE AT 20°C

	γ, dynes/cm
Water	72.8
Benzene	28.9
Carbon tetrachloride	26.9
Ethyl ether	17.0

In addition to an operational approach, surface tension has a close relationship to energy. This can be seen in terms of the units employed. Surface tension has dimensions of dyne $\cdot$ cm^{-1}; thus

$$\frac{\text{dyne}}{\text{cm}} \times \frac{\text{cm}}{\text{cm}} = \frac{\text{dyne·cm}}{\text{cm}^2} = \frac{\text{erg}}{\text{cm}^2} = \frac{\text{energy}}{\text{unit area}}.\tag{12–4}$$

Hence surface tension is an indication of surface energy. It will be shown in Chapter 14 for example that the work involved in altering the surface area of a liquid is $\gamma \cdot dA$ (that is, the surface tension times the change in area).

The interfacial tension of two liquids can be calculated indirectly from a relationship due to Antonoff. Since surface tension is an energy, and it will be shown in Chapter 14 that energy is a conserved quantity, it follows that in the ideal case the interfacial tension of two liquids, measured when each has been saturated with the other, is equal to the difference between their surface tensions (measured at the liquid-air interface). Hence the interfacial tension, at 20° C, of a water-benzene surface is 72.8 − 28.9 = 43.9 dynes/cm. Experimental measurements agree closely with this value.

Surface tension is also of interest because of the insight it gives as to fluid behavior. From thermodynamic considerations (and see Chapter 14), it can be deduced that the surface tension is equal to the change of the Gibbs free energy (G) per change in area (A), at constant temperature, pressure, and number of moles of constituents. The Gibbs free energy of a system tends to be minimized. As γ is positive, a decrease in surface area will decrease the free energy. This is consistent with the observation that the surface of liquids tends to contract.

With this background in surface tension, let us return to the question of the behavior of small oil droplets in water. Surface tension acts to reduce the surface area of liquids suspended in immiscible liquids. If two small droplets of oil in water happen to meet, their coalescence (which reduces the surface area) will be favored. As more and more droplets coalesce, the larger drops rise (if the oil is less dense than water), and shortly the oil is completely separated from the water. The oil in water emulsion is said to have been "broken." Now consider the situation when a soap is added to the oil-water mixture. The Na^+ ions are distributed throughout the aqueous medium. The remaining $H—(CH_2)_n—COO^-$ moiety is attracted to the oil-water interface. The carboxyl "head" of the molecule is hydrophilic and is orientated toward the aqueous phase. The hydrocarbon tail of the fatty acid is attracted into the oil phase. There are two interesting consequences of this alignment.

(1) Since the lipophilic (lipid loving) tail lies in the oil phase, with the negatively charged carboxyl group aligned at the oil-water interface, oil droplets acquire negative charges (which are balanced by positive ions in the aqueous phase). Each droplet exhibits electrostatic repulsion of neighboring droplets. Hence the frequency of collisions is reduced and the emulsion does not break.

(2) Soaps lower the interfacial tension. Since the tendency to reduce the surface area at an oil-water interface is lowered by the presence of a soap, the likelihood of coalescence is diminished. From thermodynamic considerations, Gibbs concluded that agents which lower the interfacial tension would tend to accumulate at the interface. This theoretical prediction has been borne out by the distribution of *surface active agents* (those which lower surface tension). The reader is referred to a paper by Snavely and co-workers for a discussion of the experimental techniques employed.

Soaps are the principal *anionic detergents*. (The head of the hydrocarbon chain bears a negative charge.) Another example of an anionic detergent is an alkyl sulfonate: $R—SO_3^- + Na^+$ (R is a bulky hydrocarbon chain or related structure). Unlike fatty acids, the sulfonate residue is a strong acid and retains its ionization in acid media (the pK is about 1). More recently, *cationic detergents* have become available; an example is

R—NH_3^+ + Cl^-. Here the head of the hydrocarbon chain bears a positive charge (and when orientated in oil droplets, each droplet bears one or more positive charges and repels other droplets). Emulsifying agents may then bear either a positive or a negative charge, as long as the hydrophilic group is associated with a hydrophobic chain which becomes distributed in the oil phase.

The process of emulsification is of importance in more than the washing away of oil deposits by soap. Lipids ingested in the diet are insoluble in the aqueous digestive fluids. They are, however, emulsified by bile acids (glycocholic acid, taurocholic acid, and others which are derivatives of cholesterol; see Section 12–3). The enzymes which digest lipids are water soluble and hence function at the water-lipid interface only. The rate of digestion is thus largely dependent upon the surface area of the lipid droplets. Through the action of the bile acids and the churning intestinal motion, lipid droplets are reduced in size and the surface area is correspondingly increased. A small fraction of dietary lipids are apparently absorbed intact (without further digestion). This occurs when the particle is reduced to a diameter of about 0.1 microns, and the process by which they cross the gut wall is termed pinocytosis (discussed in Chapter 13).

12–3 Monolayers and lipid aggregation. If a minute quantity of a substance with both lipophilic and lipophobic properties is carefully placed on a clean water surface, it tends to spread over the surface. This behavior is shown by fatty acids, among other substances. From the quantity of fatty acid added and the surface area occupied, it can be calculated that the layer on the surface is but one molecule thick (monomolecular film). The experiments are performed in a trough with measured sides so that the area of the surface film can be measured. If this is done and the film is slowly compressed by a bar at water level, then the force of the film resisting compression can be measured by a suitable device. As the film is progressively compressed, there is an increased resisting force. This is shown in Fig. 12–3. Such a resistance is understandable in terms of the area occupied by each molecule. The minimum area that can be occupied by the monomolecular film occurs when the molecules are compacted to the point of closest approach. By extrapolation of the curve in Fig. 12–3, the area occupied by each molecule can be calculated. For all the fatty acids containing from 12 to 26 carbon atoms, the area per molecule turns out to be 20×10^{-16} cm^2 (or 20 A^2). Since the area is independent of the number of carbon atoms present in the lipophilic chain, the chain obviously cannot be on the surface. The molecules are orientated with the carboxyl groups at the water surface and the hydrophobic tails pointing out of the water. This uniform orientated layer is a prototype of biologic membranes which will be discussed in Chapter 13.

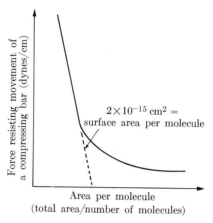

$$2\times10^{-15}\,\mathrm{cm}^2 =$$
surface area per molecule

Area per molecule
(total area/number of molecules)

Fig. 12–3. The force of a surface film of fatty acid on water resisting compression (at constant temperature) plotted as a function of the surface area.

There is an interesting way in which to think of monomolecular layers and their properties. These films have length and width, but essentially no depth. They are, in other words, "two-dimensional matter." They do follow many of the laws, suitably modified, which describe the behavior of "three-dimensional matter." It will be recalled that the ideal gas law can be expressed as:

$$pV = nRT \qquad (12\text{--}5)$$

where the notations stand for pressure, total volume, number of moles, the gas constant, and absolute temperature. A somewhat analogous expression for a surface film is

$$FA = kT, \qquad (12\text{--}6)$$

where F is the force in dyne $\cdot$ cm^{-1}, A is the area per molecule in A^2, k is a constant equal to 1.372 when these units are employed, and T is the absolute temperature. Surface films can thus be treated like two-dimensional analogues of ideal gases.

Before proceeding, we must correct the impression that fatty acids are the only substances of biologic interest which form monomolecular films. Protein monolayers have been produced and studied by several investigators. The simplest manner of writing a protein is as a linear array of its constituent amino acids (Fig. 12–4). The R groups in the figure, if all aliphatic or aromatic hydrocarbons, would be expected to project up from the surface, while the —NH—CO— (peptide) groupings would be at the water surface. In reality, the R groups of proteins are also composed of heterocyclic rings, carboxyl and sulfhydryl groupings, and other moieties.

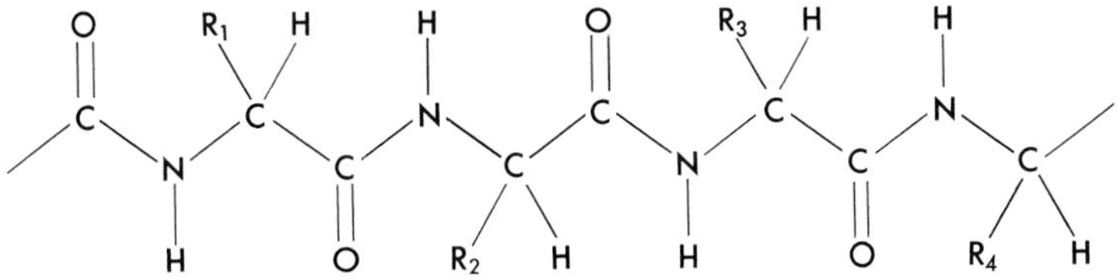

Fig. 12–4. A protein written as a linear array of amino acids. The R's represent side chains of various composition.

Hence protein orientation at the water surface is less well defined. Protein films also are subjected to changes in configuration, called denaturation, which alter their reactivity; this is an area of importance in the understanding of protein structure and function. The phosphatides, a group of lipids discussed in Section 12–5, also form monolayers on water.

In addition to monomolecular films, polymolecular films can be formed at surfaces, still with good orientation of the molecules. An example of this occurs when calcium stearate (stearic acid is a C_{18} fatty acid) is carefully placed on a water surface and a glass plate is slowly dipped through the film, perpendicular to the water. On the downward trip the plate picks up a monolayer with the hydrophobic tail against the glass plate. On the upward trip, a second layer is deposited, with the carboxyl groups in apposition to the —COOH groups of the fatty-acid molecules already there. On the next trip (another downward thrust into the water) an additional layer is added. This time, however, the hydrocarbon tails are in apposition (Fig. 12–5). In this manner layers can be constructed which are many molecules thick. The orientation shown here, carboxyl toward carboxyl and hydrocarbon toward hydrocarbon, is a good proto-

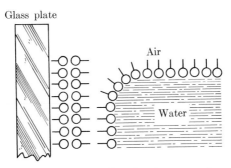

Fig. 12–5. Deposition of fatty acid molecules on a glass plate. The figure represents the reentry of the plate into the fatty acid monolayer spread on water after a previous entry and withdrawal. Observe the orientation of the molecules; the balls represent the carboxyl groups, and the lines the hydrocarbon chains. The first two layers were picked up by the glass plate during the initial entry and withdrawal.

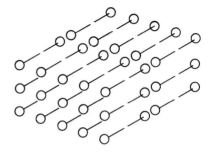

Fig. 12–6.   Arrangement of soap micelles in water. For simplicity, accompanying inorganic ions are not shown. Observe the orientation of the molecules.

type of biologic membranes and myelin described in Chapter 13. The hydrocarbon groups are attracted to each other by van der Waals forces. The reason for the carboxyl groups being in association is less clear. However, the process of polymolecular film formation is favored when divalent metals such as calcium are present. It is thus possible that the carboxyl groups are arranged with metal ions between them, such as —COO—Ca—OOC—. It is also possible that the negatively charged groups are attracted to the protons of water, so that water can be orientated between the carboxyl groups. It is of interest that this characteristic arrangement is often also shown by molecules of the fatty acid in solution. Under proper conditions of temperature, pH, and concentration, fatty-acid molecules in solution show pseudocrystalline arrangements called micelles, a term introduced by Nageli in 1858 (see Fig. 12–6). Micelles are capable of changing in size as additional molecules are added to the assemblage. Here then is a high degree of organization which occurs in solution.

12–4 Steroids.   Structurally, the steroids are derivatives of a ring system (Fig. 12–7) that, although written as planar, is in reality "puckered" and not flat. This sterically bulky molecule has many carbon atoms which can be centers of asymmetry and which can be the sites of attachment of substituents. Such asymmetries and substitutions, as well as varying numbers of double bonds, account for the almost limitless variety of steroids encountered in biologic systems. These large molecules can be

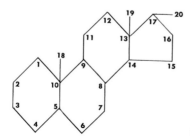

Fig. 12–7.   Structure of perhydro-cyclopentanophenanthrene, the ring compound from which steroids are derived. The carbon atoms are numbered.

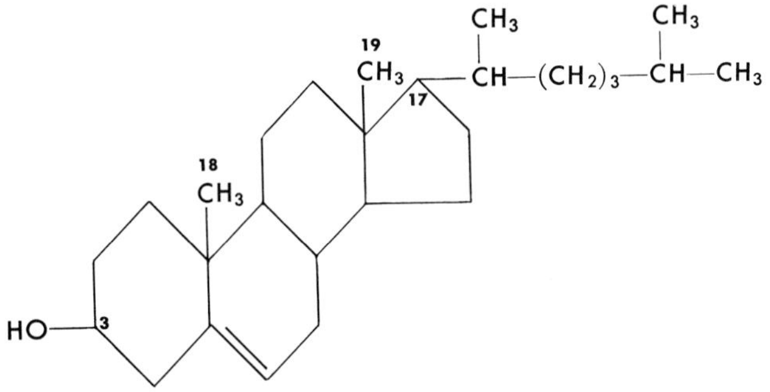

Fig. 12–8. Structure of cholesterol written in planar form. Observe the hydroxyl group at C–3, the methyl groups at C–18 and C–19, and the long chain at C–17. An unsaturated bond is also present.

expected to have but limited solubility in water, although hydrophilic groups can be added to a number of the carbon atoms.

A subclass of steroids of particular biologic interest are the sterols. These have an alcoholic hydroxyl group at C_3 and have 8 to 10 carbon atoms attached to position 17. The most prevalent sterol is cholesterol (Fig. 12–8). If for no other reason, cholesterol commands our attention because it is found in almost all insects and animals, and structural analogues occur in plants. Man (although ingesting many grams of cholesterol per day) can synthesize this molecule from simpler fragments. Cholesterol has limited solubility in water (about 0.07 mg/liter at body temperature) and is maintained in biological systems as cholesterol complexes of proteins and other entities. In blood it occurs largely as cholesterol esters. Cholesterol is an important constituent of myelin and other biologic membranes discussed in Chapter 13. Its spatial orientation in such structures is uncertain; but we might expect that the hydroxyl group would be near other hydrophilic groups in the membrane, while the major portion of cholesterol would be associated with lipophilic groupings. Because of the limited solubility of cholesterol it is not surprising that precipitation occasionally occurs (such as a cholesterol gall stone) when secretions rich in cholesterol have their water content reduced, or when the cholesterol-protein complex is denatured.

Cholesterol also merits attention as the parent compound for many sterol derivatives found in the body. For example, its principal metabolic fate is conversion to bile acids (previously mentioned) which are necessary for the emulsification of dietary lipids. Cholesterol (or its analogues) is converted to a number of hormones, principally in the adrenal gland. These substances are called, not surprisingly, adrenal steroids. Their production is limited to minute amounts each day (micrograms to milligrams), but their role in regulation of metabolism is impressive. For example, adrenal

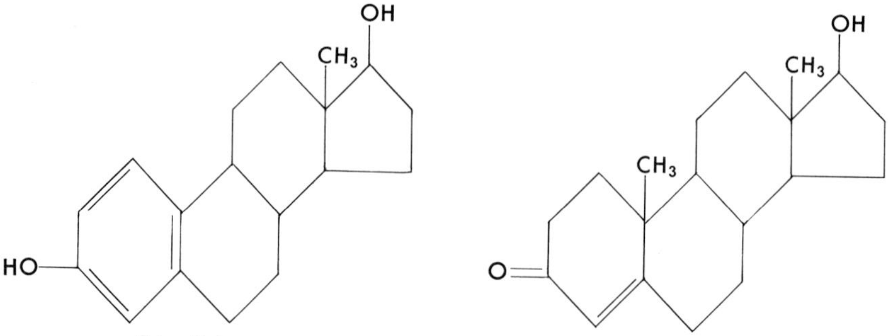

Fig. 12–9. Formulae of testosterone (a male hormone) and estradiol (a female hormone). Despite the difference in their roles, they differ at only two positions in their formulae.

steroids are involved in the control of mineral metabolism (sodium and potassium) and carbohydrate degradation. Their mode of action is unknown and remains a challenging research area. Hormones of the ovary and testis are also sterol derivatives. The relationship of molecular structure to biologic function is perhaps nowhere else pointed out so dramatically. The Figure 12–9 indicates the structures of testosterone, a male hormone, and estradiol, a female hormone. The only difference between these two molecules is the presence of an additional CH_3 and H in the testosterone molecule. Here is an example of biologic specificity at its more subtle levels, suggesting exquisite regulation of cellular events by such steroids. There are other steroids of biologic interest which cannot be discussed at length here, but one more should be mentioned. This is vitamin D. Calcium transport across the small intestine is depressed in vitamin D deficient animals, and is restored to normal within a few hours of vitamin feeding. Here then is an effect on intestinal cells or their membranes which alters the rate of absorption.

12–5 Phosphatides. The phosphatides are a group of lipids which can be considered to be derived from α-phosphatidic acid (Fig. 12–10). That is, they consist of glycerol (a previously defined trihydroxy alcohol) to which have been joined, through ester linkages, two molecules of fatty acid and one molecule of phosphoric acid. The hydrocarbon portion of the fatty acid molecules are hydrophobic, while the phosphoric acid group is hydrophilic. Thus the phosphatides can form orientated layers on a water surface, similar to those shown by fatty acids. Like soaps, phosphatides lower the surface tension at an oil-water interface and also concentrate at such an interface. Phosphatides occur in biological membranes, and there

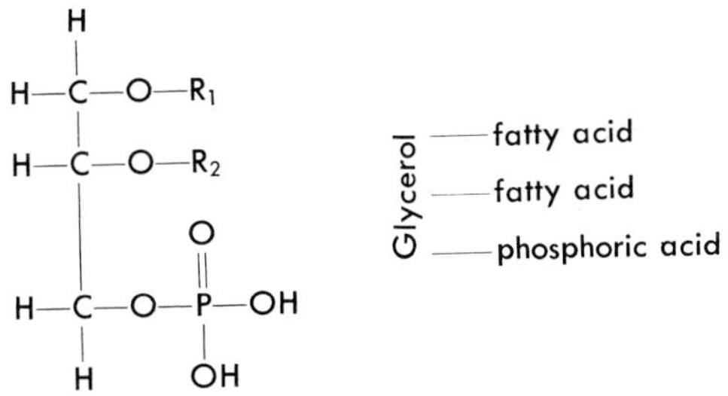

Fig. 12–10. Structure of a phosphatidic acid. R_1 and R_2 represent the residues of fatty acid molecules held in ester linkage to the glycerol.

is some evidence that they are produced and degraded at a rate more rapid than other membrane components. Their role in membranes is not known at present. However, since they show both lipophobic and lipophilic properties, they have been hypothesized to be involved in "shuttling" molecules back and forth from the aqueous cellular environment across the lipid-rich membrane to the opposite face. This is an example of the use of the properties of a molecule to postulate its possible role in biologic systems.

REFERENCES

1. H. DEUEL, *The Lipids*, 3 Vols. Interscience, New York, 1951–1957.

2. J. B. FINEAN and J. D. ROBERTSON, "Lipids and the Structure of Myelin," *Brit. Med. Bull.* **14,** 267–273 (1958).

3. A. S. C. LAWRENCE, "The Mechanism of Detergence," *Chem. & Ind.*, No. 44, 1764–1771 (1961).

4. E. S. SNAVELY, G. M. SCHMID, and R. M. HURD, "Simple Experimental Method for Verification of the Gibbs Adsorption Equation," *Nature* **194,** 439–441 (1962).

5. H. SOBOTKA, "Monomolecular Layers: Their Application in Physiology and Medicine," Vol. I., pp. 763–784, *Medical Physics*, O. Glasser (Ed.). Yearbook, Chicago, 1944.

6. L. L. M. VAN DEENEN, U. M. T. HOUTSMULLER, G. H. DEHAAS, and E. MULDER, "Monomolecular Layers of Synthetic Phosphatides." *J. Pharmacy & Pharmacology* **14,** 429–44 (1962).

CHAPTER 13

STRUCTURE OF CELLS AND MEMBRANES

CHAPTER 13

STRUCTURE OF CELLS AND MEMBRANES

13–1 Introduction. Studies of biologic systems are marked by such depth and complexity that generalizations are frequently lost, and broad principles tend to be obscured by details. However, when a principle does emerge and does possess general application, it is of invaluable aid. One of the most significant of the principles which have been pointed out in biology is *the cell theory*. In briefest terms, this concept states that all biologic creatures above the protozoa and protophyta are composed of morphologic subunits called cells. Such a simple pronouncement has the greatest implications in a study of the correlations between biologic structure and function. For instance, there must be a distinct boundary to each cell. It is known in fact that there is a limiting membrane around each and every cell. Not only does this membrane play a role in determining cell size and shape, it also influences influx of materials from the pericellular environment and the efflux of substances from the cell. Furthermore, we can ask whether there is anything between cells, or whether they are tightly packed, one against the other. Finally, we must question whether the cell itself is the smallest structural unit of the organism. The answer to this is no, and the details of cellular substructure and its relationship to cellular function will form the subject of this chapter. That is, we will examine the subcellular components and attempt to correlate known functions with these structures.

13–2 The aqueous cellular environment. Consider a hypothetical cell of spherical shape with a radius of 20 μ (1 μ = 1 micron = 10^{-6} meter = 10^{-4} cm). The volume of the cell is: $V = 4/3\pi r^3 = 3.4 \times 10^{-8}$ cm^3. Its surface area is $A = 4\pi r^2 = 5.0 \times 10^{-5}$ cm^2. This cell is approximately 80% water. Of the remaining material, about 70% is protein. Let us consider this in terms of the number of molecules involved. A kilogram of cells would contain 800 gm of water, or 44.4 moles. If all the other constituents (principally proteins) had a mean molecular weight of 500, there would be 200 gm/500 gm, or 0.4 mole. Hence each molecule within the cell would, on the average, be in the vicinity of 44.4 moles/0.4 mole or 111 molecules of water. Cellular activities can thus be understood only in terms of an appreciation of water structure and function. (See Chapter 4).

The cell is the smallest unit capable of carrying out the complex events of metabolism of food materials, energy production and storage, synthesis

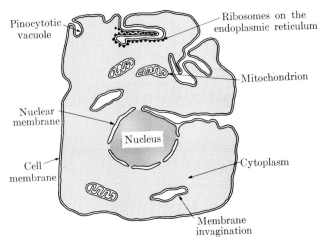

Pinocytotic vacuole

Ribosomes on the endoplasmic reticulum

Mitochondrion

Nuclear membrane

Nucleus

Cell membrane

Cytoplasm

Membrane invagination

FIG. 13–1. Schematic diagram of a mammalian cell.

of new molecules, and above all the temporal and spatial control of these processes. From amino acids, energy, and genetic information, various cells can produce at least 750 enzymes (the approximate number now recognized). In turn the enzymes catalyze metabolic events involving thousands of organic compounds. These events usually occur isothermally and isopiestically (constant temperature and pressure) under the control of multiple interrelated factors. We will try to draw a picture of the occurrence of these events in relation to the structures of the cell.

Looking closer at the microscopic organization of the cell, some regions are seen to be architecturally well defined (Fig. 13–1). Such areas obviously will have different dielectric properties and "microscopic pH" from the cytoplasm in general. Within a cell, then, there are regions which contrast vividly as to structure and physical properties. The gross term "cellular function" can only be meaningful when it is viewed as representing the interaction of the function of these components. We will, in the following sections, describe various cellular components as though they were isolated entities. In reality it is the interaction of these constituents which is of importance, and the subunits do not have an existence separate from their microenvironment. Although we will be speaking of "typical" cells, there are in reality no such entities. Cells vary in their composition from lipid engorged adipose cells to protein-rich secretory cells of the alimentary mucosa. In physical characteristics they vary from the idealized spherical cell, with a length-to-width ratio of 1 : 1, to elongated neural cells, in which the ratio is perhaps 100 : 1. The biologic variability should not make us lose sight of the basic principles underlying structure and function.

The nonaqueous component of our typical cell (20% of wet weight) consists of 14% protein, 2% lipids, 2% RNA, 1% DNA, and 1% polysaccharides. Such an analysis should be regarded as an overall view, and specific regions in the cell may deviate markedly from these figures. It is only within the past two decades that functional significance has been given to the fact that the cell is not an amorphous mass. We will see that it is structured chemically, anatomically, and functionally.

13–3 **Membrane structure and function.** Since the average membrane is only 100 A thick, light microscopy cannot begin to distinguish its structure. It is thus not surprising that our knowledge of cell membranes has been gathered largely from physical measurements. Information on membrane substructure has in turn been inferred from the results of such measurements. Much of the study of membranes has been conducted on the myelin sheath, since it can be analyzed not only in the electron microscope but also by use of x-ray diffraction and optical polarization techniques. Surrounding certain nerves in the developing nervous system are Schwann cells. As maturation of the system occurs, the Schwann cell membrane wraps about the nerve, and is wrapped over and around the nerve again and again, forming a tight sheath (Fig. 13–2). This is myelin.

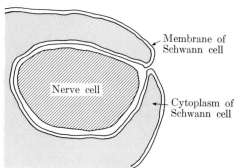

Fɪɢ. 13–2. Formation of myelin from the membrane of a Schwann cell.

In 1936, W. J. Schmidt carried out studies of this myelin sheath utilizing polarized light. A change in the direction of polarization of the emerging beam was noted. From the direction of rotation and its extent, the orientation of molecules was determined. Schmidt's interpretation was that lipid layers were orientated with their long axes in the radial direction. To account for other aspects of the data, planes of protein molecules between the lipid layers were hypothesized. X-ray diffraction studies of myelin can also be interpreted in terms of such a model.

The proposed structure is thus a "sandwich," protein alternating with lipid. Subarrangement of the lipid and protein layers is less certain (Fig.

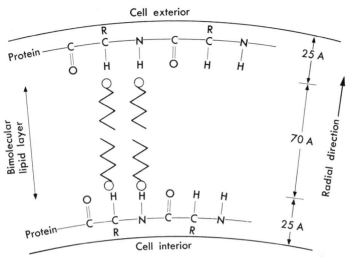

Fig. 13–3. A possible arrangement of protein and lipid in a membrane.

13–3). Within the protein-lipid "sandwich," the hydrophilic portion of the lipids face the protein, while hydrocarbon tails of the lipids probably are in proximity to each other (and held by van der Waals' forces). Electron micrographs by Sjöstrand and others tend to support this scheme of membrane structure. Sjöstrand prepared finely sliced sections of fixed peripheral nerves. The membrane contained layers with a 25-A spacing, arranged concentrically (most likely the protein). Periodic layers of about 67-A spacing were also observed, and may represent the lipids. Hence optical polarization data, x-ray diffraction studies, and electron micrographs are all consistent with the same membrane structure.

If it is true that a cell membrane is a bimolecular layer of lipid covered with protein on both sides, then the properties of the membrane should be largely explicable in terms of the properties of these constituents. Many of the characteristics of cells are consistent with a protein monolayer as the outermost surface (a review of this area is provided by Curtis).

Information as to the metabolic activity of the cell membrane is virtually nonexistent. Like other cellular components, perhaps the membrane is continually being subjected to degradative action and hence concomitant replacement. Robertson has recently presented electron micrographs of areas within the cell which he called "growth spirals." These regions appear to be producing new membranes, perhaps to replace the cell membrane in a continuous manner. One of the events of cellular division is formation of a complete membrane about each of the daughter cells. New membrane material undoubtedly appears in the process, but its site of origin is still obscure.

In the previous section our hypothetical cell of spherical shape and a 20-μ radius was noted to have a surface area of 5.0×10^{-5} cm^2. The sphere, of course, has the minimal surface area for volume enclosed, and biologic cells would in reality possess a greater surface area even without considering projections and infoldings of the membrane (a cube enclosing the same volume as the 20-μ spherical cell would have a surface area of 6.3×10^{-5} cm^2). Cells lining the intestinal lumen, as well as other cells, possess microvilli (small outward projections) of about 1 μ in length. These increase the surface area of that portion of the membrane some twenty times. The membrane about a mammalian cell has numerous folds which also increase the surface. The reason for stressing the surface of the cell membrane is that it may be a key factor in allowing substances to enter and leave the cell. It will be pointed out in Chapters 19 and 20 that the equations describing diffusion in liquids and the permeability of a membrane contain a term for area. The greater the area involved, the greater the diffusion. Nutrients and oxygen enter the cell across the membrane, and degradation products plus carbon dioxide leave via the same membrane (although perhaps at different sites). The specific and continuing role of the cell membrane in maintaining the cellular environment can perhaps be appreciated in terms of the following example. Blood plasma has a composition of $Na^+ = 145$ milliequivalents/liter, $K^+ = 5$ milliequivalents/liter. In contrast, cellular fluid is high in potassium (150 milliequivalents/liter) and low in sodium (20 milliequivalents/liter).

Passage of materials across membranes will be dealt with in detail beginning in Chapter 19. However, to give some idea of the role of the membrane, that is its function *in vivo*, let us list the mechanisms which account for materials entering the cell. These are three in number.

(1) *Passive factors.* These do not require additional energy expenditure by the cell. The principal passive factors are diffusion, hydrostatic or osmotic pressure, the Donnan equilibrium, and the existence of an electrical potential gradient. These are discussed elsewhere, but we must point out that all are influenced by the structure of the membrane.

(2) *Active transport.* This is transport which occurs in a direction opposite to that predicted by consideration of the passive factors. The simplest assumption to explain such a phenomenon (Chapter 21) is that the membrane interacts with the material being transported, forming an intermediate compound. Here the membrane is an essential part of the transport event.

(3) *Chemical conversion.* Certain substances are converted chemically (totally, or in part) to different forms upon passing into cells. For example, ascorbic acid exists in some cells largely in the form of dehydroascorbic acid. Such a process, of course, removes ascorbic acid from the internal cellular environment. A lowering of the internal concentration of a material

will allow additional molecules to pass across the membrane by diffusion (some of these concepts will be developed later in more rigorous terms, utilizing the concept of chemical potential).

The grossest statement would be that the membrane is a bag or sac surrounding the cell. We know that this is not true, since the membrane is far from passive and must be considered as an integral part of the cell. Since the membrane is the outer layer of the cell, we can ask whether it has a role in maintaining cell size and shape. That is, has the membrane distensibility, or is it rigid? If the mammalian red blood cell (erythrocyte) is placed in a solution containing less solute per unit volume of solvent than the erythrocyte itself, then fluid enters the cell, which accordingly swells. This phenomenon is an example of solvent flow due to differences in osmotic pressure (a topic quantitated in Chapter 18). Erythrocytes show no volume change in 0.9% NaCl (0.15 M). They swell when exposed to dilute saline, and finally the membrane ruptures at about 0.3% NaCl. The membrane can thus withstand limited pressure changes within the cell. To maintain cell size requires a delicate balance between fluid influx and efflux (plant cell walls of cellulose, however, have greater rigidity). Examples are known in which the membrane changes its shape rapidly. The most dramatic are the pseudopodia of amoeba, employed in propelling the organism. The electron micrographs of cells must be recognized to represent the cytoarchitecture at one instant of time. At other intervals the formed elements and membrane will change their alignment in the constant activity that is life. The membrane is also involved in the process of pinocytosis ("cell drinking"). A liquid drop with a diameter on the order of 0.1 μ at the cell's external surface can be surrounded by the membrane. A vacuole is formed and the liquid drop is then transferred to the interior of the cell. Pinocytosis is shown not only by membranes of lower animals but by those of man as well (and certain lipids may enter the intestinal mucosa by pinocytosis).

A significant portion of the mass of a membrane passes into solution in lipid solvents (Chapter 11). Chemical analysis reveals cholesterol, phospholipids and neutral fats to be the principal compounds. Of the material not solubilized by such treatment, protein appears to be the main component. We have previously discussed how lipids and protein are arranged in three-dimensional fashion to form a cell membrane.

For materials whose passage across the cell membrane is adequately explained by diffusion, we can employ various size molecules to gain insight as to the functioning of the cellular membrane. We can use progressively more bulky analogues to find the equivalent size of the "pore" through which they are passing. For example, methanol, ethanol, propanol, and so on form a series of alcohols differing from each other in chain length. Branched chain alcohols which impart sterically bulky groups to the width of the probing molecules can also be employed. Results differ from membrane to membrane, but the general statement can be made that the more bulky molecules penetrate less readily. In addition, for molecules of identical size, those possessing lipophobic groups (lipophobic means lipid hating, that is, groups which are not soluble in lipid solvents) pass with a slower velocity than those with lipophilic groups. The lipid properties of the membrane thus appear to dominate its response to diffusing molecules. This is treated further in Chapter 20, where the permeability is shown to correlate with the solubility of the probing molecule in lipid solvents versus its solubility in water (the so-called partition coefficient). Also treated at that time will be the concept that biologic membranes show varying degrees of permeability (from impermeable to fully permeable) and that this influences the measurement of osmotic pressure, since certain solute molecules may pass the membrane in addition to solvent molecules. Finally, by measurement of water flow across biologic membranes due to differences in osmotic pressure, and again due to diffusion, it is possible to measure an "equivalent pore radius." That is, if there were "pores," they would have a radius of given magnitude in order to account for the flow. The radius has been calculated to be on the order of 4 A (the theory and techniques of the procedure are discussed by Solomon). Pores have not been seen by use of the electron microscope. This is not unexpected, since a pore with a radius of 4 A would be below the limit of resolution of present electron microscopes with best contrast. Whether all pores are identical is, of course, unknown. On the basis of more rapid interchange of negatively charged ions than of ions with a positive charge between a cell and its surroundings (and vice versa in other membranes), some membranes may have electrical charges set in the pores. That is, a positively charged pore would allow negative ions to enter but would repel positive ions. The study of such electrical properties has particular importance in elucidation of nerve excitation and conduction. It would seem that the membrane has, functionally, an inhomogenous surface. One part is an ion-permeable region (perhaps pores), while the other is ion-impermeable.

Thinking of biologic systems in electrical terms is perhaps unfamiliar. Electrical properties are of importance in determining the function of membranes, and aspects of this in relationship to transport are discussed in Chapter 20. The potential difference between the faces of a cell membrane always occurs, and the internal surface of the cell is negative with respect to the exterior. A typical membrane 100 A thick has a potential difference of about 0.040 volt (40 millivolts) between its faces. This is 4×10^6 volts/cm. The capacitance of a biological membrane is approximately 1 microfarad/cm^2, while its resistance is on the order of 1000 ohms/cm^2. The dielectric constant of the membrane (about 11) is considerably below that of water (Chapter 3).

13–4 The nucleus. Although many structures can be identified by use of the electron microscope, we can ask whether these are true entities or whether they are artifacts of fixation. Part of the definitive evidence that many of these subcellular components are truly present in the cell has been provided by separation studies. That is, various components have been isolated from cells in great purity, and have been studied in detail.

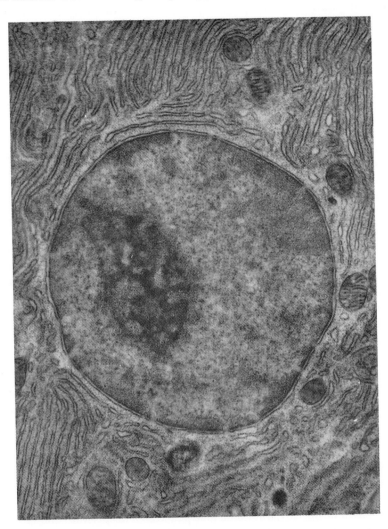

Fig. 13–4. Nucleus of a cell from the pancreas of a bat. The perinuclear membrane is not continuous, but is apparently pierced by numerous pores. Mitochondria and part of the endoplasmic reticulum (with attached ribosomes) are present. [Reprinted by permission from *Scientific American*, September 1961, p. 50.]

The principal technique for accomplishing this has been differential centrifugation (discussed elsewhere), in which subcellular entities are separated according to their density. Usually the densest region within the cell is the nucleus.

In terms of volume, the nucleus may occupy from less than 10% of the cell (as in engorged adipose tissue) all the way up to nearly 100% (in germinal cells). Bounding the nucleus is a nuclear membrane, perhaps derived from the pericellular membrane. The unique features of this membrane (Fig. 13–4) are the numerous discontinuities, which allow the cell cytoplasm to be in contact with the nuclear material. A possible reason for this is as follows: One of the principal means of nuclear control of cellular events is through the provision of messenger RNA to direct protein synthesis at the ribosomes. RNA precursors are small molecules and can likely diffuse across the membrane from cytoplasm to nucleus. The finished RNA polymer, however, has a high molecular weight (perhaps on the order of 1×10^6). Such a macromolecule should not pass across a biologic membrane with a finite velocity. Discontinuities in the nuclear membrane may thus possibly be sites at which macromolecules pass.

The erythrocyte of man (the circulating red blood cell) spends about 120 days in the peripheral circulation before being destroyed. This cell does not possess a nucleus; in addition, it does not reproduce. We may infer that presence of the nucleus is a necessary condition for cell reproduction. While necessary, the nucleus is not sufficient for occurrence of reproduction (this is shown by the fact that mature muscles and nerves, with nuclei, do not reproduce). Experiments can be performed in which amoebae or certain large algae are enucleated. The forms without a nucleus do not reproduce, although they can live for a period of days. Location of genetic material within the nucleus makes the failure of reproduction of enucleated species understandable. The events involved in cellular division are complex, with an elaborate architecture present at mitosis, as though (teleologically) to insure the proper distribution of nuclear material between the two daughter cells. Mazia and co-workers have studied the mitotic process in detail and have elucidated many of the chemical and anatomical details.

13–5 Ribosomes and protein synthesis. The classical view of the cell membrane was of a boundary layer encompassing the outer surface of the cell. The advent of electron microscopy has shown that the limiting membrane has multiple invaginations and penetrates deeply into the cell. In addition, other units within the cell (as the endoplasmic reticulum) are bounded by membranes. Are all of these membranes communicating? They all have the same basic structure (likely protein-double lipid layer-protein) and under the electron microscope appear to be about the same

Fig. 13-5. Electron micrograph showing the endoplasmic reticulum of a cell from the human submaxillary salivary gland. Observe the ribosomes as small dark particles, each with a diameter of approximately 1.5×10^{-6} cm. Parts of four mitochondria are also visible. [Reprinted by permission from *Scientific American*, September 1961, p. 76.]

dimension. According to J. D. Robertson, most of these membranes are continuous and perhaps originate from the growth spirals. This is indeed a challenging concept; most of the intracellular membranes may be extensions of the boundary membrane.

Part of the tortuous membrane protruding into the cell is referred to as the endoplasmic reticulum (Fig. 13-5). Attached to this system are particles called microsomes, about 300 A in diameter. Centrifugation of microsomes separates components called ribosomes, which can be collected and studied virtually free of other cellular components. The ribosomes are composed of lipid, protein, and ribonucleic acid, and command our attention because of their connection with protein elaboration. Ribosomes are the site of protein synthesis (see Chapter 9). It will be recalled that after amino acids are activated by ATP, they are transferred to a soluble RNA (*S*-RNA). The complex of *S*-RNA-amino acid arrives at the ribosomes for protein synthesis. The ribosomes are apparently 'coded' for the synthesis of particular proteins by a distinct type of RNA termed messenger RNA (which may come from the nucleus, see Fig. 13-6). Activated amino acids on *S*-RNA, messenger RNA, and ribosomes then interact to form proteins. Here is an excellent example of the relationship

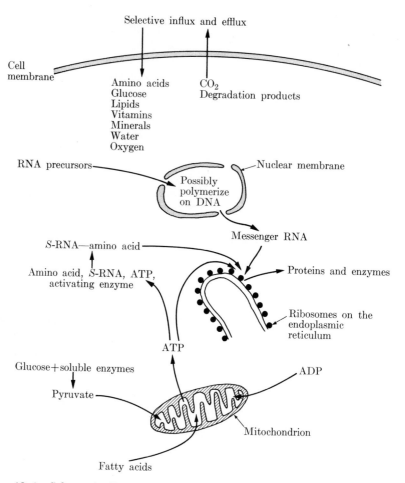

FIG. 13–6. Schematic diagram of the integration of selected cellular functions.

of structure to function. Soluble components are carried to a discrete structural unit for protein synthesis. Ribosomes, at least those from certain sites, may have additional roles to play. The production of hydroxyproline from proline (see Section 13–7) appears to be carried out by ribosomes. The ultimate role of ribosomes may thus prove to be both production and modification of proteins.

13–6 Mitochondria. Located within the cytoplasm of mammalian cells are particles called *mitochondria* (Fig. 13–7). These rod-shaped structures, 1 to 10 μ long, are concerned with three principal metabolic events:
   (1) Degradation of fatty acids.

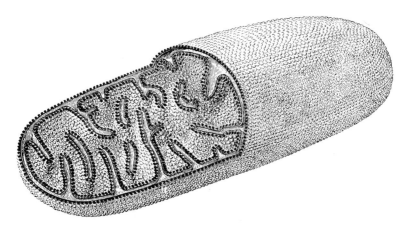

Fig. 13-7. Cross section of an idealized typical mitochondrion. The mitochondrion is approximately elliptical in shape and is about $2\,\mu$ in length. There is an outer membrane and an inner convoluted membrane to which are attached multiple small particles which are involved in energy transfer. [Reprinted by permission from *Scientific American*.]

(2) Oxidation of pyruvate via a series of steps called the citric acid cycle (pyruvate is the principal metabolic product of glucose and hence is a key intermediate).

(3) The coupling of oxidation to phosphorylation (that is, production of ATP from ADP, utilizing the energy gained by metabolism; see Fig. 13-6). ATP is an "energy-rich" compound needed in the biosynthesis of proteins and other cellular components. ATP is also the energy source for such events as muscle contraction, and one is impressed by the proximity of mitochondria to the contractile fibrils in a muscle cell.

The consensus of studies is that the mitochondrion (Fig. 13-7) is well structured, having a distinct boundary membrane. Within each mitochondrion can be seen membranous folds or partitions which are termed cristae. The cristae appear to be formed by a continuation of the inner membrane, but this point is unsettled. Cristae increase the internal surface area; there appears to be a correlation between the number of cristae in a mitochondrion and its oxidative rate. The origin of the mitochondrial membrane is still uncertain, and it may or may not be derived from the cell membrane.

The intact mitochondrial membrane, like other biologic membranes, undoubtedly has selective permeability; however, its study is made difficult by the small size of these particles. The mitochondrial membrane can be ruptured by three techniques: use of sound waves, utilization of a hypotonic medium to cause osmotic rupture, and use of deoxycholic acid (which is a surface active agent) and digitonin (which precipitates cholesterol). When mitochondria are completely fragmented and the mitochon-drial wall is recovered, so long as double membranes are present the events of oxidative phosphorylation are still shown by the fragmented mito-chondrial wall. The enzymes necessary for these occurrences must reside within or on the wall. If the events are quantitated from a number of mitochondrial walls and are further fragmented into small pieces, the same set of events is shown by the subfragments. No matter how frag-mentation is accomplished, the resulting particles still carry out the events of oxidative phosphorylation. A reasonable conclusion is that the wall contains numerous subassemblies of the enzymes and cofactors needed for oxidative phosphorylation. Cleavage of the membrane separates these units from each other but still leaves each intact. By having an assembly of enzymes in the mitochondrial wall, the nutrient undergoing processing does not have to pass into solution, but can probably move from one site to another on the wall. The cytoarchitecture of the mitochondrion may be a means of causing reactions to occur near or on the wall and in precise control, rather than by diffusion of a molecule through cell fluid.

13-7 The intercellular substance. Cells are not in direct contact, but are separated by about 150 A. We may inquire why cells frequently sta-bilize at this particular distance from each other. The first answer is that there is an extramembranous material between cells. However, this does not give us insight as to why the distance of 150 A is commonly observed. Surfaces can be expected to stabilize at that point at which the attractive forces are balanced by the repulsive forces. Attraction between membranes is possibly due to van der Waals forces. It will be recalled from Chapter 3 that between isolated particles the van der Waals force fell off as the sixth power of distance. On two parallel aligned surfaces, however, it has been calculated that the distance relationship depends on the second power of distance (see Overbeek). The repulsive force between membranes is prob-ably due to similar electrical charges. On two parallel plates the elec-trical force depends upon a logarithmic function of distance. At that point at which the van der Waals forces balance the electrical repulsive forces, stability can result. In life, however, the situation may be com-plicated by the varying dielectric properties of the intercellular material, solvent flow, and other factors. Cell stability and adhesion is thus an area of great interest at present.

What is the composition of the material occurring between cells? Succinctly, there is little directly known concerning the intercellular "cement" *in vivo*. Cells can be separated from one another by treatment with agents which combine with calcium, suggesting a Ca^{2+} rich matrix. Certain proteolytic enzymes also cause cells to separate, but this may be due to an effect on the cell wall protein, or its interaction with the cementing material, rather than to a direct effect on the cemented material itself. From areas such as those surrounding small blood vessels, quantities of intercellular substances can be obtained and shown to consist of two parts: an amorphous material and fibers. The amorphous material is primarily carbohydrate such as sulfated mucopolysaccharides (see Chapter 11). The principal fibers are composed of collagen. This substance collagen is a most ubiquitous protein, being found in nearly all animals above the sponges. In addition, collagen has wide distribution within an animal, occurring to some extent in all tissues, except perhaps the nervous system. Collagen is an interesting protein in several respects.

(1) Two principal amino acids found in collagen are proline and hydroxyproline. Apparently the latter occurs only in collagen and is produced from proline at the ribosomes.

(2) Unlike the α-helix of some proteins or the Watson-Crick helix of DNA, collagen is composed of a *three*-stranded helix held together by hydrogen bonding.

(3) Collagen fibers aggregate together. What is striking is that depending upon the pH and other factors, three distinct types of aggregation of the asymmetric collagen molecule are possible: parallel with overlap, parallel without overlap, and antiparallel without overlap (see the review by Gross).

(4) The mechanical properties of collagen are such that they lend rigidity to tissues in which they are found. Although we will not pursue these topics, an introduction to the literature on collagen is provided by Harkness and by Rich and Crick.

We have mentioned the intercellular substance briefly in order to point out its structural contrast to cells and their membranes. The intercellular material is in contact with cells, and nutrients pass through the intercellular region. In terms of composition, however, there is vivid contrast between the polysaccharide-rich intercellular substance and the lipid-rich cell.

References

1. A. S. G. Curtis, "Cell Contacts: Some Physical Considerations," *American Naturalist* 94, 37–56, (1960).

2. J. T. Davies and E. K. Rideal, *Interfacial Phenomena*. Academic Press, New York, 1961.

3. H. Davson and J. F. Danielli, *The Permeability of Natural Membranes*, 2nd Ed. Cambridge University Press, London, 1952.

4. D. E. Green and Y. Hatefi, "The Mitochondrion and Biochemical Machines," *Science* 133, 13–19 (1961).

5. J. Gross, "Collagen," *Scientific American* 204, 121–130, (May, 1961).

6. R. D. HARKNESS, "Biological Functions of Collagen," *Biol. Reviews* **36**, 399–463 (1961).

7. H. HERRMANN, "Direct Metabolic Interactions Between Animal Cells," *Science* **132**, 529–532 (1960).

8. D. MAZIA, "Mitosis and the Physiology of Cell Division," in *The Cell*, ed. by J. Brachet and A. E. Mirsky, Vol. 3, pp. 77–412. Academic Press, New York, 1961.

9. J. T. G. OVERBEEK, "The Interaction Between Colloidal Particles," in *Colloid Science*, H. R. Kruyt, Vol. I, pp. 245–277. Elsevier, Amsterdam, 1952.

10. A. RICH and F. H. C. CRICK, "The Molecular Structure of Collagen," *J. Mol. Biol.* **3**, 483–506 (1961).

11. J. D. ROBERTSON, "The Membrane of the Living Cell," *Scientific American* **206**, 64–72, (April, 1962).

12. A. K. SOLOMON, "Pores in the Cell Membrane," *Scientific American* **203**, 146–156 (December, 1960).

CHAPTER 14
ELEMENTS OF THERMODYNAMICS

CHAPTER 14

ELEMENTS OF THERMODYNAMICS

14–1 Introduction. Requisite to an understanding of the functional behavior of biological systems is an understanding of some of the laws describing the behavior and properties of physical chemical systems. Thermodynamics is a physical science which, based primarily upon two principles or postulates, embraces a large domain of science and provides a systematic approach to a study of function. It is in its essence a mathematical science. From the first two principles or laws of thermodynamics, there may be deduced, with mathematical rigor and exactness, a large number of consequences to which physical, chemical, and biological systems have been found to conform. The elements of thermodynamics are developed in this chapter—not in all detail nor with the complete rigor found in advanced treatments, but hopefully with sufficient detail and logic to promote a basic understanding and to underscore the inherent power of thermodynamics as a tool of scientific thought. It cannot be overemphasized that some understanding of thermodynamics is mandatory for an understanding of biological systems.

Central to some comprehension of thermodynamics is the concept of energy (introduced in Chapter 2), a concept which is much less a part of everyday experience than is, for instance, that of mass. However, like mass, energy is a conserved quantity. This fact simplifies many of the considerations in thermodynamics and indeed forms the basis of the entire science. It would be well to indicate here that even though energy in all its forms is a conserved quantity, its *absolute* values remain undefined. Only changes in energy are operationally measurable. Mass, on the other hand, possesses an operationally definable absolute value. A given quantity of mass is referable to a zero quantity. However, when a body of substance is viewed with respect to its position and state of existence in our universe, it is apparent that an absolute zero energy is quite impossible to define meaningfully. It becomes necessary to assign some given state as a state of reference, or reference point; i.e., some particular but arbitrary state may be assigned zero energy. No difficulty is thus presented if one is consistent with respect to this reference state in considering any change in the energy.

14–2 Definitions. Before embarking upon the formal statements of the first and second principles of thermodynamics, it is desirable first to define clearly certain terms that are essential. Thermodynamics deals with energy, i.e., changes in energy associated with prescribed changes in the state of matter as determined by changes in such variables as temperature, pressure, volume, mass, etc. *Matter* is composed of discrete particles, but it is only collections or populations of these particles of which the average energy, certain properties, or the state are really measurable. Thus, thermodynamics is a *macroscopic* science and deals only with collections of atoms or molecules sufficiently large to enable certain macroscopic properties to be measured and assigned. The properties and energies of individual molecules cannot be measured, although from statistical theory, energy levels may be assigned to individual molecules or groups of molecules. See Fig. 14–1.

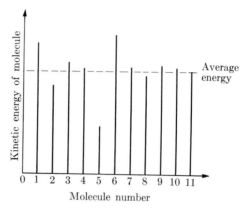

Fig. 14–1. Kinetic energies of individual molecules. The average energy of a population of molecules is the only energy that is operationally accessible to measurement.

A collection of molecules to which attention is directed and whose properties may be measured constitutes a *thermodynamic system*. A system is set apart from the remainder of the universe, termed the *environment*, by *boundaries*, real or conceptual. Thus a thermodynamic system may be the living cell and its boundary the cell membrane, or the system may be a subcellular element like a mitochondrion; or it may be a collection of these. On the other hand, it may be a particular chemical system in a vessel or an entire biological organism. In every case, however, the system is that collection of matter which is under study. Boundaries, real or conceived, may be such as to allow matter to cross between the system and the environment, resulting in an *open system;* or the boundary may be impenetrable to matter, giving a *closed system*. The walls may be *thermally conducting* or *thermally insulating*. In the former case, if the environment is an infinite heat reservoir at a given temperature, the system is at this constant temperature. Boundaries may be such as to completely isolate the system, allowing no interaction between system and environment. Systems so bounded are *isolated systems*. A system itself may be *homogeneous* or may consist of a number of *phases*, a phase being that portion of the system which is uniform and homogeneous. Thus a mixture of ice and liquid water comprises a two-phase system, as does a mixture of oil and water which are immiscible. A *component* is an independent chemical entity of the system. Thus sodium chloride may be a component; but the sodium ions alone cannot be conceivably a component, for it must always be accompanied operationally by an anion to preserve electrical neutrality. It is convenient to refer to dependent parts of a component as individual *species* of the system.

With reference not merely to its state of aggregation (e.g. gas, liquid, or crystal), the *state* of a thermodynamic system must be specified in terms of values of all *variables* necessary to describe the system. Such variables fall into two classes—those *extensive* in character, such as mass (quantity of each component), volume, energy, surface area, electric charge, etc., and those *intensive* in character which do not depend upon the extent or size of the system, such as temperature, pressure, concentration of each component, surface tension, electrical potential, etc.

As previously indicated, thermodynamics is concerned with *changes in the state* of a system. Changes in state involve some *process* which determines the manner in which the change in state is brought about. We deal here primarily with *equilibrium processes* (also called *reversible processes*) which involve, for a change in state, a continuous succession of equilibrium states between the initial and final equilibrium states. Such a process is an idealized mathematical one, for in any real case, one must always be slightly displaced from equilibrium to achieve a change, however slight this may be. Equilibrium itself is, in fact, a conceptual situation in that it is one which involves no further change in time of any of the vari-

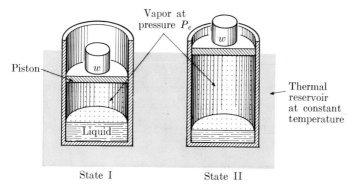

FIG. 14–2. Illustration of a change in state of a system involving the reversible isothermal evaporation of a quantity of liquid water at its equilibrium vapor pressure, P_e.

ables describing the system. For mathematical exactness, this involves infinite time. For experimental purposes, a reasonable length of time suitable for the particular conditions must suffice.

To illustrate a reversible process, one may consider a two-phase one-component system consisting of liquid water in equilibrium with its vapor and in thermal contact with an infinite heat reservoir, as seen in Fig. 14–2. The change in state involves evaporation of a portion of the liquid to the vapor, and since the system is isothermal (has a constant temperature), the equilibrium vapor pressure is unchanged throughout the process. The volume changes by a continuous succession of infinitesimal increments, dV, a differential quantity (see appendix for the meaning of the differential), attended by the simultaneous absorption from the heat reservoir of an infinitesimal quantity of heat, dq. In such a process or its reverse, therefore, neither the temperature nor the vapor pressure depart from their equilibrium values by more than an infinitesimal. In a *nonequilibrium* or *natural process*, such may not be the case.

14–3 The first principle of thermodynamics. The first principle of thermodynamics is a statement of the conservation of energy. This is a statement not subject to proof but only to repetitive experimental verification. It is a postulate, therefore, which states that for a given change in state of a thermodynamic system, energy changes in this system are quantitatively accountable in terms of the energy changes experienced in the environment of the system. This implies that the energy is a unique function of the state of the system and possesses a characteristic value for each state.

Consider first the simplest case in which a system is completely isolated from the environment. Such a system by definition cannot exchange energy or mass with its environment. Its boundaries are thermally insulated, rigid, and impenetrable to matter or other environmental influences. It is apparent that such a system, initially in internal equilibrium, can experience no change in state and thus no change in the internal energy, U. Both the heat absorbed by the system from the environment, designated a positive q, and the work done by the system on the environment, designated a positive w, are zero:

$$\Delta U = 0, \quad q = 0, \quad w = 0. \quad (14\text{–}1)$$

Consider next a system which is closed to the exchange of matter, as above, but which is merely thermally insulated from the environment. In this case, work, either positive or negative, may be done by the system on the environment with a resultant change in the state of the system. The first principle then states that the change in internal energy of the system plus the work done by the system is zero. Mathematically,

$$U_2 - U_1 + w = 0$$

or

$$\Delta U = -w, \qquad (14\text{–}2)$$

where U_2 and U_1 designate the final and initial energy, and Δ the change in a thermally insulated system.

Consider thirdly a system which is still closed to the exchange of matter, but is now not thermally insulated. A quantity of heat, q, may now be absorbed by the system from the environment and an amount of work, w, may be done by the system on the environment to accompany a given change in state of the system. The first principle then states that the change in internal energy of a closed system is always the difference between the heat absorbed and the work done. Mathematically,

$$U_2 - U_1 = q - w = \Delta U. \qquad (14\text{–}3)$$

For an infinitesimal change in state,

$$dU = q - w. \qquad (14\text{–}4)$$

It is a fact that neither q nor w are properties of the system, and their individual magnitudes depend upon the particular manner in which a change in state is achieved; however, their difference, finite in Eq. (14–3) and infinitesimal in Eq. (14–4), is indeed a property of the state of the system, independent of the manner or particular path by which the change in state is effected.

In an overall cyclic process, defined as a sequence of processes in which the system is ultimately returned to its initial state, it is evident that ΔU must be zero since the internal energy U is a function only of the state of the system. However, q and w are in general not zero, although for the entire cycle the total q must equal the total w. In a cyclic process there is therefore an equivalence between the heat absorbed and the work done.

14–4 Thermodynamic work. Thermodynamic work may appear in several forms depending on the processes involved. Such work, however, always has the dimensions of energy. For instance, in the example cited in Section 14–2 and illustrated in Fig. 14–2 involving the reversible evaporation of liquid water to vapor at the equilibrium vapor pressure, P_e, the differential reversible work done by the system is $P_e\, dV$. With pressure in units of dyne $\cdot$ cm^{-2} and volume in cm^3, $P_e\, dV$ has the dimensions of dyne-cm (a force acting through a distance) or ergs (a unit of energy). The total work involved in such a reversible process in going from an initial state to a final state is the sum of all the bits or infinitesimal amounts of

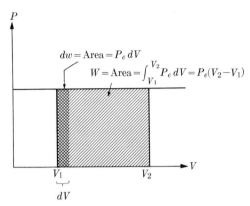

FIG. 14–3. Representation of the work done by the system of Fig. 14–2. The work represents an area.

work in passing from one equilibrium state to another. Mathematically, this involves an integration, a procedure introduced in Chapter 3 and outlined further in the Appendix. In this example, as has been stated, the pressure P_e is a constant. The sum of dV or $\int_{V_1}^{V_2} dV$, from the initial volume V_1 to the final volume V_2, is simply $V_2 - V_1$. The total work is therefore

$$P_e(V_2 - V_1) = P_e \, \Delta V, \qquad (14\text{–}5)$$

as shown in Fig. 14–3. In general, however, the pressure varies as the volume varies, and integration must be carried out such that one sums properly the product of that pressure which corresponds to a particular volume as it is changed by an infinitesimal. For instance, assume we have as our system a quantity of ideal gas for which it is well known that the product $pV = C$, where C is a constant for a given constant temperature. Then $p = C/V$, and

$$\int_{V_1}^{V_2} p \, dV = C \int_{V_1}^{V_2} \frac{dV}{V}. \qquad (14\text{–}6)$$

This last integral now contains a single variable, V, in the integrand; this is a necessary condition before the mathematical operation can be carried out. [This particular type of integral occurs with such frequency in the physical sciences that a special function, the natural logarithm, has been defined for it (see Appendix).] The result is

$$
\begin{aligned}
w &= C \int_{V_1}^{V^2} \frac{dV}{V} = C \int_{V_1}^{V_2} d \ln V \\
&= C \ln V_2 - C \ln V_1 = C \ln \frac{V_2}{V_1},
\end{aligned}
\qquad (14\text{–}7)
$$

Table 14-1

Units of Energy in Common Use
and Their Conversion Factors

	erg	joule	gram-calorie	kilogram-calorie	kilogram-meter	watt-hour	electron-volt	liter-atm
1 erg	1.00	$1.00 \cdot 10^{-7}$	$2.39 \cdot 10^{-8}$	$2.39 \cdot 10^{-11}$	$1.02 \cdot 10^{-8}$	$2.78 \cdot 10^{-11}$	$6.29 \cdot 10^{11}$	$9.87 \cdot 10^{-11}$
1 joule	$1.00 \cdot 10^{7}$	1.00	$2.39 \cdot 10^{-1}$	$2.39 \cdot 10^{-4}$	$1.02 \cdot 10^{-1}$	$2.78 \cdot 10^{-4}$	$6.29 \cdot 10^{18}$	$9.87 \cdot 10^{-3}$
1 gm-cal	$4.186 \cdot 10^{7}$	4.186	1.00	$1.00 \cdot 10^{-3}$	$4.27 \cdot 10^{-1}$	$1.16 \cdot 10^{-3}$	$2.63 \cdot 10^{19}$	$4.13 \cdot 10^{-2}$
1 kcal	$4.186 \cdot 10^{11}$	$4.186 \cdot 10^{3}$	$1.00 \cdot 10^{3}$	1.00	$4.27 \cdot 10^{2}$	1.16	$2.23 \cdot 10^{22}$	$4.13 \cdot 10^{1}$
1 kg-m	$9.81 \cdot 10^{7}$	9.81	2.34	$2.34 \cdot 10^{-3}$	1.00	$2.72 \cdot 10^{-3}$	$6.17 \cdot 10^{19}$	$9.68 \cdot 10^{-2}$
1 watt-hr	$3.60 \cdot 10^{10}$	$3.60 \cdot 10^{3}$	$8.60 \cdot 10^{2}$	$8.60 \cdot 10^{-1}$	$3.67 \cdot 10^{2}$	1.00	$2.26 \cdot 10^{22}$	$3.55 \cdot 10^{1}$
1 ev	$1.59 \cdot 10^{-12}$	$1.59 \cdot 10^{-19}$	$3.80 \cdot 10^{-20}$	$3.80 \cdot 10^{-23}$	$1.62 \cdot 10^{-20}$	$4.42 \cdot 10^{-23}$	1.00	$1.57 \cdot 10^{-21}$
1 liter-atm	$1.01 \cdot 10^{9}$	$1.01 \cdot 10^{2}$	$2.42 \cdot 10^{1}$	$2.42 \cdot 10^{-2}$	$1.03 \cdot 10^{1}$	$2.82 \cdot 10^{-2}$	$6.37 \cdot 10^{20}$	1.00

and thus the work is proportional to the logarithm of the ratio of final and initial volumes.

The above are two examples of "pressure-volume" work, the first involving constant pressure and the second involving a known relation between pressure and volume, the so-called equation of state of a perfect gas. There are, however, many other types of thermodynamic work. Electrical work involving simple charged particles was introduced in Chapter 3. For a system of particles at an electrical potential ψ, we may conceptually charge these with successive infinitesimal increments of charge dq. The infinitesimal electrical work is $dw_e = \psi \, dq$. The resultant electrical work is

$$w_e = \int_0^Q \psi \, dq, \qquad (14\text{–}8)$$

commencing with uncharged particles and introducing a total charge, Q. If ψ is expressed in volts and q in coulombs, then w_e has the dimensions of volt coulombs = joules = 10^7 ergs.

Similarly there is, in general, work involved in altering the surface area of a phase or system, for at phase boundaries there is a surface tension, or an energy per unit area, γ, arising from asymmetry of intermolecular forces for molecules in the surface (see Chapters 4 and 12). Surface tension has the dimensions of dyne $\cdot$ cm^{-1}, and is in one dimension analogous to the pressure of a fluid or gas in two dimensions. The differential work involved in altering the surface area is $dw_a = \gamma \, dA$, and the total reversible work is given by

$$w_a = \int_{A_1}^{A_2} \gamma \, dA. \qquad (14\text{–}9)$$

Further examples of thermodynamic work are considered in the chapters which follow.

It should be mentioned that in considering more than one kind of work simultaneously the units in which work is expressed should be the same. In other words, before adding and subtracting electrical work, pressure-volume work, or surface work, it is necessary that each be expressed in the same units. The units in common use are calories, joules, ergs, electron volts, and liter-atmospheres. The conversion factors for these units are found in Table 14–1.

14–5 Heat, heat capacity, and thermal equilibrium. In our discussion of the first principle of thermodynamics in Section 14–3, a quantity q, termed "heat absorbed," was introduced. In one's experience the flow of heat from one body to another is associated with changes in the "thermal" energy of these bodies, which in turn is related to their "temperature."

However, it is to be recognized that temperature may be measured in numerous ways, each representing some property of the particular system used. Thus the volume of a constant quantity of liquid or gas serves as a measure of temperature, as in the ordinary mercury thermometer, or the electrical resistance of a conducting metal, as in a resistance thermometer. Innumerable temperature scales may be envisaged.

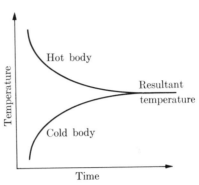

FIG. 14–4. The approach to thermal equilibrium when a hot and cold body are placed in thermal contact.

In one's everyday experience is also the observation that two systems originally at different temperatures will undergo a change when placed in thermal contact with each other. The change is such that the originally warmer system becomes cooler, and vice versa. During this change, heat or thermal energy is transferred from the warmer to the cooler body, and if left in isolation for a sufficiently long time, no measurable difference in temperature continues to exist. This final state is one of *thermal equilibrium*. In this approach to thermal equilibrium (see Fig. 14–4) the magnitude of q, referring to the quantity of heat transferred, depends upon both the original difference in temperature and the *heat capacities* of the two bodies. The heat capacity is a property of the material composing the system and is most commonly expressed in terms of a unit quantity of the matter in a given state. Thus the *specific heat capacity* is expressed as heat absorbed (ergs, joules, calories, etc.) per gram-degree, the degree referring to a suitable temperature scale. The *molar heat capacity* would be expressed, for instance, in calories $\cdot$ mole^{-1} $\cdot$ degree^{-1} C. Since the heat capacity for a given material differs as to whether or not changes in volume (expansion or contraction) of the system are permitted during the thermal change, two different heat capacities are recognized; C_v is that associated with a constant volume process and C_p that associated with a constant pressure process. Expressed mathematically in differential form, we have

$$dq = C_p \, dT \quad \text{(constant pressure)},$$
$$dq = C_v \, dT \quad \text{(constant volume)},$$

(14–10)

or, in integral form,

$$q = \int_{T_1}^{T_2} C_p \, dT. \tag{14-11}$$

Statements pertaining to thermal equilibrium are often designated by some authors as the zeroth principle of thermodynamics (see Guggenheim). Such a statement may read as follows: If two systems are each in thermal equilibrium with a third system, they are in turn in thermal equilibrium with each other and are therefore at the same temperature.

14–6 The second principle of thermodynamics. As indicated above, the quantity of heat absorbed by a system undergoing a change in state is, in general, dependent upon the manner in which the change is effected, although the difference, $q - w$, is always a unique function of the change in state of the system and is independent of the path involved in any change. As a part of the statement of the second principle, it is postulated that there exists a function termed the *entropy*, S, which, like the internal energy, U, is a unique function of the state of the system (apart from an arbitrary constant, since only changes in either S or U are measurable) and depends upon its extent. It is further postulated that the entropy may change in two distinct ways: (1) by interaction of the system with its environment, d_eS, or (2) by internal changes taking place in the system, d_iS. The total entropy change in differential form is

$$dS = d_eS + d_iS. \tag{14-12}$$

The quantity d_eS is related to the heat absorbed by a system,

$$d_eS = \frac{q}{T}, \tag{14-13}$$

where T is the *absolute temperature* (a temperature having only positive quantities) and is defined by Eq. (14–13). It is seen in this equation that the absolute temperature T appears in the denominator. This suggests that T can only approach an absolute zero but can never actually reach it. On the other hand, if one had defined a different temperature scale, for example $T' = 1/T$, the resultant thermodynamics would then have heat passing from a lower to a higher T'. It is evident that $T' = 0$ is equally impossible to $T = 0$, for $T' = 0$ implies an infinite temperature on our original T-scale.

The quantity d_iS is always positive for real processes occurring in nature, but is zero for all reversible equilibrium processes. This is a very important point, for it associates the entropy function, at least the portion d_iS, with the variable time. In other words, changes occurring in our universe are associated with this dimension of time, and with this is established a "direction" to this change, a direction along positive time. The postulate that d_iS is greater than zero for natural processes says that such processes are, in their essence, irreversible in time. This points out the conceptual nature of the idealized processes which are called reversible and accounts for the statement that the entropy of the universe is continually increasing, since only natural processes are occurring.

In summary, we see that

$$d_iS = 0 \quad \text{(reversible changes)},$$
$$d_iS > 0 \quad \text{(real or natural changes)},$$

(14–14)

which, together with Eqs. (14–12) and (14–13), lead to

$$dS = \frac{q}{T} = \frac{dq_{\text{rev}}}{T} \quad \text{(reversible changes)},$$
$$dS > \frac{q}{T} \quad \text{(real or natural changes)};$$

(14–15)

these statements comprise the second principle of thermodynamics.

14–7 The entropy function. It is seen that a function S has been postulated as part of the second principle. This is a state function of the system. Its changes, resulting from interaction of the system with the environment, involve the quantity of heat absorbed, q, divided by the absolute temperature, T. Entropy, being a property of the system and having the dimensions of energy per degree, may be given a statistical interpretation as well. In this respect, it is related to the degree of order-disorder of the system, which in turn relates to the extent of our detailed knowledge of the system, such as the precision with which we may specify the positions of the individual molecules of which it is composed. A crystal, for instance, is well ordered, and the molecular positions may be well established. As the crystal absorbs heat q and its temperature increases, the molecules vibrate with greater amplitude about their mean lattice position and there is, in general, expansion of the crystal. The entropy, according to Eq. (14–12), increases with positive q, since T is always positive; and the larger the entropy, the less precise can be our specification of the molecular positions at any instant. Quantitatively, the entropy change may be computed as

$$S - S_0 = \int_{T_0}^{T} \frac{dq_{\text{rev}}}{T} ,$$

(14–16)

where S_0 is the reference value of entropy at the temperature T_0. Alternatively one may combine Eq. (14–10) with Eq. (14–16) and obtain

$$S - S_0 = \int_{T_0}^{T} C_p \frac{dT}{T} = \int_{T_0}^{T} C_p \, d\ln T. \qquad (14\text{–}17a)$$

If C_p is a constant, independent of temperature in the range T_0 to T, as is frequently the case for small intervals of temperature, then the integral is similar to that of Eq. (14–7) and gives

$$S - S_0 = C_p \ln \frac{T}{T_0}. \qquad (14\text{–}17b)$$

At the melting point of a substance, a quantity of heat is absorbed without change in temperature, and the crystal becomes a liquid in which the molecular positions become considerably less certain. Randomness is considerably increased in the liquid state compared with the crystalline state, and the entropy is likewise increased by an amount related to the heat absorbed on melting, the so-called heat of fusion. Further heat absorption, causing the liquid to increase in temperature or to evaporate at an equilibrium vapor pressure to become a gas phase, leads to even greater randomness and a further increase in entropy. In this manner, one can imagine how entropy is related to the degree of randomness of molecular position and energy (potential and kinetic) in a system, and, intuitively, how entropy is related to information. In other words, the more detailed knowledge that we possess of these systems with regard to molecular position, energies, etc., the lower is the entropy of that system; the less pre-

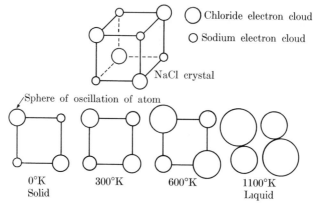

FIG. 14–5. Diagrammatic sketch illustrating the effect of increasing temperature on the randomness and uncertainty of position of Na^+ and Cl^- in crystal lattice and liquid NaCl. Increased randomness and uncertainty are associated with increased entropy.

cisely we can specify the molecular positions and energies at any instant, the greater is the entropy of the system. Entropy is therefore related to the randomness; and the more random a system, the higher is its entropy. We attempt to illustrate this in Fig. 14–5.

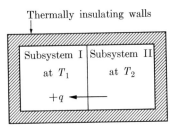

Thermally insulating walls

Subsystem I | Subsystem II
at T_1 | at T_2

$+q$

Fig. 14–6. Diagram illustrating two subsystems in thermal contact with each other but thermally insulated from the environment. An amount of heat, q, is transferred from II to I. See text for entropy changes involved.

If one accepts the entropy function S, together with the absolute temperature T, for which values are always positive, one may easily show that the statement $d_iS > 0$ for a real natural process, is reasonable and within the realm of experience. Consider two subsystems, I and II, in thermal contact with each other but thermally insulated from the environment. (See Fig. 14–6.) Let I be at temperature T_1, and II at a different temperature, T_2. Allow a quantity of positive heat, q, to be absorbed by subsystem I, whereupon its differential entropy change

$$d_eS^{\mathrm{I}} = \frac{1}{T_1}\, q.$$

This small amount of heat can come only from II, since otherwise the walls are thermally insulated. Thus subsystem II loses an amount of heat, q, or absorbs an amount of $-q$, giving a differential entropy change,

$$d_eS^{\mathrm{II}} = -\frac{1}{T_2}\, q.$$

The total entropy change for the two subsystems taken together is

$$dS = d_eS^{\mathrm{I}} + d_eS^{\mathrm{II}} = d_iS,$$

since $d_eS = 0$ for the whole system, it being insulated from the environment. Combining these relations, one obtains

$$d_iS = q\left(\frac{1}{T_1} - \frac{1}{T_2}\right) > 0. \qquad (14\text{–}18)$$

Since q, the heat absorbed by subsystem I, is taken as positive, it is evident on examining Eq. (14–18) that T_2 must be larger than T_1 for the inequality to hold; the inequality is part of the second principle of thermodynamics. As everyone appreciates, the natural flow of heat is from a warmer to a cooler body, and thus the inequality is perfectly reasonable and logical.

14–8 Some important thermodynamic relations. Our statements of the first and second principles of thermodynamics may be combined to form a *fundamental* relation. From this relation, together with certain additional definitions, all thermodynamic relations may be derived. If we consider only reversible changes, for which $d_iS = 0$, then, as before,

$$dU = q - w \qquad (14\text{–}4)$$

and

$$d_eS = dS = \frac{q}{T}, \qquad (14\text{–}19)$$

and then here $q = T\,dS$. These two relations may be combined to give

$$dU = T\,dS - dW, \qquad (14\text{–}20)$$

where dW is understood to include all reversible work, such as compression, surface, electrical, gravitational, and magnetic. We limit our discussion for the moment to compression work, whereupon

$$dW = P\,dV,$$

and Eq. (14–20) becomes

$$dU = T\,dS - P\,dV. \qquad (14\text{–}21)$$

This gives the differential internal energy change associated with these reversible changes in a closed system. If the system is thermally insulated from the environment, then $dS = 0$ and $dU = -P\,dV$. If the system is bounded by rigid heat-conducting walls, then $dV = 0$ and $dU = T\,dS$. In any case, however, Eq. (14–21) is valid only for systems in which mass does not leave or enter the system.

Often it is necessary to consider biological systems not as closed systems but as open systems, since matter may cross the boundaries. For instance, certain chemical compounds may enter a living cell, and others leave. Glucose on entering a cell may undergo a complex series of chemical transformations ultimately involving the utilization of oxygen and resulting in the formation of carbon dioxide and water which must be eliminated across the boundary.

It is important, therefore, to generalize the relation of Eq. (14–21) to include open systems. This may be done in the following manner. Let us assume that our system is composed of a total of c different components.

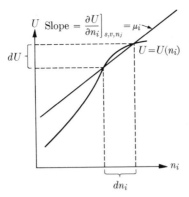

FIG. 14-7. Graphic illustration of the partial derivative, $(\partial U/\partial n_i)_{S,V,n_j} = \mu_i$.

We may number these components successively and designate a particular one, say the ith, by a subscript i. If we reversibly transfer an infinitesimal quantity dn_i into the system from the environment, this may be attended by an increase in internal energy dU. Thus dU is related to dn_i; but the problem is how to compute this, since dU is also a function of dS and dV. Conceptually, we may add dn_i moles to our system, having the system contained in rigid thermally insulating walls such that both dS and dV are zero. Then dU is a function only of dn_i (assuming still the absence of other forms of work, and that no other component, n_j, is being transferred). Written in functional notation, we have

$$U = U(n_i) \qquad \begin{cases} dS = 0, \\ dV = 0, \\ dn_j = 0, \end{cases} \qquad j = 1, 2, \ldots, c, \quad j \neq i, \qquad (14\text{-}22)$$

where j refers to all components other than the ith. The relation between dU and dn_i becomes simply

$$dU = \frac{\partial U}{\partial n_i}\bigg]_{S,V,n_j} dn_i, \qquad (14\text{-}23)$$

where the quantity in the bracket is known as the partial derivative, the derivative of $U = U(n_i)$ with S, V, and n_j held constant. This relation is graphically portrayed in Fig. 14-7. The partial derivative defines the rate with which U changes with respect to increasing n_i by an infinitesimal amount, dn_i, holding all the other variables, S, V, and all n_j, $j \neq i$, constant. This slope at any point multiplied by the magnitude of the change, dn_i, then gives the magnitude of change in U, dU. This partial derivative is given the symbol μ_i and is called the chemical potential of the ith component, a most important concept in chemical thermodynamics; this will be elaborated upon in the following chapter.

For each component there is a relation like Eq. (14–23). Therefore, for the total change in U, we must include all such expressions, giving

$$dU = T\,dS - P\,dV + \frac{\partial U}{\partial n_1}\bigg]_{S,V,n} dn_1 + \frac{\partial U}{\partial n_2}\bigg]_{S,V,n} dn_2 + \cdots \frac{\partial U}{\partial n_c}\bigg]_{S,V,n} dn_c.$$

(14–24)

Using a conventional sum notation, we may conveniently write Eq. (14–24) as

$$dU = T\,dS - P\,dV + \sum_{i=1}^{c} \frac{\partial U}{\partial n_i}\bigg]_{S,V,n_j} dn_i,$$

(14–25)

or

$$dU = T\,dS - P\,dV + \sum_{i=1}^{c} \mu_i\,dn_i.$$

(14–26)

Equation (14–25) or (14–26) now expresses any changes in internal energy in terms of reversible changes in the entropy, volume, and mass of all constituents. It is the form necessary in considering transfers of mass between systems or transfer of mass between subsystems within a whole system which itself may be closed to the environment. However, the expression is rather inconvenient. Practically and conceptually, it is difficult to devise or imagine a reversible process involving the transfer of matter holding both the entropy and volume constant. In other words, the variables S and V are not the most ideal in dealing with open systems. For this reason, other *energy functions* have been defined in terms of U, T, S, P, and V, such that convenient variables result.

14–9 Gibbs free energy. A very convenient and useful energy function may be defined which results in a differential equation explicit in the variables temperature, pressure, and mass, T, P, and n_i. These variables are easily handled, both experimentally and conceptually. This function is here given the symbol G to emphasize that J. Willard Gibbs (1876) was its author. Many American texts utilize the symbol F.* G is defined by

$$G \equiv U + PV - TS,$$

(14–27)

which on differentiation gives

$$dG = dU + P\,dV + V\,dP - T\,dS - S\,dT.$$

(14–28)

---

* See Guggenheim, p. 20, for a list of symbols for energy functions in current use.

Solving Eq. (14–28) for dU, substituting into Eq. (14–26), and rearranging, one obtains

$$dG = -S\,dT + V\,dP + \sum_{i=1}^{c} \mu_i\,dn_i, \qquad (14\text{--}29)$$

an equation explicit in the variables T, P, and n_i. In this relation, μ_i is given the interpretation,

$$\mu_i = \frac{\partial G}{\partial n_i}\bigg]_{T,P,n_j}. \qquad (14\text{--}30)$$

This interpretation is entirely consistent with the original. Because of this interpretation, μ_i, the chemical potential of component i, is sometimes called the partial molar free energy of i when n_i is expressed in units of moles. It represents the increase of Gibbs free energy of the system on the reversible addition of dn_i moles of substance i, holding the temperature, pressure, and mass of all other components constant.

14–10 Other energy functions. Other energy functions are frequently used in thermodynamics. For reference purposes we define them here:

The enthalpy, H, is defined by

$$H \equiv U + PV, \qquad (14\text{--}31)$$

giving the differential form

$$dH = dU + p\,dV + V\,dP, \qquad (14\text{--}32)$$

which, when combined with Eq. (14–26), results in

$$dH = T\,dS + V\,dP + \sum_{i=1}^{c} \mu_i\,dn_i. \qquad (14\text{--}33)$$

The Helmholtz free energy, A, is defined by

$$A \equiv U - TS, \qquad (14\text{--}34)$$

giving the differential form

$$dA = dU - T\,dS - S\,dT, \qquad (14\text{--}35)$$

which, when combined with Eq. (14–26), results in

$$dA = -S\,dT - P\,dV + \sum_{i=1}^{c} \mu_i\,dn_i. \qquad (14\text{--}36)$$

14–11 Summary. We have attempted in the foregoing to develop in a concise fashion the fundamental relations resulting from the first and second principles of thermodynamics. These fundamental relations are

$$dU = T \, dS - P \, dV + \sum \mu_i \, dn_i, \qquad (14\text{-}26)$$
$$dH = T \, dS + V \, dP + \sum \mu_i \, dn_i, \qquad (14\text{-}33)$$
$$dA = -S \, dT - P \, dV + \sum \mu_i \, dn_i, \qquad (14\text{-}36)$$
$$dG = -S \, dT + V \, dP + \sum \mu_i \, dn_i. \qquad (14\text{-}29)$$

Each equation must also contain the appropriate expression for dW for forms of work other than compression work. The chemical potential of component i may be given any of the following interpretations:

$$\mu_i \equiv \frac{\partial U}{\partial n_i}\bigg]_{S,V,n_j} \equiv \frac{\partial H}{\partial n_i}\bigg]_{S,P,n_j} \equiv \frac{\partial A}{\partial n_i}\bigg]_{T,V,n_j} \equiv \frac{\partial G}{\partial n_i}\bigg]_{T,P,n_j}. \qquad (14\text{-}37)$$

From the fundamental relations, all other thermodynamic relations may be derived. In the chapters which follow, we will make use of some of these relations, drawing more heavily upon intuitive logic than upon the formalism presented above. We will find especially useful for biological systems the Gibbs energy function and the chemical potential function. Both are used freely in the discussions which follow.

REFERENCES

1. W. J. MOORE, *Physical Chemistry*, 3rd Ed. Prentice-Hall, New York, 1962.
2. F. DANIELS and R. A. ALBERTY, *Physical Chemistry*, 2nd Ed. Wiley, New York, 1955.
3. A. B. PIPPARD, *Elements of Classical Thermodynamics*. Cambridge University Press, 1960.
4. J. T. EDSALL and J. WYMAN, *Biophysical Chemistry*, Vol. I, Chapter 4. Academic Press, New York, 1958.
5. E. A. GUGGENHEIM, *Thermodynamics—An Advanced Treatment for Chemists and Physicists*. Interscience, New York, 1949.
6. J. W. GIBBS, *Collected Works*, Vol. I. Yale University Press, New Haven, Conn., 1948, also Dover, New York.

CHAPTER 15

EQUILIBRIUM AND THE ENERGY FUNCTIONS

CHAPTER 15

EQUILIBRIUM AND THE ENERGY FUNCTIONS

15–1 Introduction. In the preceding chapter the essential elements of thermodynamics have been introduced and briefly discussed. The concepts themselves provide a scheme of precise mathematical logic for considering some aspects of biological systems. Before indicating any application of these principles, however, we shall discuss further in this chapter the concept of equilibrium and its relation to the various thermodynamic energy functions. Also, we elaborate further our discussion of the chemical potential, since it is a concept of such central importance. The relations of the chemical potential to the common experimentally measured variables, such as pressure and concentration, are developed.

15–2 Mechanical equilibrium. The idea of static mechanical equilibrium presents no great difficulties. A body at rest relative to some point in space is said to be in mechanical equilibrium with respect to this reference space coordinate system. The reference point may be some point on the earth's surface or any other convenient point. Suffice it to say that in such static equilibrium the body is experiencing no net force and thus is not undergoing acceleration, positive or negative, relative to our position of reference. With respect to other coordinate systems, this may not be true, as is easily imaginable. More generally speaking, a body in static mechanical equilibrium has constant energy. Moreover, the fact that a mechanical system has constant energy, provided that this energy is not being exchanged with the environment, suggests that indeed this fact may be used as a general criterion for mechanical equilibrium.

To illustrate simple mechanical equilibrium and to point out its relation to energy, as well as the relation of energy to the stability of equilibrium, it is instructive to consider a particular example. Let this system consist of a spherical steel ball. We place this in a rounded bowl, which may be of a variety of shapes, but which, for mathematical simplicity, we will assume to be of such a shape that the center of the ball describes a paraboloid surface. A section along the axis of such a shape is illustrated in Fig. 15–1, in which the direction of the gravitational field is indicated as being downward. As is intuitively reasonable, the rest point of the ball is at the lowest point of the surface, and it is here at this equilibrium point that the energy of the ball is also at a minimum. Neglecting for the moment any kinetic energy considerations involved in displacing the system, the potential energy, is a function only of the height above the bottom. Since the sur-

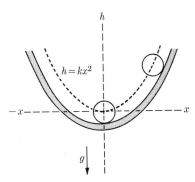

Fig. 15-1. Sketch illustrating stable mechanical equilibrium. The system consists of a sphere confined to a surface such that its center describes a parabola of revolution. See text for discussion.

face described by the center of the sphere is a parabola of revolution, the equation in two dimensions,

$$h = kx^2,\qquad(15\text{-}1)$$

describes the axial section through such a surface if we choose the center of the sphere while at the bottom as the origin of our coordinate system (h, x). The height is h; x is a horizontal displacement, and k is a proportionality constant. Arbitrarily choosing our reference point of zero potential energy with our system at the bottom, we may write the energy equation as

$$E = mgh,\qquad(15\text{-}2)$$

where E is the potential energy (kinetic energy is nonexistent with the system stationary), m is the mass of the sphere, and g is the acceleration due to gravity. Combining (15-1) and (15-2) gives

$$E = kmgx^2,\qquad(15\text{-}3)$$

and on differentiating we obtain

$$dE = 2kmgx\,dx.\qquad(15\text{-}4)$$

Equation (15-4) shows us clearly that the energy is a minimum at equilibrium, as judged by the following facts.

(1) Any infinitesimal displacement, $\pm dx$ at $x = 0$ results in zero energy change, $dE = 0$; that is, $dE/dx = 0$.

(2) For any further displacement from the origin, dE is positive, since x is now not equal to zero and has the same sign as dx; that is

$$dE/x\,dx > 0,$$

or d^2E/dx^2 (the second derivative) is > 0.

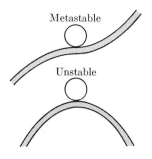

FIG. 15–2.   Sketches illustrating
metastable and unstable equilibrium.

In addition, the fact that the energy is at a minimum suggests also that the equilibrium point is a stable point. This is in contrast to unstable and metastable equilibria, such as are illustrated in Fig. 15–2. In both these cases the surfaces to which the sphere is confined provide for a zero change in energy for infinitesimal displacements from the equilibrium position. However, in the metastable case further displacement *may* lead to a decrease in the energy of the system, depending on the direction of displacement, whereas in the unstable case a finite displacement *always* leads to a decrease in energy. Thus stable equilibrium is characterized by a true minimum in the energy in relation to all conceivable small displacements from equilibrium. No such true minimum exists for metastable and unstable equilibrium. In summary we have

$$dE \geq 0, \quad \text{stable equilibrium,}$$
$$dE \lessgtr 0, \quad \text{metastable equilibrium,} \qquad (15\text{--}5)$$
$$dE \leq 0, \quad \text{unstable equilibrium,}$$

for displacements from the equilibrium position.

15–3 Thermodynamic equilibrium. Equilibrium in a thermodynamic system is quite analogous to that illustrated by the simple mechanical system described in the foregoing section. Thermodynamics, however, deals more generally with the behavior of systems composed of matter. It does not demand detailed knowledge that matter is composed of atoms and molecules, but is concerned only with macroscopic behavior. Nonetheless, matter is composed of atoms and molecules which as individual units are mechanical systems and may themselves be described in classical mechanical terms. As mechanical systems, it is the average behavior of large populations of these atoms and molecules with which thermodynamics is concerned. A connection between mechanics and thermodynamics exists however; this is the field of statistical mechanics or statistical thermodynamics. In any real sense, thermodynamic equilibrium, concerned with the average mechanical behavior of a large number of mechanical systems, is a dynamic equilibrium. Such an equilibrium is composed of a large number of continual small changes taking place among the elemental parts of the overall system, these individual parts continually exchanging energy through collision and change of position. The average energy change, averaged over the entire system, however, is zero.

Consider, for example, a liquid in equilibrium with its vapor. The individual molecules are in continual movement. The path of each individual molecule is extremely complicated as it experiences collisions with its neighbors, altering both its kinetic and potential energy. At any one instant it may exist in the liquid phase, and at another, in the vapor phase. When averaged, however, the number of molecules leaving the liquid to enter the vapor phase in an interval of time is equal to the number entering the liquid from the vapor phase. An analogous situation prevails in a chemical reaction at equilibrium. At any one instant a particular molecule may be identified as a reactant species, and at the next instant as a product species. However, on the average the number of molecules undergoing transformation from reactant to product and from product to reactant in an interval of time is the same. In both these examples a dynamic equilibrium exists. The average energy of the system, composed of the kinetic and potential energies of the elemental parts of the system, is a constant. Furthermore, quite analogous to the simple mechanical system illustrated in the foregoing section, the energy of a thermodynamic system at equilibrium is at a minimum with respect to infinitesimal displacements in those variables necessary to describe the system. This is true whether the energy function be the internal energy U, the enthalpy H, the Helmholtz free energy A, or the Gibbs free energy G. The variables in each case refer to those associated with each function in the fundamental equations (14–26), (14–33), (14–36), and (14–29). Thus for infinitesimal changes in

$$S \text{ and } V, \quad dU = 0, \qquad S \text{ and } P, \quad dH = 0,$$
$$T \text{ and } V, \quad dA = 0, \qquad T \text{ and } P, \quad dG = 0, \tag{15–6}$$

for closed system whose total mass is a constant. The concept that the energy functions are at a minimum in stable equilibrium states is of central importance in thermodynamics. Of equal importance is the fact that the entropy function at equilibrium is at a maximum, a fact that would appear to be quite reasonable considering that the entropy has an interpretation which is associated with the statistical randomness of the system. A system at equilibrium is in a state of maximum randomness, a state of least order consistent with the values of the variables describing this equilibrium. (See Section 14–7.) Any order ascribed to such factors as thermal differences in different parts of a system or concentration differences in different parts of a liquid or gaseous phase will have disappeared in the equilibrium state.

15–4 Irreversible and reversible processes. In the previous two sections it was evident that systems, both mechanical and thermodynamic, at stable equilibrium had minimum energy consistent with any restraints imposed. Let us consider further the mechanical system illustrated in Fig. 15–1 and examine in particular the approach to the stable equilibrium position at the bottom of the bowl. Let us assume that the bowl is filled with a viscous fluid. If the steel ball is released from some position on the side of the bowl it will descend slowly toward its equilibrium position. In its descent, the energy of the ball is gradually being transferred to the viscous medium. In being transferred, this energy, both potential and kinetic (kinetic since it is assumed to be moving with finite velocity), appears as heat, so-called frictional heat. The ball will eventually come to rest at the stable equilibrium point. The process of approaching this point occurs naturally, and the energy of the system decreases to reach a minimum at equilibrium. Such a natural process, attended by a decrease in energy, is also called an irreversible process, for the energy transferred from the system in this case and appearing as heat is not available in its entirety by any conceivable mechanism or process to restore the system to its original initial state corresponding to the starting position. As indicated in Section 14–8, such a natural irreversible process is attended by an increase in entropy of the system, and it reaches a maximum at equilibrium. Indeed, this increase in entropy is here manifest in the appearance of heat and resultant increase in temperature of the system. The entropy being a function of the state of the system, the magnitude of increase may be computed by conceptually bringing about this same change in state by some reversible means and applying Eq. (14–17b). The original potential energy of our mechanical system with the ball not at the bottom becomes "dissipated" in approaching equilibrium and appears as entropy. Entropy is created in such a process from other forms of energy.

On the other hand, we may conceive of a process whereby at every position of the sphere within the bowl, its mass is exactly counterbalanced by another mass. The system and its countermass are so coupled that any decrease in the potential energy of our system is attended by a corresponding increase in the potential energy of the countermass. At every position the system is in virtual equilibrium, and if displacements toward the bottom to achieve the same change in state discussed above are carried out by slow infinitesimal increments such that the velocity is virtually zero, then frictional forces due to the viscosity of the medium do not enter into consideration. Under these circumstances, the ball may approach the bottom completely reversibly; such a process is known as a reversible process. The original potential energy of the ball is completely transferred as potential energy to the countermass. None is dissipated to appear as entropy. Reversible processes are only conceptual and idealized. They do not occur in nature but can only be approximated by experiment.

15–5 Thermodynamic energy functions. In the previous chapter and again in this chapter it has been indicated that thermodynamics deals with energy functions or thermodynamic potentials, of which there are four principal ones. These are the internal energy U, the enthalpy H, the Hemholtz free energy A, and the Gibbs free energy G. Each function, a mathematical construct or abstraction in itself, has its own particular usefulness depending on the variables employed in an experiment or in its interpretation. For instance, the internal energy function is most useful in considering systems of constant volume which are thermally insulated, for in such systems, closed to the exchange of matter, the internal energy remains unchanged with a change in state. However, such restrictions are not convenient in dealing with many systems, including biological systems, and hence other energy functions have been devised.

Of particular usefulness in considering biological systems is the Gibbs free energy. In this function, the explicit variables are the temperature and pressure (see Eq. 14–29). Systems of constant temperature and pressure are easily and conveniently realized. Furthermore, changes in Gibbs free energy, ΔG, are interpretable as a measure of systems to do useful work, the maximum energy available from one system to alter another. Thus ΔG is a measure of the maximum available energy from a system to "drive" a chemical reaction, lift a weight against an opposing gravitational field, or cause an electric current to flow, assuming in each instance that proper coupling can be realized. This maximum work is the maximum theoretically realizable with the system perfectly coupled such as to be in mutual equilibrium throughout as the change is effected; in other words, the process is reversible. This interpretation of the Gibbs free energy will become clearer as we develop further the entire concept of this function in later chapters and illustrate with specific examples.

Another frequently used energy function is the enthalpy, H, often designated the heat content because of its interpretation as such. The enthalpy is valuable in considering systems undergoing phase changes at constant pressure, such as the evaporation of water from liquid to vapor. Here the change in enthalpy, ΔH, is the heat absorbed, q, by the system at a constant temperature; thus $\Delta H = q = T\Delta S$. For water, $\Delta H_{\text{vap}} = 9717$ cal $\cdot$ mole^{-1} (1 atm, 373.16°K). The enthalpy is also of value in studying chemical reactions, the so-called heats of chemical reactions. Some chemical reactions are endothermic, absorbing heat during reaction; others are exothermic, giving off heat during reaction. The enthalpy of neutralization, or formation of water from its constituent ions, H^+ and OH^-, each at a concentration of one molar, is $\Delta H_0 = -13,360$ cal $\cdot$ mole^{-1} (1 atm, 298.16°K). The negative sign indicates that a negative quantity of heat is absorbed or that this reaction is exothermic. It is important in considering tabulated thermodynamic data that the enthalpy and Gibbs free energy not be confused with each other. This often occurs in biochemical

literature through use of the terms endothermic or endergonic and exothermic or exergonic in which there may be some ambiguity as to whether
these terms refer to ΔH or ΔG. From the definition of G in terms of H,
Eqs. (14–27) and (14–31), it is quite evident that the two differ by an
entropy term.

15–6 The chemical potential. Emphasis was given in the foregoing
section to a particular energy function, the Gibbs free energy G; G, in its
general form, applies to the energy of the entire system under consideration, such as a particular chemical reaction carried out under appropriate
conditions in a vessel, or even an entire biological cell or organism, in which
certain chemical entities, such as foodstuffs and waste products, may
cross the boundary of the system. In this respect, it is evident that G is
an extensive quantity. Like volume, it depends upon the extent of the
system or its mass. In contrast, such quantities as density (mass per unit
volume), concentration (moles per unit volume), or temperature and pressure are intensive in character and do not depend upon the extent of a
system directly. For many purposes in dealing with chemical substances
in various biological and physical chemical systems, it is found convenient
to use an energy quantity which is likewise intensive in character. As such
it would depend, therefore, not upon the total amount of a particular
chemical component but only upon its state, that is, its particular state of
aggregation, its concentration, its pressure and temperature, and the like.
It will be recalled that the chemical potential defined by Eqs. (14–23) and
(14–37) has such intensive character. Taking the definition in terms of
the Gibbs free energy,

$$\mu_i = \left[\frac{\partial G}{\partial n_i}\right]_{T,P,n_j} , \qquad (15\text{–}7)$$

we find that the chemical potential of component i is the increase in the
Gibbs free energy of the entire system under consideration with an addition of the infinitesimal quantity (moles) of i, dn_i, to the system, keeping
the temperature, pressure, and quantity of all other components, n_j,
constant. A graphical representation of μ_i is seen in Fig. 14–7. Recall
that μ_i is also

$$\left.\frac{\partial U}{\partial n_i}\right]_{S,V,n_j} \qquad \text{as well as} \qquad \left.\frac{\partial G}{\partial n_i}\right]_{T,P,n_j} .$$

For a pure one-component system, it may be deductively reasoned from
Eq. (15–7) that μ_1 is simply the Gibbs free energy per mole of 1; in other
words, it is G/n_1 at a given temperature and pressure. The total G is
simply $n_1\mu_1$. If the system is composed of more than one component it is
still reasonable that the chemical potential of each component be related

to its amount per unit quantity of the entire system. However, there is always a degree of molecular interaction between components, and μ_i is not generally equal to G/n_i but is given properly by Eq. (15-7). Graphically, this implies that there is not necessarily a straight-line relation belation between G and n_i, but the relation may be curvilinear as portrayed in Fig. 14-7. Nevertheless, in a multicomponent system it turns out mathematically that the total free energy at a given temperature and pressure is given by

$$G = n_1\mu_1 + n_2\mu_2 + \cdots + n_c\mu_c = \sum_{i=1}^{c} n_i\mu_i. \qquad (15\text{-}8)$$

The subscripts refer to the particular components of which there are a total of c, and the summation extends to include all of these.

The chemical potential of a component, μ_i, is a measure of the potential of a mole of the substance to do useful work, for instance, by undergoing a chemical change. Many examples of this will be given in discussions below. In this respect, the chemical potential of a substance bears a relation to this substance, analogous to the relation that an electrical potential bears to an electrical charge. The greater the electrical potential or voltage, the greater the amount of electrical work obtainable from a given amount of charge. Indeed, in dealing with charged ionic substances, it becomes quite convenient at times to discuss the chemical potential of each of the charged species separately, whereupon it is necessary to add an electrical potential term to the chemical potential of these species. Thus if the electrical potential in a given region of the system is denoted by ψ, and the valence of the ionic species, k, is z_k (reckoned positive for cations and negative for anions), and F is the faraday,* the electrical portion of the total potential is $z_k F \psi$. The total potential for a charged species, called the *electrochemical potential*, $\bar{\mu}_k$, and is

$$\bar{\mu}_k = \mu_k + z_k F \psi. \qquad (15\text{-}9)$$

15-7 Relations of the chemical potential. We have indicated some of the general properties of the chemical potential in the foregoing paragraphs but have not yet indicated how this energy function relates to various variables such as pressure of a gaseous substance, concentration of a substance in solution, and the like. It was indicated that μ_i represented the maximum useful work available of this substance, i, in a particular state. For our purposes, then, it is perhaps simplest to indicate in some detail

---

* The faraday is the electronic charge per gram-equivalent. The electronic charge on an electron is $1.6 \cdot 10^{-18}$ coulomb. Avogadro's number is $6.02 \cdot 10^{23} \cdot$ $F = N\epsilon = 96{,}489$ coulombs per gram-equivalent.

TABLE 15-1

VALUES FOR THE GAS CONSTANT R IN
DIFFERENT ENERGY UNITS

R = 1.9864 cal · deg^{-1} C · mole^{-1}
R = 8.3136 · 10^7 ergs · deg^{-1} C · mole^{-1}
R = 8.3136 joules · deg^{-1} C · mole^{-1}
R = 0.08207 liter-atm · deg^{-1} C · mole^{-1}

how this may be computed for a gaseous substance and argue the derivation of relations for other substances in other states of aggregation by analogy.

Chemical potential of a gas. Consider a system consisting of an ideal gas. It is well known that an ideal gas behaves according to the equation, $PV = nRT$, where n is the number of moles, R is the gas constant having the dimensions of energy · mole^{-1} · degree^{-1} (see Table 15–1), and T is the absolute temperature. Since we are computing energy per mole to obtain the chemical potential, we let $n = 1$. The differential reversible work done by a gaseous system on the environment on expansion is

$$dw = P \, dV. \tag{15-10}$$

Since μ_g, the subscript g referring to the gas, represents the reversible work, any infinitesimal work done by the system, dw, is attended by the change $-d\mu_g$ in the potential. Thus

$$d\mu_g = -P \, dV. \tag{15-11}$$

However, from the equation for an ideal gas,

$$d(PV) = P \, dV + V \, dP = d(RT) = 0, \quad T = \text{constant.} \tag{15-12}$$

It follows that

$$d\mu_g = V \, dP, \quad T = \text{constant,} \tag{15-13}$$

and substituting for V from the gas equation, $V = RT/P$, we have

$$d\mu_g = RT \, \frac{dP}{P}, \quad T = \text{constant.} \tag{15-14}$$

Integrating both sides of this equation from some given initial state, where the potential is μ_g^0 and the pressure is P_0, to a final state, with potential

μ_g and pressure P, we obtain in a manner similar to Eq. (14–7)

$$\int_{\mu_g^0}^{\mu_g} d\mu_g = RT \int_{P_0}^{P} \frac{dP}{P} = RT \int_{P_0}^{P} d(\ln P), \qquad (15\text{--}15)$$

giving

$$\mu_g - \mu_g^0 = RT \ln \frac{P}{P_0}. \qquad (15\text{--}16)$$

The significance of μ_g^0, the chemical potential of g at P_0, is quite evident, for it forms merely a starting point or reference point from which changes in μ_g may be conveniently measured. As has been stated, only changes in energy are measurable, and here the change is $\mu_g - \mu_g^0$. This implies that we are free to choose our reference point in a way that suits us most conveniently. In this regard it has become conventional to take the value $P_0 = 1$ atm at any particular temperature as the reference point. Thus Eq. (15–16) becomes

$$\mu_g = \mu_g^0 + RT \ln P_g, \qquad (15\text{--}17)$$

which is our final result and expresses the chemical potential of a gas explicitly as a function of its pressure.

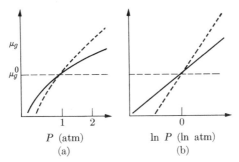

Fig. 15–3. Sketches of the function of $\mu_g = \mu_g^0 + RT \ln P$. Graph (a) shows the function with pressure P plotted on a linear scale, whereas in Graph (b), P is on a logarithmic scale. The two curves of each plot represent the function at two different temperatures.

The relation is illustrated graphically in Fig. 15–3. It is to be noted that as the pressure increases, the chemical potential of a gas increases, a fact intuitively reasonable in our concept of the chemical potential as a measure of the potential of the substance to do useful work. A gas under high pressure certainly has greater potential than one under low pressure. It is also to be noted, however, that μ_g may assume either positive or negative values, depending on the values of P and μ_g^0. It is quite conventional in tabulating values of μ_g^0 to take this arbitrarily as zero for an element which is naturally a gas at 1-atm pressure and 298.16°K. Thus $\mu_g^0 = 0$ if the gas is, for example, O_2, N_2, Cl_2, etc., but $\mu_g^0 \neq 0$ for gases such as CO_2, NO, or NO_2 (which are not pure elements) or I_2 or Br_2 (which are not gases giving 1-atm pressure at 298.16°K).

Equation (15–17) has been derived considering the gaseous substance as a pure gas, a one-component system with a total pressure P. However, the same equation is valid in a mixture of gases if P is taken not as the total pressure but as the partial pressure p, that is, the pressure it would have if it were present alone. This is a consequence of the fact that the total pressure is the sum of the partial pressures of each gas present, a fact known as Dalton's law. The equation was also derived considering the gas to behave as an ideal gas, a kind of behavior which does not exist in actual fact but which is approximated by many real gases at low pressures (say, less than 1 atm). To be strictly correct, then, for real gases we must replace p by a conceptual quantity, the effective pressure, the so-called fugacity. This is a consequence of the fact that molecules of a real gas interact with each other (ideal gases do not) and occupy some actual volume (ideal gases are point molecules having only mass and no volume). At reasonable total pressures the interaction is generally one of molecular attraction such as to make the effective pressure lower than would be expected had the gas been considered ideal. Further discussion of these interactions and the corrections involved is given in Section 15–8, but for our purposes we will generally assume an equivalence between the actual partial pressure and the fugacity.

Chemical potential of a solute. A solute dissolved in a solvent is, in some ways, much like a gas in free space. For a gas, the pressure is proportional to the number of molecules per unit volume, as may be seen by rearranging the ideal gas equation to give

$$p = \frac{n}{V} RT = c_g RT. \tag{15–18}$$

Therefore, it is reasonable to suppose that the chemical potential of a solute would have a relation to its concentration analogous to that of gas to its pressure. Indeed, for a solute component i in solution,

$$\mu_i = \mu_i^0 + RT \ln c_i. \tag{15–19}$$

It is evident that if the concentration unit employed for c_i is moles i per liter of solution (molar concentration), then when the concentration is one mole per liter ($c_i = 1$) $\mu_i = \mu_i^0$. This is our reference point. As in the case of a gas, solutes in general are not ideal, but the molecules show a degree of interaction with the solvent, with each other and with other solute molecules, so that to be mathematically and rigorously correct, c_i

must be replaced by the activity of i, a_i, the activity representing an effective concentration. Deviations of the effective concentration from the actual concentration may become quite appreciable, especially in more concentrated solutions. In electrolyte solutions there is considerable electrostatic attraction between positive and negative ions; as a consequence, the activity may be considerably less than the actual concentration would suggest, even in fairly dilute solutions. Further discussion of this point is given in Section 15–8. In general, for our purposes here we will consider $c_i = a_i$.

Chemical potential of a crystal. For a solid crystalline substance c, which of course does not change in concentration, μ is quite reasonably a constant at a given temperature and pressure. For a pure crystalline substance,

$$\mu_c = \mu_c^0, \tag{15–20}$$

for a given temperature and pressure.

Chemical potential of a solvent. The solvent component of a solution also has a concentration, for an increased concentration of solute in the solution means less solvent in a given volume. It is convenient, however, to choose the manner of expressing the concentration of a solvent in such a manner that there is unit concentration for a pure solvent. One concentration unit that has this property is the mole fraction. The mole fraction of a substance, j, is defined as

$$x_j \equiv \frac{n_j}{\sum_{i=1}^{c} n_i}. \tag{15–21}$$

The mole fraction, x_j, is therefore the number of moles of substance j in the system divided by the total number of moles present. This total is obtained by summing over all substances, i, which includes j. It is evident that if we have a pure solvent, s, then $x_s = n_s/n_s = 1$. Our expression for the chemical potential of a solvent s then assumes the form

$$\mu_s = \mu_s^0 + RT \ln x_s, \tag{15–22}$$

where $\mu_s = \mu_s^0$ for the pure solvent s. The chemical potential of the solvent is then always lowered by addition of solute, for then $x_s < 1$, and $\ln x_s < 0$. Again, as with the partial pressure of a gas and the concentration of a solute, one must, in a rigorous sense, speak of a solvent activity which may be different from the true mole fraction because of molecular interactions. For our purposes we will, in general, consider the activity and mole fraction to be equal.

Chemical potential of an ionic species. Ionic species are like other solutes in solution except that they are not independently variable, as is a component. It is frequently convenient to speak rather artificially of the chemical potential, or rather the electrochemical potential of an ionic solute species, especially in the consideration of certain membrane phenomena which involve transfer of ionic charge from one side to the other. For an ionic species, k, we may combine Eqs. (15-9) and (15-19) to obtain the electrochemical potential

$$\bar{\mu}_k = \mu_k + RT \ln c_k + z_k F \psi. \tag{15-23}$$

If a salt B ionizes into ν_+ cations C and ν_- anions A, according to the chemical equation

$$B \rightleftharpoons \nu_+ C + \nu_- A, \tag{15-24}$$

then the chemical potential of the salt, μ_B, is equal to the sum of the electrochemical potentials of the constituent ions, each multiplied by the stoichiometric number ν, according to the relation

$$\mu_B = \nu_+ \bar{\mu}_C + \nu_- \bar{\mu}_A. \tag{15-25}$$

The electrical potential term does not appear in μ_B since

$$\nu_+ z_C + \nu_- z_A = 0, \tag{15-26}$$

a statement of the fact that the salt itself is electrically neutral.

In summary it is to be noted that the relations for the chemical potential always take a very similar form, namely a constant plus a logarithmic term. To reiterate, we know that for a pure crystalline substance c,

$$\mu_c = \mu_c^0; \tag{15-20}$$

for a gas g,

$$\mu_g = \mu_g^0 + RT \ln p_g; \tag{15-17}$$

for a solute i in solution,

$$\mu_i = \mu_i^0 + RT \ln c_i; \tag{15-19}$$

for a solvent s of a solution,

$$\mu_s = \mu_s^0 + RT \ln x_s; \tag{15-22}$$

and the electrochemical potential of an ionic species is

$$\bar{\mu}_k = \mu_k^0 + z_k F \psi = \mu_k^0 + RT \ln c_k + z_k F \psi. \tag{15-23}$$

Considerable use of these equations will be made in the following chapter. It will be noted in Chapters 16 and 18 that, with use of the chemical potential, many of the empirical "laws" of nature expounded by different scientists are given a common basis.

15–8 Molecular interactions and activity coefficients. It has been indicated that energy is the fundamental quantity considered in the rigorous mathematical development of thermodynamics. Energy is a quantity that is conserved. In developing the relations for the chemical potential of various substances in the foregoing section, we noted equations that relate the fundamental energy quantity with the experimentally measurable quantities, such as pressure and concentration; we indicated that to be rigorous in all real nonidealized systems we must replace these measurable quantities with their thermodynamic exact quantities. Thus partial pressures of gases are to be replaced by their fugacities, and concentrations of solutes or solvents, by their activities or effective concentrations. This is so because there is always a degree of molecular interaction. This interaction is not a constant but depends on factors inherent in the structure of the molecules and their proximity to each other. Their average proximity is, of course, related to the concentration. Ideal solutions and gases are conceptual quantities which show no interactions. Real solutions and gases approach this behavior as the intermolecular distances become so great that no further interaction exists. What about solute in a solvent? Even in the most dilute solution, are not solute and solvent in close proximity? The answer is, of course, in the affirmative. However, the interaction between a solute and its solvent in a state of infinite dilution is taken into account in the standard chemical potential, μ_i^0, of the solute i. The μ_i^0 properly represents the chemical potential of solute i when it has unit activity, $a_i = 1$, but in the hypothetical state of behaving ideally, i.e., as though there were only interaction of solute molecules with each other. With standard solvent-solute interaction relegated to μ_i^0, it is then only the changes in this solute-solvent interaction together with all of the solute-solute interactions which must be accounted for in any differences between a physical concentration and the thermodynamic effective concentration or activity.

On the basis of the discussions advanced in Chapter 3, it is not difficult to imagine molecular interactions of an attractive nature being quite significant at small intermolecular distances. Such attractions in uncharged molecules are attributable to dipoles, permanent or induced, and lead to a decrease in the intermolecular potential energy. In this way, the attractions act more or less as a restraining influence on the molecules in their normal random molecular motion, thus decreasing their effectiveness, on the average, as a population of molecules. This comprises a decrease in average potential energy of the molecules and is manifest by an activity somewhat less than its physical concentration would indicate. The chemical potential computed from its activity would be less than that computed from its physical concentration.

On the other hand, if molecular interaction as such is to be repulsive in nature, say for example that proximities are close enough to result in volume interference or crowding, the intermolecular potential energy is not as low as it would otherwise be, and the effective concentration or thermodynamic activity may be larger than the actual physical concentration. This is observed frequently in more concentrated solutions.

Quite formally we may relate physical concentration to thermodynamic activity by such relations as

$$f_g = \alpha_g p_g \qquad (15\text{–}27)$$

for a gas, where f_g is the effective pressure or fugacity, and α_g is a factor which, when multiplied by the partial pressure p_g, gives f_g and is known as the fugacity coefficient. Similarly, for a solute A in solution,

$$a_A = \alpha_A c_A, \qquad (15\text{–}28)$$

or

$$a_A = \gamma_A m_A, \qquad (15\text{–}29)$$

where a_A is the thermodynamic activity, c_a is the concentration in moles per liter of solution (molar scale), m_A is the concentration in moles per kilogram of solvent (molal scale), and α_A and γ_A are the activity coefficients for the appropriate concentration scales. Finally, we recognize a relation for the mole fraction scale of concentration giving

$$a_S = g_S x_S, \qquad (15\text{–}30)$$

where a_S is the mole fraction activity as for a solvent, and g_S is the coefficient relating this to the true mole fraction, x_S. As such, the coefficients in Eqs. (15–27) to (15–30) are purely empirical coefficients. Their values in general are functions of the partial pressure or concentration and must be determined from experiment. Thermodynamics, *per se*, does not specify any functional relation. Nonthermodynamic considerations must be exploited in the formulation of any theoretical relation. This is difficult at best even with relatively crude models, and except for the cases of ionic charges and some dipolar interactions, little theoretical work of a general nature has been done.

In our consideration and understanding of the thermodynamics of biological systems at the present state of refinement, by and large we can assume unit fugacity coefficients for all gases under conditions of normal biologic function. Similarly, in consideration of living systems, we can generally assume unit activity coefficients for nonionic solutes, since we are dealing with relatively dilute solutions. This is not to imply that we should not or need not consider the interaction in studying molecules of biological interest, for it is from many such studies that extrapolations to living systems must be made to further our understanding. The importance of interactions among electrically charged constituents in biological systems is considerably greater and is such that it is often necessary to consider activity coefficient corrections. This is so because primary coulombic forces are so much larger and are effective over a so much greater distance than are the secondary coulombic forces arising from dipoles, permanent or induced. Therefore, even at the ionic concentrations prevalent biologically, ionic interactions are quite pronounced, and activity coefficients of electrolytes, even in dilute solutions, depart rather significantly from unity. However, in this particular area theory has been developed by Debye and Hückel. A simplified, concise, and lucid development of the Debye-Hückel theory of ionic interaction is to be found in MacInnes. A more advanced derivation of this theory is to be found in Harned and Owens.

REFERENCES

1. J. T. EDSALL and J. WYMAN, "Activity Coefficients" and "Debye-Hückel Theory," in *Biophysical Chemistry*, Vol. I, pp. 198, 282. Academic Press, New York, 1958.

2. D. M. MacINNES, *The Principles of Electrochemistry*, Reinhold, New York, 1939, also Dover, New York.

3. H. S. HARNED and B. B. OWENS, *The Physical Chemistry of Electrolytic Solutions*. Reinhold, New York, 1950.

4. W. J. MOORE, *Physical Chemistry*, 3rd Ed., Prentice-Hall, New York, 1962.

5. S. GLASSTONE and H. S. TAYLER, *A Treatise on Physical Chemistry*, Vol. 1, Van Nostrand, Princeton, 1942.

6. G. M. LEWIS and M. RANDALL, *Thermodynamics*, McGraw-Hill, New York, 1961.

7. R. A. ROBINSON and R. H. STOKER, *Electrolyte Solutions*, Butterworths Scientific Publications, London, 1955.

8. F. W. SEARS, *Thermodynamics, the Kinetic Theory of Gases, and Statistical Mechanics*, Addison-Wesley, Reading, Mass., 1953.

CHAPTER 16

PHYSICAL AND CHEMICAL EQUILIBRIA

CHAPTER 16

PHYSICAL AND CHEMICAL EQUILIBRIA

16–1 Introduction. In the previous two chapters we have developed the elements of thermodynamics and the concept of energy and energy functions. The chemical potential received special emphasis for it represents the maximum work available from a chemical component of a system. Be it a physical, chemical, or biological system, the chemical potential forms a unifying concept in understanding many of the empirical laws discovered for these systems. Paramount to this understanding is also the concept that at equilibrium the various energy functions or thermodynamic potentials are at a minimum. We have emphasized the Gibbs free energy function in our considerations in that it is an explicit function of the variables, temperature and pressure. Furthermore, the Gibbs free energy is always given by the sum of the chemical potentials of each component comprising a system times its mole quantity (or factors proportional to this quantity), according to Eq. (15–8), and hence the chemical potential itself becomes a convenient and important entity with which to deal with equilibrium and, as will be seen later, nonequilibrium processes.

Living biological systems are not equilibrium systems. Physical and chemical processes are going on in the cell continually. These processes form the very basis of the cell functioning as a living system. The cell converts chemical compounds entering the cell as foodstuffs, such as glucose, to other compounds. From these reactions it gains free energy to expend in the various processes useful to the cell and to the entire organism. The entire system of chemical reactions is indeed very complex. Many of the reactions have been well worked out by biochemists, but many are still not understood. In any case, it is true that in all these processes the very fact that they occur denotes that there is a decrease in the overall free energy, a consequence of the principles of thermodynamics. If the biological systems are not equilibrium systems, then why, it may be asked, is it necessary to consider many of the physical and physical-chemical laws dealing with equilibrium? The answer is that equilibrium processes are the simplest ones, and an understanding of these is a necessary prerequisite to an understanding of processes which are not at equilibrium. Systems not at equilibrium, isolated from the environment, always approach an equilibrium state. Furthermore, many parts of a living biological system may often, to a good approximation, be considered as being in equilibrium; this greatly simplifies one's understanding. For these reasons, then, a good deal of emphasis is placed on an understanding of physical and chemical equilibria. We consider these in two main categories—simple equilibrium between phases of a system, and equilibrium of chemical reactions. Fundamentally, however, these are the same in principle. Each will be illustrated with pertinent and important biological examples.

16–2 Phase equilibria. Phase equilibria are perhaps the simplest of all equilibria to consider and are most easily visualized and understood intuitively. Treated from the viewpoint of the chemical potential, there is a common pattern to the relevant equations, providing considerable simplicity.

(a) *Solubility of a solid phase.* An excess of a solid crystalline substance A, when placed in a solvent, dissolves in the solvent until the solution is saturated with respect to this substance. At this point, the system is in equilibrium at a given temperature, and we may write for the process:

$$A \text{ (crystal)} \rightleftharpoons A \text{ (satd. soln.)}. \tag{16–1}$$

This equation is a statement of a change in state and indicates a transfer of one mole of substance A from the crystalline state (written on the left) to the dissolved state (written on the right), the dissolved state being a saturated solution of this substance. The system is in equilibrium at all times during this transfer. Thus the free energy change, ΔG, for this change in state is zero, and since the free energy in each state is simply the chemical potential in this state times the number of moles considered, we have

$$\Delta G = \mu_{A(\text{satd. soln.})} - \mu_{A(\text{crystal})} = 0. \tag{16–2}$$

Utilizing the expressions for the chemical potentials for these two states, namely Eqs. (15–19) and (15–20), one obtains

$$\mu_{A(\text{soln.})}^0 + RT \ln c_{A(\text{satd. soln.})} - \mu_{A(\text{crystal})}^0 = 0. \tag{16–3}$$

This may be rearranged to put the reference potentials, constants for a particular temperature and pressure, on one side:

$$\mu_{A(\text{soln.})}^0 - \mu_{A(\text{crystal})}^0 = -RT \ln c_{A(\text{satd. soln.})}, \tag{16–4}$$

which indicates that the right-hand side must also be a constant. Thus, $c_{A(\text{satd. soln.})}$ is a constant at a particular temperature and pressure, characteristic for the solid crystal and the particular solvent employed, and may be replaced by K_s, the solubility constant, which thus defines an equilibrium constant. The left-hand side of Eq. (16–4) is the *standard free energy change*, ΔG^0, for the process of Eq. (16–1). Thus

$$\mu_{A(\text{satd. soln.})}^0 - \mu_{A(\text{crystal})}^0 = \Delta G^0 = -RT \ln K_s, \tag{16–5}$$

showing that an equilibrium constant at a particular temperature bears a definite relation to the standard free energy. The ΔG^0 has a very definite interpretation which becomes obvious on studying Eq. (16–3). It represents that quantity of free energy available in dissolving one mole of the crystalline solid in one molar solution of this substance, maintaining the solution always at this unit concentration (or unit activity). This is an abstract process, unobtainable in actuality, but is a valuable conceptual one. In biochemical literature, it is often abused because of failure to understand its correct interpretation. To add some possible clarity here, let us assume that a saturated solution of A is less than one molar; Eq. (16–4) or (16–5) then indicates that ΔG^0 is a positive quantity, which is tantamount to saying that external work is required to bring the solution to a one-molar concentration. (This is a hypothetical state, for it would be supersaturated.) If, however, the saturated solution of A is greater than 1 molar, then ΔG^0 is negative, indicating that the process of bringing a saturated solution to that of a one-molar concentration is attended by a free-energy decrease. This is, therefore, the natural direction for the process, and under these conditions this quantity of free energy is available to do useful work, provided proper coupling could be obtained.

There are many factors which affect the solubility of a given substance and which thus determine the individual magnitude of the standard chemical potentials, μ^0. Stable crystals are associated with stable lattice structures, indicating a high degree of attractive interaction in the crystal between the individual molecules. If this interaction is greater than the interaction of these molecules with the solvent, then the substance is poorly soluble, as is often the case of organic "nonpolar" molecules in an aqueous system. If, however, the attractive interaction with solvent is greater than the mutual interaction in the crystal, the molecules tend to become "solvated" by the solvent molecules and may be quite soluble, as is the case of "polar" molecules in aqueous systems. Because water is so polar (see Chapter 4) and portions of many biological molecules are polar, the interaction between water and these molecules is generally quite large. Water is therefore a good solvent. For salts, the attractive energy or force between ion pairs (oppositely charged species) is inversely proportional to the dielectric constant of the medium. Thus a medium such as water, with its high dielectric constant, is very effective in reducing this electrical attractive force, and even though there is considerable lattice stability of ionic crystals, these crystals may be quite soluble. Certainly, ionic salts are, in general, more soluble in aqueous systems than in solvents which have a lower dielectric constant, such as organic solvents.

Before considering some biological examples of saturated solutions of interest, we first indicate a variation of the simple equations (16–2) through (16–4) that results from considering saturated salt solutions. For a salt,

$C_{\nu_+}A_{\nu_-}$, that in solution dissociates into its constituent ions (ν_+ cations of C, and ν_- anions of A), the chemical equation for equilibrium is

$$C_{\nu_+}A_{\nu_-} \text{ (crystal)} \rightleftharpoons \nu_+ C + \nu_- A \text{ (satd. soln.)}. \qquad (16\text{–}6)$$

At equilibrium, the change in free energy, ΔG, for this change in state is

$$\Delta G = \mu(\text{salt, satd. soln.}) - \mu(\text{salt, crystal}) = 0, \qquad (16\text{–}7)$$

and is thus, according to Eqs. (15–19) and (15–20),

$$\nu_+ \mu_C^0 + \nu_+ RT \ln c_{C(\text{satd.})} + \nu_- \mu_A^0 + \nu_- RT \ln c_{A(\text{satd.})} - \mu_{CA(\text{crystal})}^0 = 0. \qquad (16\text{–}8)$$

Rearranging, we obtain

$$\nu_+ \mu_C^0 + \nu_- \mu_A^0 - \mu_{CA(\text{crystal})}^0 = -RT \ln c_C^{\nu_+} c_A^{\nu_-} \text{ (satd.)}. \qquad (16\text{–}9)$$

The left-hand side, at a particular temperature, is made up only of constants and is equal to ΔG^0 for the process of Eq. (16–6). Therefore, the right-hand side must be a constant. Comparing with Eq. (16–5), we have

$$K_{\text{sp}} = c_C^{\nu_+} c_A^{\nu_-} \text{ (satd. soln.)}. \qquad (16\text{–}10)$$

K_{sp} is the solubility product constant, and the equation states that the product of the concentrations of cation and anion, each raised to the power of their stoichiometric number in the salt, is a constant at saturation. Independent variations may be made in one charged species by addition of other salts with a common ion, resulting in a dependent variation in the other ion.

In illustration of the solubility product constant and the importance of energy considerations we can discuss briefly the relations of plasma calcium and phosphate ions to bone. In human plasma, the concentration of trivalent phosphate, PO_4^{3-}, is about 10^{-7} mole $\cdot$ liter^{-1}; that of Ca^{2+} is about $1.25 \cdot 10^{-3}$ mole $\cdot$ liter^{-1}. We may consider bone to be composed principally of $Ca_3(PO_4)_2$, which from best estimates has a solubility product of the order of 10^{-25}. It is quite evident that the product

$$(C_{Ca^{2+}})^3 (C_{PO_4^{3-}})^2 = (1.25 \cdot 10^{-3})^3 (10^{-7})^2 \cong 2 \cdot 10^{-23} \qquad (16\text{–}11)$$

is a considerably larger number than is the solubility product constant. This would indicate that the plasma is supersaturated with respect to bone salt! Why is it then that indiscriminate precipitation does not occur? This is not a simple problem, but available evidence suggests that a nucleation center, a matrix on which to form, is required. After all, to precipitate directly from solution requires a five-body collision among the appropriate ion and each in correct orientation, an occurrence which is extremely improbable. If, however, the solid salt $CaHPO_4$ were first to form from Ca^{2+} and HPO_4^{2-} and then rearrangement of these occurred by the reaction

$$3CaHPO_4 = Ca_3(PO_4)_2 + 2H^+ + HPO_4^{2-}, \qquad (16-12)$$

then the probability of occurrence would be much greater since only a bimolecular collision is required. Estimates of the K_{sp} for $CaHPO_4$ are about $1 \cdot 10^{-6}$ and HPO_4^{2-} has a concentration of about $7 \cdot 10^{-4}$ mole $\cdot$ liter^{-1} in human plasma. The ionic product is then

$$(C_{Ca^{2+}})(C_{HPO_4^{2-}}) \cong 1 \cdot 10^{-6}. \qquad (16-13)$$

The fact that the ionic product and the solubility product constant are nearly the same is indicative that the plasma is very nearly a saturated solution of this salt. This bone-salt problem points out a fact of importance thermodynamically. The process forming $Ca_3(PO_4)_2$ directly from the ions is one that by calculation would be attended by a decrease in free energy of the system. Energetic considerations indicate that it may occur. It does not occur, however, because of kinetic considerations. The formation of solid $CaHPO_4$ could occur if there were an increase in the concentration of one of the ions. For instance, a chemical reaction generating an increased concentration of HPO_4^{2-} in a specific locale would suffice. It is to be emphasized that energy considerations indicate only what is possible or impossible, and not necessarily what will or will not actually occur. Thermodynamics is, in this respect, dissociated from any mechanistic points of view.

(b) *Solubility of gases in solvents.* Gases dissolve in liquids just as solids do, and their solubility is again related to the degree of interaction that they show toward the particular solvent. Aside from these factors which depend upon the innate properties of the particular gas and solvent, it is reasonable to suppose that the amount of gas dissolved is related to its particular partial pressure in the system at a particular temperature, for as indicated before (Eq. 15–18) the partial pressure is proportional to the concentration of the gas in the gas phase. We may write the chemical equation for change in state as

$$G \text{ (gas)} \rightleftharpoons G \text{ (satd. soln.)}, \qquad (16-14)$$

in which one mole of gas G is transferred from the gas state to that of a saturated solution. At equilibrium,

$$\Delta G = \mu_g \text{ (satd. soln.)} - \mu_g \text{ (gas)} = 0, \qquad (16-15)$$

and, using the appropriate relations for the chemical potential in each

TABLE 16–1

SOLUBILITY CONSTANTS f AND α OF VARIOUS GASES
IN WATER AT 38°C

Gas	α^*	$f\dagger$
N_2	0.012	0.0007
O_2	0.024	0.0014
CO_2	0.546	0.0325

* Cubic centimeters of gas, corrected to 0°C and 1 atm pressure, per cc of solution per atm partial pressure.

† Millimoles of gas per liter solution per mm Hg partial pressure.

phase, Eqs. (15–19) and (15–17), we have

$$\mu^0_{g(\text{soln.})} + RT \ln c_{g(\text{satd.})} - \mu^0_{g(\text{gas})} - RT \ln p_g = 0. \quad (16\text{--}16)$$

Rearranging this gives

$$\mu^0_{g(\text{soln.})} - \mu^0_{g(\text{gas})} = -RT \ln \frac{c_{g(\text{satd.})}}{p_g}. \quad (16\text{--}17)$$

Since the left-hand side is equal to ΔG^0 and is made up only of constants at a given temperature, the right-hand side must likewise be a constant, which may be written

$$\frac{c_{g(\text{satd.})}}{p_g} = k_h \quad \text{or} \quad c_{g(\text{satd.})} = k_h p_g. \quad (16\text{--}18)$$

This relation is known as Henry's law and states that the concentration of dissolved gas at equilibrium is proportibnal to the partial pressure of this gas in the vapor phase, the proportionality constant being k_h. The constant k_h is constant only at a given temperature and has the general dimensions of concentration pressure^{-1}. Its particular dimensions are thus dependent upon the particular concentration units and pressure units employed. In biochemical and physiological literature, two different constants of Henry's law are in common use. Values of these constants for several gases appear in Table 16–1.

The average partial pressure of oxygen in the alveoli of the lungs is about 100 mm Hg. If the blood were assumed to be water, how much O_2 would be dissolved per liter? We calculate this to be

$$100 \cdot 0.0014 \cdot 10^{-3} = 1.4 \cdot 10^{-4} \text{ mole} \cdot \text{liter}^{-1}.$$

If we assume that the human body consumes 200 ml · min^{-1} or about $0.9 \cdot 10^{-2}$ mole O_2 min^{-1} at rest, and we further assume that all O_2 is removed from the circulation on passing through the capillaries, this means that the blood flow would need to be

$$\frac{0.9 \cdot 10^{-2}}{1.4 \cdot 10^{-4}} = 65 \text{ liters/min,}$$

indeed, a rather large figure. Other factors must obviously be responsible for carrying these quantities of oxygen in the blood.

(c) *Vapor pressure of a solvent.* Volatile solvents have a very definite vapor pressure, or partial pressure in an equilibrium vapor phase. This vapor pressure is not only a function of the temperature, reaching one atmosphere at the "boiling" point at sea level, but is also dependent upon the presence of dissolved solute, which in effect lowers the concentration of the solvent. This relation, describing the vapor pressure lowering resulting from the presence of a dissolved solute and known as Raoult's law, is easily derived from considerations of the chemical potential of the liquid solvent S and its equilibrium vapor pressure. For the change in state, we may write the physical equation at a given temperature as

$$S \text{ (solv.)} \rightleftharpoons S \text{ (gas).} \tag{16-19}$$

Equating the chemical potentials on each side, since the free-energy change is zero ($\Delta G = 0$), we obtain, using Eqs. (15–22) and (15–17),

$$\mu_{s(\text{solv.})}^0 + RT \ln x_s = \mu_{s(\text{gas})}^0 + RT \ln p_s. \tag{16-20}$$

Rearrangement gives

$$\mu_{s(\text{gas})}^0 - \mu_{s(\text{solv.})}^0 = -RT \ln \frac{p_s}{x_s}. \tag{16-21}$$

The left-hand side is a constant, ΔG^0, and therefore the right-hand side must be likewise a constant, giving

$$\frac{p_s}{x_s} = k_r \quad \text{or} \quad p_s = k_r x_s. \tag{16-22}$$

This states that the equilibrium vapor pressure of a volatile solvent of a solution is proportional to its mole fraction, the proportionality constant (known as Raoult's constant) being k_r. We may determine k_r, since, with pure solvent, $x_s = 1$ and $p_s = p_s^0$ (the vapor pressure of the pure solvent). Hence,

$$k_r = p_s^0 \quad \text{and} \quad p_s = p_s^0 x_s. \tag{16-23}$$

From the definition of mole fraction given by Eq. (15–21), we know that

$$\sum_{j=1}^{s} x_j = 1$$

and if we separate from the sum the fraction x_s by writing

$$x_s + \sum_{j=1, j \neq s}^{s} x_j = 1,$$

then

$$x_s = 1 - \sum_{j=1, j \neq s}^{s} x_j \equiv 1 - X_A, \qquad (16\text{-}24)$$

where X_A is defined by this equation and is the sum of all species mole fractions excluding x_s, this is, the total solute mole fraction. Substituting Eq. (16-24) into Eq. (16-23), one obtains

$$p_s = p_s^0(1 - X_A) \qquad (16\text{-}25a)$$

or

$$\frac{p_s^0 - p_s}{p_s^0} = X_A. \qquad (16\text{-}25b)$$

Equations (16-25) state that the fractional lowering of the pure solvent vapor pressure due to the presence of solute is equal to the mole fraction of the added solute, an alternative form of Raoult's law.

In dilute solutions, X_A is approximately proportional to the total molar concentration, as may be deduced by the following argument. From the definition of X_A and mole fraction,

$$X_A = \frac{\sum_{j=1, j \neq s}^{s} n_j}{n_s + \sum_{j=1, j \neq s}^{s} n_j}. \qquad (16\text{-}26)$$

For a liter of dilute aqueous solution, $n_s \cong 55.5$. The term $\sum_{j=1,\ j \neq s}^{s} n_j$ is $\ll 55.5$, and may therefore be ignored in the denominator of Eq. (16-26) in comparison to n_s. Multiplying both sides by n_s, we obtain for the one liter

$$55.5 X_A = \sum_{j=1, j \neq s}^{s} n_j = \sum_{j=1, j \neq s}^{s} c_j = C_A, \qquad (16\text{-}27)$$

where C_A is the total molar solute concentration. This result, when combined with Eq. (16-25b), gives

$$\frac{p_s^0 - p_s}{p_s^0} = \frac{C_A}{55.5} \qquad (16\text{-}28)$$

for the vapor-pressure lowering of an aqueous solution due to the presence of dissolved solute whose total molar concentration is C_A. It is important to note in considering mole fractions that each species of the system is to be properly counted in totaling the number of moles; e.g., each separate ionic species must be counted. One liter of a one-molar solution of sodium chloride has one mole of Na^+ and one mole of Cl^-.

Biological systems are aqueous systems, and although the presence of the many dissolved solutes totaling approximately 0.300 molar does lower the vapor pressure of the water, the effect is quantitatively small. The vapor pressure of pure water at 38°C is 49.69 mm Hg (Ref. 2, p. 447) and

$$\Delta p = \frac{0.30}{55.5} \, 49.69 = 0.27 \text{ mm Hg.}$$

Temperature variations *per se* may be quantitatively more important than solute in altering vapor pressure, for at this temperature the vapor pressure of water varies about 3 mm Hg per degree centigrade.

Raoult's law, however, is important in many physical chemical measurements of biological importance. It forms the basis of some of the more precise measurements of molecular interaction of solutes in solutions. It is the basis of the fact that the freezing point of a solution is lower than that of pure solvent, and the boiling point is elevated over that of a pure solvent.

16–3 Equilibrium of a chemical reaction. Chemical reactions do not differ in principle from the type of physical reactions that we have been considering in the foregoing section. The physical reactions of phase equilibria involve the transfer of a chemical entity from one region of the system to another, leaving the entity unchanged except for location. A chemical reaction, on the other hand, is merely a modification of one or more chemical entities without necessarily involving, on the average, a change in physical location. Thermodynamically, the same energy considerations may be applied. Using the chemical potential concepts developed, we are here led to the law of mass action. For a fairly general chemical reaction equation at equilibrium, we write

$$aA + bB \rightleftharpoons pP + qQ \tag{16–29}$$

in which the lower-case letters are the stoichiometric numbers involved in the reaction, and the upper-case letters are the chemical compounds. This equation is again a statement of a change in state in which a moles of A react with b moles of B forming p moles of P and q moles of Q; the reaction occurs such that at all times the reactants and products are in mutual equilibrium. Since the free energy in each state (the reactant state and the product state) is given by the sum of the products of the mole quantities (stoichiometric numbers) and chemical potentials of the substances, and since the change in free energy, ΔG, is zero, we have

$$p\mu_P + q\mu_Q - a\mu_A - b\mu_B = \Delta G = 0. \tag{16–30}$$

If we substitute for the chemical potential of each constituent its relation to the concentration (Eq. 15–19), we obtain

$$p\mu_P^0 + pRT \ln c_P + q\mu_Q^0 + qRT \ln c_Q$$
$$-a\mu_A^0 - aRT \ln c_A - b\mu_B^0 - bRT \ln c_B = 0. \qquad (16\text{–}31)$$

Rearranging gives

$$p\mu_P^0 + q\mu_Q^0 - a\mu_A^0 - b\mu_B^0 = -RT \ln \frac{c_P^p \cdot c_Q^q}{c_A^a \cdot c_B^b}. \qquad (16\text{–}32)$$

The left-hand side is made up only of constants and equals ΔG^0 at a particular temperature; therefore, the right-hand side must be likewise a constant. Comparison to Eq. (16–5) shows that

$$K = \frac{c_P^p \cdot c_Q^q}{c_A^a \cdot c_B^b}, \qquad (16\text{–}33)$$

where K is the reaction equilibrium constant at the particular temperature, and the equation is the law of mass action. This applies to all chemical reactions at equilibrium and is of great significance in considering innumerable biochemical reactions. We should again direct our attention to the interpretation of the quantity ΔG^0 forming the left-hand side of Eq. (16–32), for it is a quantity frequently quoted in biochemical literature and oftentimes used erroneously. If the chemical reaction of Eq. (16–29) were not carried out at equilibrium but were carried out under the conditions such that each of the reactants on the left-hand side of Eq. (16–29) and each of the products on the right-hand side were held at unit activity during the course of the reaction of a moles of A with b moles of B to give the products, then the reaction would be attended by a free energy change to ΔG^0. This can perhaps be made clearer by rewriting Eq. (16–30) for the equilibrium reactions in the form of an energy balance equation, namely,

$$a\mu_A + b\mu_B + \Delta G = p\mu_P + q\mu_Q. \qquad (16\text{–}34)$$

Of course, at equilibrium $\Delta G = 0$, which then allows the equality of Eq. (16–30). However, if each of the reactants and products is held constant at unit activity, then for each, $\mu_i = \mu_i^0$, and in this case,

$$a\mu_A^0 + b\mu_B^0 + \Delta G = p\mu_P^0 + q\mu_Q^0, \qquad (16\text{–}35)$$

which on rearranging gives

$$\Delta G = p\mu_P^0 + q\mu_Q^0 - a\mu_A^0 - b\mu_B^0 = \Delta G^0 = -RT \ln K. \qquad (16\text{–}36)$$

Under arbitrary conditions not representing equilibrium, the maximum free energy available for useful work, such as to "drive" another chemical reaction appropriately coupled, is then correctly given by Eq. (16–34). It is not given by Eq. (16–35), where $\Delta G = \Delta G^0$, which represents a very definite, generally unobtainable condition for the reaction in which each of the substances are at unit concentration throughout the reaction. This distinction is an important one and well worthy of comprehension.

Referring to Eq. (16–34), we note that if ΔG is negative, the reaction may proceed from left to right, but if ΔG is positive, the conditions are such that the reaction may proceed from right to left. In other words, if the free energy of the reactants, $a\mu_A + b\mu_B$, is greater than that of the products, $p\mu_P + q\mu_Q$, then from Eq. (16–34), the direction of decreasing free energy for the system, i.e., the direction of the natural process in Eq. (16–29), is from left to right. If the system is closed so that none of the constituents can be added or taken away, the free energy of the system at constant temperature and pressure may continue to decrease until its minimum value is reached at equilibrium.

In the foregoing paragraph we have been careful to use the words "may proceed" rather than "will proceed." This is so because this is all that thermodynamics can indicate. Energy considerations distinguish what is or what is not possible, but no more. A classical example of this is a mixture of hydrogen and oxygen gas, which at ordinary temperatures fail to react with each other to produce water, although such a reaction would be attended by a large free energy decrease. Whether or not a reaction will actually occur is a matter of kinetic considerations and will be discussed in Chapters 22 and 23.

A number of examples of chemical reaction equilibria are discussed in the following chapter, which deals with proton transfer reactions.

16–4 Free energy change and coupling of chemical reactions. In previous discussions of the Gibbs free energy we have indicated its interpretation in terms of the maximum available energy of a system for performance of useful work. Such useful work may take a variety of forms. For example, if our systems consist of one chemical reaction it may be used to drive another, provided appropriate coupling between the two reactions exists. Up to this point we have not yet indicated what this appropriate coupling might be. Since this matter is of great importance to the entire energy economy of the living cell it is worthy of further discussion at this time. The cell derives its energy from certain foodstuffs such as glucose and oxygen, and utilizes this energy in the performance of other cellular functions. Such cellular functions may be the mechanical work on the environment associated with muscular contraction, or it might be the synthesis of chemical compounds preparatory for the cell to reproduce itself in division. Even though considerations of the mechanisms of coupling must be de-

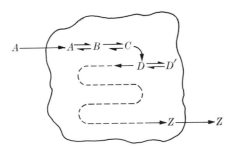

Fig. 16–1. Diagrammatic illustration of a living cell in which A, a foodstuff, is conceived to enter, and then by a series of reactions it is ultimately converted to Z, which leaves the cell as a waste product. These intermediates are not in true equilibrium, although there may be side reactions which can be in true equilibrium, such as D with D'.

ferred until Chapter 23, the free energy considerations may be illustrated by a very simple system. (See Fig. 16–1.)

Consider two chemical reactions:

$$A \rightleftharpoons P + Q, \tag{16–37a}$$

$$B + Q \rightleftharpoons R, \tag{16–37b}$$

which are assumed to occur in the same mixture of constituents. Let us further assume that chemical potential conditions are such at a given time that reaction (16–37a) may proceed from left to right, but that reaction (16–37b) may proceed from right to left. In other words,

$$\Delta G_a = \mu_P + \mu_Q - \mu_A = \mu_P^0 + \mu_Q^0 - \mu_A^0 + RT \ln \frac{c_P \cdot c_Q}{c_A} < 0 \tag{16–38a}$$

whereas

$$\Delta G_b = \mu_R - \mu_B - \mu_Q = \mu_R^0 - \mu_B^0 - \mu_Q^0 + RT \ln \frac{c_R}{c_B \cdot c_Q} > 0. \tag{16–38b}$$

To be more specific let us assume that the particular conditions exist such that the free energy changes per mole unit through the reaction would be $\Delta G_a = -5000$ cal $\cdot$ mole^{-1} and $\Delta G_b = +4000$ cal $\cdot$ mole^{-1}; each is computed for the reactions proceeding from left to right as is conventional. Such conditions might be realized if, for instance, the concentration of Q were very small, making μ_Q a large negative value. It is to be noted that proceeding from right to left the free energy change for (16–37b) would be -4000 cal $\cdot$ mole^{-1}, and this would be the direction of the natural process. The two reactions proceed essentially independently except for their mutual dependency on the concentration of Q or μ_Q. Reaction a proceeds forward, and reaction b moves in the reverse direction. Each would "dissipate" its free energy as heat, creating entropy. If, however, the reactions were so coupled that substance B could "obtain" the substance Q, not from free solution but instead directly from A by reacting with A in the overall reaction

$$A + B \rightleftharpoons P + R, \qquad (16\text{-}39)$$

then the total free energy change would be

$$\Delta G = \Delta G_a + \Delta G_b = \mu_P^0 + \mu_R^0 - \mu_A^0 - \mu_B^0 + RT \ln \frac{c_P \cdot c_R}{c_A \cdot c_B}. \qquad (16\text{-}40)$$

Under our assumed conditions this free energy change is -1000 cal $\cdot$ mole^{-1}. In this manner reaction (16-37b), having a positive free energy change, is "driven" by reaction (16-37a), which had a negative free energy change. As long as $\Delta G_a + \Delta G_b$ is negative, the overall reaction given by Eq. (16-39) may proceed from left to right; and in terms of Eqs. (16-37), reaction a is doing useful work in converting B to R in reaction b.

There are numerous examples of reaction coupling to be found among the complex metabolic transformations that occur in the living cell. It is appropriate to mention here the reaction coupling involving the transfer of a phosphate group from adenosine triphosphate (ATP) to creatine (Cr) and its reverse, the transfer of phosphate from phosphoryl-creatine (CrP) to adenosine diphosphate (ADP). The ATP-ADP system is central to the entire concept of biological metabolic energy.

Taken individually, the hydrolysis reactions may be written simply as

$$\text{ATP} + \text{H}_2\text{O} \rightleftharpoons \text{ADP} + \text{P} \qquad (16\text{-}41\text{a})$$

and

$$\text{CrP} + \text{H}_2\text{O} \rightleftharpoons \text{Cr} + \text{P}, \qquad (16\text{-}41\text{b})$$

where P represents inorganic phosphate. Analysis of these reactions indicates that both ATP and CrP are unstable in the sense that the equilibrium points are both far to the right. The standard free energy changes, ΔG^0, have large negative values, of the order of -6000 to -8000 cal $\cdot$ mole^{-1}. Although precise data are lacking, available evidence suggests that in the functioning muscle cell the conditions are such that the actual free energy changes (ΔG, not ΔG^0) also have rather large negative values, due to the rather low concentration of inorganic phosphate that prevails. In other words, the individual reactions are themselves far from equilibrium. Even so, the reactions do not proceed at a very significant rate under these conditions unless they are enzymatically catalyzed. However, there exists in muscle tissue, where this system is found, an enzyme, creatine kinase. This enzyme allows these two reactions to be closely coupled, such that the phosphate may be directly transferred from one molecule to the other without entering the solution pool of inorganic phosphate. The combined reaction may be written as

$$\text{ATP} + \text{Cr} \rightleftarrows \text{ADP} + \text{CrP}. \qquad (16\text{–}42)$$

In that both of the individual reactions have large negative standard free energy changes as written in Eqs. (16–41), the combination of the two as in Eq. (16–42) would be expected to have a small standard free energy change. The equilibrium constant given by

$$K = \frac{c_{\text{ADP}} \cdot c_{\text{CrP}}}{c_{\text{ATP}} \cdot c_{\text{Cr}}}$$

is estimated to be about $1 \cdot 10^{-1}$. (See Ref. 4.) The standard free energy change may be estimated to be $\Delta G^0 = -RT \ln K = +1400 \text{ cal} \cdot \text{mole}^{-1}$. In all probability the conditions in resting muscle are such that this system is close to equilibrium (see Ref. 5), and therefore ΔG would be approximately zero.

16–5 Measurement of the chemical potential. In all of the foregoing treatments of equilibria in this chapter, the chemical potential function has been utilized to provide unity of concept in the various empirically discovered physical-chemical laws. The solubility constant, the solubility

TABLE 16–2

STANDARD FREE ENERGIES OF SOME CHEMICAL
REACTIONS OF BIOLOGICAL IMPORTANCE*

	$\Delta G'$,† Kcal	pH
Glucose $\rightleftarrows$ 2 lactate$^-$ + 2H$^+$	−47.4	7.0
Glucose + ATP^{4-} $\rightleftarrows$ glucose 6P^{2-} + ADP^{3-} + H$^+$	−5.1	7.0
ATP^{4-} + H$_2$O $\rightleftarrows$ ADP^{3-} + HPO$_4^{2-}$ + H$^+$	−8.9	7.5
ADP^{3-} + H$_2$O $\rightleftarrows$ AMP^{2-} + HPO$_4^{2-}$ + H$^+$	−9.5	7.5
Enolpyruvate 2P^{3-} + ADP^{3-} + H$^+$ $\rightleftarrows$ pyruvate + ATP^{4-}	−6.0	7.0
Pyruvate$^-$ + DPNH + H$^+$ $\rightleftarrows$ lactate$^-$ + DPN$^+$	−5.4	7.0
Succinate^{2-} + $\frac{1}{2}$O$_2$ $\rightleftarrows$ fumarate^{2-} + H$_2$O	−36.1	7.0
DPNH + $\frac{1}{2}$O$_2$ + H$^+$ $\rightleftarrows$ DPN$^+$ + H$_2$O	−52.4	7.0
Glucose + 6O$_2$ $\rightleftarrows$ 6CO$_2$ + 6H$_2$O	−686.5	—
Glycylglycine + H$_2$O $\rightleftarrows$ 2 glycine	−3.59	—

* Selected from tables compiled by Burton in Ref. 7.
† $\Delta G'$ refers to unit activity (molal) of all substances in aqueous solution except the gaseous substances (CO$_2$ and O$_2$), which are at 1 atm pressure, and the H$^+$, which is at the pH noted.

product of salts, Henry's law on gas solubility, Raoult's law on the vapor pressure of solutions, and the law of mass action are individual statements of the underlying principle of equilibrium, namely that for such equilibria a change in state at constant temperature and pressure is attended by zero free energy change. This fact draws these several phenomena, as well as others, into a common interpretation and points out their essential similarity.

However, it still remains that what is measured experimentally is not the chemical potential itself nor the standard chemical potential. Instead what must be measured are the actual variables, such as concentration or activity and partial pressures as may be computed from total pressures and chemical analyses of the vapor. It is from these measurements that equilibrium constants may be assessed which in turn allow computation of standard free energy changes and standard chemical potentials. It is often difficult to measure equilibrium constants in biological systems especially when the concentrations of one or more of the constituents in the reaction is very low and, therefore, analysis is subject to considerable error. A useful expedient sometimes is to combine a series of chemical reactions which, when summed, give an overall reaction whose equilibrium constant it is desired to measure. In any case the energy quantities are always derived quantities, but the standard energies associated with given changes in state provide an important means of tabulating much information pertaining to the behavior of physical chemical systems. (See Ref. 6). Table 16–2 lists the standard free energies of a number of chemical reactions of biological interest.

REFERENCES

1. E. A. GUGGENHEIM, *Thermodynamics.* Interscience, New York, 1949.
2. J. T. EDSALL and J. WYMAN, *Biophysical Chemistry*, Vol. I. Academic Press, New York, 1958.
3. R. A. ROBINSON and R. H. STOKES, *Electrolyte Solutions.* Butterworths, London, 1955.
4. L. NODA, S. KUBY, and H. A. LARDY, "Adenosinetriphosphate-Creatine Transphosphorylase. IV. Equilibrium Studies," *J. Biol. Chem.* **210,** 83 (1954).
5. H. J. HOHORST, M. REIM, and H. BARTELS, "Studies on the Cretine Kinase Equilibrium in Muscle and the Significance of ATP and ADP Levels." *Biochem. Biophys. Res. Comm.* **7,** 142 (1962).
6. F. D. ROSSINI, D. D. WAGMAN, W. H. EVANS, S. LEVINE, and I. JAFFE, *Selected Values of Chemical Thermodynamic Properties.* Circular of the National Bureau of Standards 500, U. S. Government Printing Office, Washington, D. C. (1952).
7. H. A. KREB and H. L. KORNBERG, *Energy Transformations in Living Matter*, a survey with an Appendix by K. Burton. Springer-Verlag, Berlin, 1957.

CHAPTER 17

ACID-BASE EQUILIBRIA

257

CHAPTER 17

ACID-BASE EQUILIBRIA

17-1 Introduction. In the previous chapter we have discussed equilibrium of chemical reactions and have developed the law of mass action from relations involving the chemical potential. There are innumerable kinds of chemical reactions in chemistry as well as in biological systems. However, a very important class of reactions, especially in biology, involves the association and dissociation of the simple proton, H^+, with special groups. A brief introduction to these matters was given in Chapter 4. This reaction, being a simple ionic reaction, attains equilibrium with great rapidity. The half-life of these proton associations has been determined in a series of elegant experiments to be of the order of 10^{-10} sec. (See Ref. 1.) Since these reactions likewise involve a charged moiety, the H^+, the reaction must involve an alteration in electrical charge of the group with which it is involved. Furthermore, since biological systems are aqueous systems, any reaction involving proton association or dissociation with a particular group must also involve such a reaction with water. The bare proton as such does not exist except in transit. The proton is of nuclear dimensions and is quickly taken into the orbital electron clouds of other atoms sharing an electron. In aqueous solution, therefore, it is more proper to write for the state of hydrogen ion, the ion H_3O^+ or even $H_9O_4^+$ (see Ref. 2) rather than merely H^+. H_3O^+ is termed the hydronium ion. We must recognize this hydronium ion as an entity, but to simplify the writing of chemical reactions we will write them not as

$$R—H + H_2O \rightleftharpoons R^- + H_3O^+ \qquad (17\text{-}1)$$

for the exchange of a proton from a group or molecule, R, to H_2O, but instead in the simpler form

$$R—H \rightleftharpoons R^- + H^+. \qquad (17\text{-}2)$$

The latter form implicitly assumes the involvement of water.

17-2 Definition of acid and base. We employ herein the definition of Brönsted: *An acid is any substance that is a proton donor and is thus capable of dissociating a proton from a particular group. A base, on the other hand, is a proton acceptor and thus has a group capable of associating with a proton.* Obviously, since these reactions of proton dissociation or association are

258

reversible (i.e., may be reversed) any acid on donating a proton results in a base and any base on accepting a proton becomes an acid. Therefore, for each acid, we may properly identify a conjugate base. In reaction (17–2), RH is the acid, whereas R^- is its conjugate base. This being the case, we need only speak of acid groups and their properties and not reiterate by speaking of base groups and their properties.

There are many atoms to which atomic hydrogen may be covalently or partially covalently bonded. Bonds such as that of

$$-\overset{\displaystyle |}{\underset{\displaystyle |}{C}}-H$$

are very stable, and one would not expect any significant dissociation into

$$-\overset{\displaystyle |}{\underset{\displaystyle |}{C}}^- \qquad \text{and} \qquad H^+$$

under ordinary conditions. At the other extreme, the bond of H—Cl is largely an electrostatic bond, and in aqueous solution with its high dielectric constant, together with the high affinity of H_2O for the proton to form H_3O^+, complete dissociation of HCl results by the reaction

$$HCl + H_2O \rightarrow H_3O^+ + Cl^-. \tag{17–3}$$

Certainly, HCl is recognized as a strong acid, and one does not usually associate with methane, CH_4, any acid properties.

From this discussion it must be apparent that there are degrees of acid strength. Strong acids are good proton donors and give up their protons readily, whereas weak acids give up their protons less readily. There exists a continuum of acid strengths which, given the same conditions, must be inversely related to the bond energy between group and proton; the stronger the bond, the more stable the association and the weaker its acid function. Applying these same considerations to bases (conjugate bases), we find that the stronger the base, the better it may accept a proton and the stronger must be the proton-base bond. Therefore, strong acids yield weak bases, and weak acids yield strong bases, the two functions being inversely related. We may illustrate this with the two substances, acetic acid and ammonium ion. Acetic acid dissociates according to the reaction

$$HAc \rightleftharpoons H^+ + Ac^-, \tag{17–4}$$

yielding a proton and an acetate ion. Ammonium ion dissociates as follows:

$$NH_4^+ \rightleftharpoons H^+ + NH_3, \tag{17–5}$$

yielding a proton and ammonia which, of course, in aqueous solution is associated with water and may be written as NH_4OH. Acetic acid is normally thought of as a weak acid, but ammonium ion is a still weaker acid. NH_4OH is thought of as a moderately strong (or weak) base, but acetate ion is a still weaker base. We will discuss in Section 17–5 the more quantitative aspects of these relations in terms of the standard free energies and equilibrium constants.

17–3 Definition of pH. The concept of pH is central to any discussion of acid-base equilibria. (See Chapter 4.) It is defined as

$$pH \equiv -\log a_{H^+}, \qquad (17\text{–}6)$$

and we look upon p as an operator, telling the reader to take the logarithm to the base of 10 of what follows and multiply the result by minus one. The H of pH refers to the concentration of H^+, or more properly the effective thermodynamic concentration, the H^+ activity, a_{H^+}. We will not concern ourselves at this juncture with certain operational difficulties associated with this definition but will just accept it. These operational difficulties are somewhat sophisticated. We will describe in Chapter 18 some principles inherent in the electrometric measurement of pH where it becomes apparent that certain assumptions must be made.

Characteristically, the hydrogen ion activity may be varied widely. In aqueous systems the extremes of a_{H^+} may be somewhat greater than one molar to somewhat less than 10^{-14} molar. These extremes correspond to pH values of somewhat less than zero (i.e., a negative number) to somewhat larger than 14. The logarithmic function of pH then provides a convenience, for it, in effect, contracts a large concentration scale into a unit change for each 10-fold change in a_{H^+}.

We note here that pH is directly related, or proportional to, an energy associated with a given activity of H^+. Thus from Eq. (15–19) the relation between the chemical potential of H^+ and pH is

$$\mu_{H^+} = -2.3 \, RT \, pH, \qquad (17\text{–}7)$$

having taken $\mu_{H^+}^0 = 0$ at $a_{H^+} = 1$ (pH = 0), as is conventional.

17–4 The dissociation of water; pK. Water is the ubiquitous biological solvent and has many unique properties, as has been pointed out in Chapter 4. Among its important properties is that of dissociating into hydrogen ion and hydroxyl ion by the chemical reaction

$$H_2O \rightleftharpoons H^+ + OH^-, \qquad (17\text{–}8)$$

or more properly (see Section 17–1 and Chapter 4)

$$2H_2O \rightleftharpoons H_3O^+ + OH^-. \qquad (17\text{–}9)$$

In the very purest water at 25°C, H^+ is found to be just about $1 \cdot 10^{-7}$ molar, and due to electrical neutrality demanding an equal number of positive and negative charges, the OH^- concentration is the same. At equilibrium, the chemical potential relations are for this change in state

$$\mu_{H^+}^0 + RT \ln c_{H^+} + \mu_{OH^-}^0$$
$$+ RT \ln c_{OH^-} - \mu_{H_2O}^0 - RT \ln x_{H_2O} = \Delta G = 0, \qquad (17\text{–}10)$$

which on rearranging gives

$$\Delta G^0 = \mu_{H^+}^0 + \mu_{OH^-}^0 - \mu_{H_2O}^0 = -RT \ln \frac{c_{H^+} \cdot c_{OH^-}}{x_{H_2O}}. \qquad (17\text{–}11)$$

The term on the right-hand side is, of course, a constant, since that on the left is a constant. It is apparent also that x_{H_2O} in pure water is unity to a very good approximation, thus

$$\frac{c_{H^+} \cdot c_{OH^-}}{x_{H_2O}} = K_w = 1 \cdot 10^{-14} \cong c_{H^+} \cdot c_{OH^-}, \qquad (17\text{–}12)$$

and

$$\Delta G^0 = -2.3 \cdot 1.99 \cdot 298(-14) = 19{,}100 \text{ cal} \cdot \text{mole}^{-1}. \qquad (17\text{–}13)$$

This indicates that to dissociate one mole of water at unit activity into H^+ and OH^-, each also at unit activity, requires the expenditure of 19,100 cal. Water is a very weak acid. The pH of pure water at 25°C is $-\log 10^{-7} = 7.00$, a value which is frequently termed neutral.

In discussing acid dissociation reactions and their equilibrium constants it has again become the practice to use logarithmic relations. Thus from rearrangement of Eqs. (17–11) and (17–12), we obtain

$$\frac{\Delta G^0}{2.3RT} = -\log c_{H^+} - \log \frac{c_{OH^-}}{x_{H_2O}} = -\log K_w = pK_w. \qquad (17\text{–}14)$$

The last relation defines pK in a fashion analogous to that of pH.

Equation (17–14) may be rearranged further to put it into a conventional form giving

$$pH = pK_w + \log \frac{c_{OH^-}}{x_{H_2O}}. \qquad (17\text{–}15)$$

It is this type of logarithmic relation generalized for any acid in equilibrium with its dissociation products, H^+ and conjugate base, that is commonly used. Written for the general case it is

$$pH = pK + \log \frac{c \text{ (conjugate base)}}{c \text{ (acid)}}. \qquad (17\text{--}16)$$

This equation is the logarithmic form of the law of mass action for acid dissociation equilibria and is known as the Henderson-Hasselbalch equation. In view of the fact that the pK is directly related to the standard free energy of the reaction ($\Delta G^0 = 2.3\ RT\ pK$), it has become rather conventional to tabulate the dissociation constants of acids in terms of pK. It is deduced that the lower the value of a pK, the stronger is the acid; the higher the value of a pK, the weaker is the acid.

It should be noted that the concentrations appearing in Eqs. (17–14), (17–15), and (17–16) should in fact be activities, the effective concentration, in order for K to be a true thermodynamic constant. Consistent with the foregoing chapters, however, we consider for our purposes concentrations and activities to be nearly the same. (See Section 15–8.) In many textbooks in the biochemical literature, K is often primed when it refers to an equilibrium constant based on concentrations and is unprimed when it refers to activities. However, the hydrogen ion or pH, being measured electrochemically (see Section 18–3), is expressed as an activity. The reader should note carefully how a particular author defines his equilibrium constants. We will not distinguish between a primed and an unprimed K in our discussions.

17–5 Monobasic acids; titration curves. The term "monobasic acid" applies to those molecules possessing a single group capable of dissociating a proton. Such substances as acetic acid and ammonium ion are typical examples. We discuss acid-base equilibrium in these simple molecules first before going on to more complex molecules. In the study of acid-base equilibria, one generally does a "titration" and plots the results as titration curves. In its essence this generally consists of measurements on a succession of equilibrium points, each representing an increment of change in conditions. Our problem herein will be to examine the theoretical aspects of these titration curves in a general manner.

In an actual titration experiment, one may commence with a solution of a given acid at a known concentration. The pH of the solution is measured and recorded. A known increment of a solution of a suitable strong base such as NaOH or KOH is added. The added OH^- reacts with some of the H^+, and a new equilibrium point is established at a slightly lower c_{H^+}. The pH is measured and recorded, followed again by the addition of another known increment of OH^-. The process is continued until the acid has been titrated to any desired state of completion (dissociation). Alternatively, one may commence with a solution of the conjugate base and add increments of a strong acid, such as HCl, measuring the pH as before. One may even commence with a mixture of acid and conjugate base and titrate first in one manner and then in the other.

At each point in the titration, the proton dissociation reactions are assumed to be in equilibrium, an assumption well justified since equilibrium in these types of reactions is approached exceedingly fast. For the acid, we abbreviate with the symbol HA, and for the conjugate base, A^-. The two reactions that are in simultaneous equilibria are then

$$HA \rightleftharpoons A^- + H^+ \qquad (17\text{--}17)$$

and

$$H_2O \rightleftharpoons OH^- + H^+, \qquad (17\text{--}18)$$

for which the two equilibrium relations may be written

$$K_a = \frac{c_{H^+} \cdot c_{A^-}}{c_{HA}}, \qquad (17\text{--}19)$$

$$K_w = c_{H^+} \cdot c_{OH^-}. \qquad (17\text{--}20)$$

In addition, if we designate our added strong base as B^+OH^- and its concentration in the solution titrated as c_B, we have an additional equation based on the principle of electrical neutrality. This is

$$c_{H^+} + c_{B^+} = c_{A^-} + c_{OH^-}. \qquad (17\text{--}21)$$

Finally, we have conservation of the acid plus conjugate base, namely

$$C_T = c_{HA} + c_{A^-}. \qquad (17\text{--}22)$$

These are four equations containing the four variables, c_{H^+}, c_{A^-}, c_{HA}, and c_{OH^-}, the two constants, K_a and K_w, and the two experimentally known quantities of the system, C_T and c_B. Since Eqs. (17–19) and (17–20) are, strictly speaking, thermodynamic equations in which the concentrations should in actuality be replaced by activities, whereas Eqs. (17–21) and (17–22) are mass or charge conservation equations and contain true concentrations, any combination of these necessitates additional assumptions or theoretical corrections pertaining to the relation between the physical concentrations and the thermodynamic effective concentrations or activities. For our purposes here we take these two as equivalent, although formal corrections of the type discussed in Section 15–8 may be easily included.

The experimental problem in the case of an acid group of unknown properties is generally to determine the value of K_a from titration data. In principle this is possible provided we measure one of the variables

(c_{H^+} or pH) and know the value of K_w, for then we have the four equations relating five unknown quantities. This is sufficient to establish a single relation between the two quantities pH and pK. However, in analyzing titration data it is convenient to establish a more or less uniform scheme. In this respect the introduction of a new variable representing the fractional extent to which an acid has dissociated its proton to become a conjugate base, or conversely, the fractional extent to which it is still an acid, considerably simplifies any analysis. Let us define this variable, a dimensionless number, as

$$\bar{h} = \frac{c_{HA}}{c_T} = \frac{c_{HA}}{c_{HA} + c_{A^-}}, \qquad (17\text{-}23)$$

which represents that fraction of the total acid associated with a proton. For the monobasic acid case, $\bar{h}$ has a maximum value of unity, and a minimum value of zero. However, identical considerations may be applied to molecules with more than one acidic group as developed in the following section, whereupon the maximum value would correspond to the number of such acid groups per molecule. From Eq. (17-23) it is evident that

$$1 - \bar{h} = \frac{c_{A^-}}{c_{HA} + c_{A^-}}. \qquad (17\text{-}24)$$

The ratio c_{A^-}/c_{HA} is then

$$\frac{c_{A^-}}{c_{HA}} = \frac{1 - \bar{h}}{\bar{h}}. \qquad (17\text{-}25)$$

Taking the logarithmic form of Eq. (17-19) (the Henderson-Hasselbalch equation) and substituting from Eq. (17-25), we have

$$\text{pH} = \text{p}K_a + \log \frac{c_{A^-}}{c_{HA}} = \text{p}K_a + \log \frac{1 - \bar{h}}{\bar{h}}. \qquad (17\text{-}26)$$

This equation relates pH to pK_a in terms of our new variable, $\bar{h}$, which is evaluated from the known quantities C_T and c_{B^+} together with Eqs. (17-20) and (17-21).

In Fig. 17-1 we plot the function, $\bar{h}$, versus pH, for two simple monobasic acids, acetic acid and ammonium ion. These curves are characteristic and are derived from titration data as we have described. Several points of interest emerge.

(1) There is a central point of symmetry, about which $\bar{h} = 0.5$. This point is an inflection point characterized by a maximum absolute value (value disregarding algebraic sign) in the slope. From Eq. (17-26), it is evident that at this point pH = pK_a, since

$$\log \frac{1 - 0.5}{0.5} = \log 1 = 0.$$

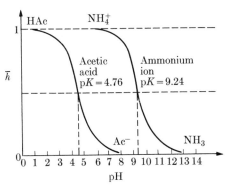

FIG. 17–1. Hydrogen ion dissociation curves of acetic acid and ammonium ion. See text for discussion.

This provides a means, therefore, of determining the pK of any monobasic acid.

(2) At values of pH $\ll$ pK_a the curve has an asymptote at $\bar{h} = 1$. In other words, at high concentrations of hydrogen ion, the HA form predominates.

(3) At values of pH $\gg$ pK_a, the curve has an asymptote at $\bar{h} = 0$. In other words, at low concentrations of hydrogen ion, the A^- form predominates.

(4) Curves of all monobasic acids plotted in this fashion are identical in form, the point of inflection where pH = pK_a being the only distinguishing characteristic. Referring to Fig. 17–1, we see that curves to the left are for stronger acids than those to the right.

(5) Without too much difficulty, the value for the slope of the curve may be derived from Eq. (17–26). This slope is

$$\frac{d\bar{h}}{d(\text{pH})} = -2.303\bar{h}(1 - \bar{h}), \qquad (17\text{–}27)$$

whence it is evident that its absolute value is a maximum when $\bar{h} = 0.5$. This slope has significance in terms of hydrogen ion or pH buffering. At the point of symmetry where pH = pK_a, buffering is at a maximum. This means that for an addition of a given amount of strong base or acid to the system at this pH, the least change in pH will result. This may be obvious from the curves. This fact is utilized in preparation of standard pH solutions to avoid possible errors resulting from slight accidental contamination, and also in preparation of solutions where it is desirable to maintain a reasonably constant pH in spite of possible H^+ being produced or consumed by some reaction. The concept of buffering is especially important in biology where the regulation and control of pH is of prime importance in the normal functioning of living systems.

TABLE 17-1

THE pK_a VALUES FOR VARIOUS BIOLOGICAL COMPOUNDS
AND BIOLOGICALLY IMPORTANT FUNCTIONAL GROUPS

Acid	Group and reaction	pK_a
Aspartic acid	$-\alpha-COOH = \alpha-COO^- + H^+$	1.99
Phosphoric acid	$H_3PO_4 = H_2PO_4^- + H^+$	2.15
Glycine	$-COOH = -COO^- + H^+$	2.35
Formic acid	$HCOOH = HCOO^- + H^+$	3.75
Lactic acid	$CH_3-CH(OH)-COOH =$	
	$CH_3-CH(OH)-COO^- + H^+$	3.86
Aspartic acid	$-\beta-COOH = \beta-COO^- + H^+$	3.90
Succinic acid	$HOOC-CH_2-CH_2-COOH =$	
	$HOOC-CH_2-CH_2-COO^- + H^+$	4.21
Acetic acid	$CH_3-COOH = CH_3-COO^- + H^+$	4.76
Succinic acid	$HOOC-CH_2-CH_2-COO^- =$	
	$^-OOC-CH_2-CH_2-COO^- + H^+$	5.64
Histidine	$HN\;\;\;\;NH^+ = HN\;\;\;\;N + H^+$	6.00
Carbonic acid	$H_2CO_3 = HCO_3^- + H^+$	6.35
Phosphoric	$H_2PO_4^- = HPO_4^{2-} + H^+$	7.20
Ammonium ion	$NH_4^+ = NH_3 + H^+$	9.24
Glycine	$^+H_3N-CH_2-COO^- =$	
	$H_2N-CH_2-COO^- + H^+$	9.78
Trimethylammonium ion	$(CH_3)_3NH^+ = (CH_3)_3N + H^+$	9.80
Aspartic	$^2-R-NH_3^+ = {}^2-R-NH_2 + H^+$	10.00
Carbonic	$HCO_3^- = CO_3^{2-} + H^+$	10.33
Tyrosinol OH	$R-\langle\bigcirc\rangle-OH = R-\langle\bigcirc\rangle-O^- + H^+$	10.95
Water	$H_2O = OH^- + H^+$	14.00

In Table 17-1 we collect the pK's of some representative acids and acid groups of biological significance. Much could be discussed relative to the acid strength and the associated structure of the group, for this has been an area of intensive investigation. It has become recognized that neighboring atoms may modify the pK of an acid group according to factors based primarily on coulombic considerations or electron orbital shifts associated with the electronegativity of the atoms. The reader is referred elsewhere (e.g., Edsall and Wyman) for a thorough discussion of this subject.

17–6 Polybasic acids. As may have been noted in Table 17–1, many of the acids have several groups from which hydrogen ion dissociation occurs. For example, glycine has both a carboxyl group and an amino group. Phosphoric acid has three protons to dissociate. Aspartic acid has two carboxyl groups and an amino group. Each acid group has its own characteristic pK, although due to mutual influences of neighboring groups and the necessity to satisfy all equilibria simultaneously, "hybrid" pK's are frequent. (See Edsall and Wyman, Chapter 8.)

The titration curves of polybasic acids may become quite complex. In general, the simple Henderson-Hasselbalch equation (Eq. 17–16) cannot be applied, for it takes into account only one of the several pK's, and equilibrium for all acid groups must obtain simultaneously. However, if the pK's are widely different, as for example in the case of glycine, the acid functions "titrate" in widely different regions on the pH scale. To a good approximation, therefore, each group behaves as a monobasic acid and each follows closely an expression of the form of Eq. (17–16).

In Fig. 17–2, we plot the titration curve of glycine, again plotting $\bar{h}$ versus pH. The maximum value for $\bar{h}$ is, of course, 2; but it is evident that two widely separated S-shaped curves exist. These are not very different from those which would be obtained in the titration of ammonium acetate. Compare Fig. 17–1. The lowest pK of glycine, pK_1, is lower than the pK of acetic acid by 2.4 pH units. This is due primarily to the presence of the neighboring positively charged amino group, causing electrostatic repulsion of the proton on the carboxyl group, making it dissociate more easily. The higher pK of glycine, pK_2, is slightly higher than that of NH_4^+ due

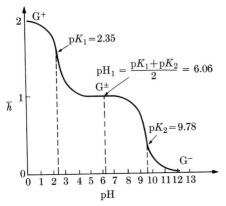

FIG. 17–2. Hydrogen ion dissociation curve of glycine in a plot of $\bar{h}$ vs. pH. The isoelectric pH is designated pH$_1$.

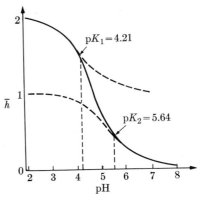

FIG. 17–3. Hydrogen ion dissociation curve of succinic acid in a plot of $\bar{h}$ vs. pH. The projected dissociations of each carboxyl group are indicated by the dashed lines.

to the presence of the neighboring negatively charged carboxyl group, causing electrostatic attraction of the proton to the amino group and making it dissociate less easily.

From Fig. 17–2 it is evident that at low pH the predominant species present is $^+\text{H}_3\text{N}$—CH_2—COOH, which may be abbreviated as G^+. At the very high pH's, the predominant species must be H_2N—CH_2—COO^-, abbreviated G^-. Over a wide central range of pH where $\bar{h}$ is near unity, the predominant species must be $^+\text{H}_3\text{N}$—CH_2—COO^-, abbreviated $\text{G}^\pm$; $\text{G}^\pm$ is the zwitterionic or "dipolar ion" form. In passing from a net positive charge at low pH to a net negative charge at high pH, there must exist a particular pH where, on the average, the net charge per molecule is zero. This pH is known as the isoelectric pH and is a point characteristic for each amino acid. In fact, it is a definite experimentally obtainable point for any polyacid that is an ampholyte; an ampholyte possesses both positive and negative charged acid groups. However, if a molecule possesses acid groups all of a similar charged type such as succinic acid or phosphoric acid, the state of zero net charge is attained only asymptotically at a pH extreme.

For polybasic acids in which the individual pK's are not widely separated, the titration curves approximate an equation such as (17–16) only near the inflection point where $\text{pH} = \text{p}K_i$; $\text{p}K_i$ refers to the pK of a particular group. In the region between the individual pK's, there is a compromised merging or averaging of what otherwise would be two independent S-shaped curves. In Fig. 17–3 we note this by the broken lines in the titration curve of succinic acid, which has the two pK's of 4.21 and 5.64.

It is instructive to write the analytical equations for polybasic acids. This may be done in a completely general manner for a substance having an arbitrary number N of acid groups per molecule. For each acid group we may write an equilibrium reaction representing a change in state:

$$\text{AH}_i \rightleftharpoons \text{AH}_{i-1} + \text{H}^+ \qquad (i = 1, 2, \ldots, N), \qquad (17\text{–}28)$$

and for each we write an equilibrium equation

$$K_i = \frac{c_{\text{AH}_{i-1}} \cdot c_{\text{H}^+}}{c_{\text{AH}_i}} \qquad (i = 1, 2, \ldots, N), \qquad (17\text{–}29)$$

where AH_i, with $i = 0, 1, 2, \ldots, N$, represents the ith species of acid which contains i protons. Thus the subscript i is used to indicate the number of protons on the molecule in a particular state of dissociation as well as to designate the successive dissociation constants, K_i, relating to the successive proton dissociations. The total concentration of A is

$$C_\text{T} = \sum_{i=0}^{N} c_{\text{AH}_i}. \qquad (17\text{–}30)$$

Equations (17–29) and (17–30) are $N + 1$ equations in the $N + 1$ variables c_{AH_i}, $i = 0, 1, \ldots, N$, and may therefore, in principle, be solved for these variables in terms of the N dissociation constants and C_T. There are several schemes for accomplishing this, but the simplest is the successive elimination of the species other than c_{AH_0}, employing Eqs. (17–29). Thus

$$c_{AH_1} = \frac{c_{AH_0} \cdot c_{H^+}}{K_1},$$

$$c_{AH_2} = \frac{c_{AH_1} \cdot c_{H^+}}{K_2} = \frac{c_{AH_0} \cdot c_{H^+}^2}{K_1 K_2},$$

$$\vdots$$

$$c_{AH_N} = \frac{c_{AH_{N-1}} \cdot c_{H^+}}{K_N} = \frac{c_{AH_0} \cdot c_{H^+}^N}{K_1 K_2 \cdots K_N}. \tag{17–31}$$

These express each species concentration as a function of c_{AH_0}, c_{H^+}, and the individual equilibrium constants.

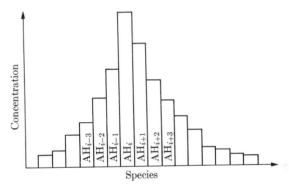

FIG. 17–4. A representative equilibrium distribution of molecular species of the component A at a particular pH.

Under any particular conditions, i.e., at a particular pH, there will be in solution a certain distribution of molecular species among all the possible kinds, AH_0 to AH_N, such that each has a particular concentration. A representative distribution is portrayed in Fig. 17–4 as an example. Taking all species into account we may compute an average or mean number of protons bound per molecule of component A in all its forms present. Such an average is precisely analogous to the case discussed for a monobasic acid in dynamic equilibrium. We designated this average as $\bar{h}$, and stated that it represented that fraction of the total component present which was associated with a proton. See Eq. (17–23). In the present case of a polybasic acid we recognize that the total concentration of component A is given by Eq. (17–30), but the total concentration of associated hydrogen ion is

$$\text{Concentration of bound } H^+ = \sum_{i=0}^{N} i c_{AH_i}. \qquad (17\text{--}32)$$

Therefore, the average number bound per molecule of A present is

$$\bar{h} = \frac{\sum_{i=0}^{N} i c_{AH_i}}{\sum_{i=0}^{N} c_{AH_i}}. \qquad (17\text{--}33)$$

Substituting in Eq. (17–33) from the appropriate Eqs. of (17–31), one obtains

$$\bar{h} = \frac{\sum_{i=0}^{N} i \kappa_i c_{H^+}^i}{\sum_{i=0}^{N} \kappa_i c_{H^+}^i}, \qquad (17\text{--}34)$$

where the κ's are defined as

$$\kappa_i = \frac{1}{K_0 K \cdots K_i} = \frac{1}{\prod_{j=0}^{i} K_j} \qquad (i = 0, \ldots, N),$$

$$\kappa_0 = K_0 \equiv 1. \qquad (17\text{--}35)$$

Equation (17–34) is our final result expressing $\bar{h}$ as a function of the hydrogen ion concentration (activity) and the products of the individual constants.

Obviously, if N becomes very large (greater than 2 or 3) the relation becomes rather complex. There exist special techniques for handling the cases for N being rather small, but in the general case for large N the detailed analysis of titration data is very difficult and virtually impossible without electronic computor techniques. In practice, $\bar{h}$ may be computed from the actual titration data, and c_{H^+} may be computed from measurements of pH, and therefore the problem resolves itself into finding the N unknown equilibrium constants that will provide a satisfactory fit of the function $\bar{h}$ to pH.

One who is versatile in handling the foregoing equations may, without great difficulty, show that the slope of the titration curve relating $\bar{h}$ to pH is

$$\frac{d\bar{h}}{d(\text{pH})} = -2.303 \, (\overline{h^2} - \bar{h}^2), \qquad (17\text{--}36)$$

where

$$\overline{h^2} = \frac{\sum_{i=0}^{N} i^2 \kappa_i c_{H^+}^i}{\sum_{i=0}^{N} \kappa_i c_{H^+}^i}.$$

The term in parenthesis of Eq. (17–36) is known in statistical terms as the variance of $\bar{h}$, which is the mean square deviation from the mean $\bar{h}$.

Thus the magnitude of the variance gives the spread in the statistical distribution of the number of protons bound per molecule. The standard deviation is the square root of the variance. The magnitude of the slope on plots of $\bar{h}$ versus pH is then proportional to the variance. From our discussions of the slope of these plots in the case of monobasic acids, a maximum slope is seen to occur at those points where pH $=$ pK_i. In the case of glycine and succinic acid, we may see from Figs. 17-2 and 17-3 that this is likewise true. These arguments may be carried over to even more complex molecules with multiple acidic groups.

17-7 Protein titration curves. As has been discussed in Chapters 5 through 7, proteins are composed of many amino acids. Even though most of the carboxyl and amino groups of these amino acids are involved in peptide bond formation, thus not being proton donors at ordinary pH's, many of the amino acid side-chains (R-groups) have functional acid groups which confer upon the proteins their charge state and significantly determine many of their properties.

Because of the rather large number of amino acid residues and functional acid groups, it may be well imagined that titration curves defining the acid-base equilibria of proteins are extraordinarily complex. The situation is often aggravated by the fact that the very process of carrying out a titration leads to subtle structural alterations in the protein. This tends to happen as the pH departs significantly from neutrality, and its occurrence suggests an unfolding of the tertiary structure to make available for titration certain acid groups not apparently accessible in the native protein.

A detailed analysis of titration data is beyond the scope of this introduction. Any analysis must be made along the lines suggested in the previous section. We illustrate some titration curves of horse hemoglobin in Fig. 17-5. Of considerable interest with this molecule as with other hemoglobins are the differences observed in the titration curve when the molecule either is or is not associated with O_2 (or CO). On association with O_2 there is a decrease of the pK of some four groups, presumably the histidine imidazolium groups closely associated with the hemes, to which O_2 becomes associated. This means that these groups become slightly stronger acids, and at a given pH would dissociate hydrogen ion to some degree when O_2 is bound, and bind hydrogen ion when O_2 becomes dissociated. This important phenomenon is intimately concerned with the circulatory transport of CO_2. (See any general textbook of biochemistry or human physiology for a description.)

Proteins are polyampholytes and, possessing both positively and negatively charged groups, bear in general a net charge. As in the case of the simpler polyampholytes, such as the amino acids, there exists some pH at which point the average algebraic charge is zero. This is known as the

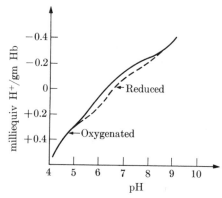

FIG. 17–5. The titration curves of horse hemoglobin. The milliequivalents of H^+ associated or dissociated per gram of hemoglobin is plotted vs. pH.

isoelectric pH, pH_I, and is characteristic for each protein under specific conditions. At pH values of less than pH_I, the protein would bear a net positive charge, whereas at pH values greater than pH_I, it bears a net negative charge. The net charge determines its direction of migration in an imposed electric field, and measurements of this "electrophoresis" serve to determine the isoelectric point. In the case of horse hemoglobin, the isoelectric point of Hb is 6.85 under prescribed conditions, whereas the isoelectric point of $Hb(O_2)_4$ or $Hb(CO)_4$ is 6.60. This change in isoelectric point is attributable to the phenomenon mentioned above of a decrease in the pK of some groups when the hemes are associated with O_2. (See Chapter 7.)

REFERENCES

1. M. EIGEN and L. DeMAEYER, "Hydrogen Bond Structure, Proton Hydration, and Proton Transfer in Aqueous Solution," *Structure of Electrolyte Solutions*, pp. 64–85, ed. by W. J. Hamer. Wiley, New York, 1959.

2. H. D. BECKEY, *Report on the 4th International Congress on Electromicroscopy*, Springer-Verlag, Berlin, 1958.

3. J. T. EDSALL and J. WYMAN, *Biophysical Chemistry*, Vol. I. Academic Press, New York, 1958.

4. R. A. ROBINSON and R. H. STOKES, *Electrolyte Solutions*. Butterworths, London, 1955.

CHAPTER 18

EQUILIBRIA ACROSS MEMBRANES

CHAPTER 18

EQUILIBRIA ACROSS MEMBRANES

18–1 Introduction. As has been indicated in Chapter 13, membranous structures are prevalent among biological systems. They not only serve as the limiting boundaries of cells but also are prominent features of much of the intracellular structure and subcellular entities such as the mitochondria. The membranous laminar structures are composed of lipids and proteins in some complex but presumably ordered array. Since the structures separate fluid phases, it is imperative for us to understand some of the properties of these membranes and the manifest effect they have in reflecting the properties of the liquid systems they separate. Through such membranes pass many chemical substances as well as energy (heat and work), but many other chemical substances appear to penetrate poorly if they penetrate at all. In this respect, the boundaries are "semipermeable," a loosely defined word implying a degree of selectivity in the penetrability of the membrane to different chemical substances. One may conceive of membranes which are ideally semipermeable, and in certain cases this ideality is approached by some artificial membranes. In a thermodynamic sense, this idealization permits one to deal with many membrane phenomena from an equilibrium viewpoint. This simplifies considerably much of the treatment and is basic to an understanding and appreciation of real living systems. In this chapter, we will develop some of the considerations concerning equilibria across membranes, utilizing our concepts of the chemical potential already developed. We reserve for Chapter 20 a discussion of the many nonequilibrium transport processes that may occur.

18–2 Osmotic pressure. Osmotic pressure is of such importance biologically it is imperative that its nature be firmly understood. With the use of the chemical potential developed in Chapters 14 and 15, the principal osmotic equations are easily derived and provide a logical basis for understanding. Consider a liquid system divided into the two subsystems, I and II, by a rigid membrane across which can exist a pressure difference and which is ideally semipermeable to the solvent alone. Let there be dissolved in the solvent S on side II a quantity of solute, A, to which the membrane is impermeable. Let the temperature of the entire system be uniform and at some constant value T.

We now consider the transfer of a mole of solvent from subsystem I to subsystem II under the conditions that they are in equilibrium with each other. The change in state may be written

$$S^{\mathrm{I}}(x_s^{\mathrm{I}},\ P^{\mathrm{I}},\ T) \rightleftharpoons S^{\mathrm{II}}(x_s^{\mathrm{II}},\ P^{\mathrm{II}},\ T), \tag{18–1}$$

with the conditions that $x_s^{\mathrm{I}} = 1$, $x_s^{\mathrm{II}} < 1$, and $P^{\mathrm{I}} \neq P^{\mathrm{II}}$, and where x_s is the mole fraction of solvent. The free energy change in terms of the chemical potentials is

$$\mu_s^{\mathrm{II}} - \mu_s^{\mathrm{I}} = \Delta G = 0. \tag{18–2}$$

Substituting the relation of the chemical potential to the mole fraction (Eq. 15–22), we obtain

$$\mu_s^0(P^{\mathrm{II}}) + RT \ln x_s^{\mathrm{II}} - \mu_s^0(P^{\mathrm{I}}) = 0, \tag{18–3}$$

where the parentheses are used to indicate a functional relation of the standard chemical potentials to the total pressure, a relation with which we must now reckon. As indicated in our discussion of the relations for the chemical potential (Section 15–4), the change in potential of a gas with change in pressure is given by $d\mu = v\, dP$ (Eq. 15–10). From the fundamental thermodynamic equations, Eq. (14–29), applied to the solvent, we may also write

$$d\mu_s = \bar{v}_s\, dP = d\mu_s^0, \tag{18–4}$$

where $\bar{v}_s$ is the molar volume of the solvent. This indicates that an increase in pressure increases the potential, increasing the potential of the system to do useful work. Our problem now is to evaluate $\mu_s^{0\mathrm{II}} - \mu_s^{0\mathrm{I}}$ in terms of the difference in pressure of these two phases at equilibrium which will satisfy Eq. (18–3). This is done by integrating Eq. (18–4) between the appropriate limits (see Appendix). Thus

$$\int_{\mu_s^{0\mathrm{I}}}^{\mu_s^{0\mathrm{II}}} d\mu_s^0 = \int_{P^{\mathrm{I}}}^{P^{\mathrm{II}}} \bar{v}_s\, dP. \tag{18–5}$$

The left-hand integral is simply $\mu_s^{0\mathrm{II}} - \mu_s^{0\mathrm{I}}$. To evaluate the right-hand integral, the functional relation between $\bar{v}_s$ and the pressure is required. For our purposes we are quite justified in assuming the liquid to be incompressible and thereby take $\bar{v}_s$ to be a constant. Integration then gives simply $\bar{v}_s(P^{\mathrm{II}} - P^{\mathrm{I}})$. Putting these results into Eq. (18–3) gives

$$\bar{v}_s(P^{\mathrm{II}} - P^{\mathrm{I}}) + RT \ln x_s^{\mathrm{II}} = 0. \tag{18–6}$$

Since $x_s^{\mathrm{II}} < 1$, the second term is negative; thus P^{II} must be greater than P^{I}. In other words, for equilibrium to exist in this system the pressure on the side of pure solvent must be less than that on the side in which the solvent contains a dissolved solute. The difference in pressure, $P^{II} - P^{I}$, is defined as the osmotic pressure, π. Thus

$$\pi = -\frac{RT}{\bar{v}_s} \ln x_s^{II}. \qquad (18\text{-}7)$$

To the extent that x_s^{II} may be taken as the activity of the solvent, this equation is an exact expression for the osmotic pressure except for our reasonable approximation that the liquid is incompressible. In its essence then the osmotic pressure is to be considered as the increase in pressure required to raise the chemical potential of the solvent of a solution to that of the pure solvent. However, we must recognize that operationally the osmotic pressure concerns only that solute to which a semipermeable membrane is ideally impermeable. (In Section 20–5 we discuss more fully the properties of nonideal semipermeable membranes.)

Since most biological systems are dilute aqueous systems wherein the total concentration of solute rarely exceed 0.4 molar, the value of x_s in Eq. (18–7) is very close to unity. For instance, in an 0.4 molar solution,

$$x_s \cong \frac{55.5}{55.5 + 0.4} = 0.9928.$$

With this in mind we are justified in making further simplifying approximations and in this way eliminate the logarithmic term of (18–7). Since $x_s = 1 - X_A$, where X_A is the total solute mole fraction as defined in Eq. (16–24), we may expand $\ln x_s$ in a power series (see Appendix), giving

$$\ln (1 - X_A) = -X_A - \frac{X_A^2}{2} - \frac{X_A^3}{3} - \cdots , \qquad (18\text{-}8)$$

and for small values of X_A we are justified in retaining only the first term. Also we have

$$X_A = \frac{n_A}{n_s + n_A} \cong \frac{n_A}{n_s}, \qquad (18\text{-}9)$$

where n_A and n_s refer to the total number of moles of solute; furthermore, since $n_s \bar{v}_s = V$, the volume, we have

$$\frac{n_A}{n_s} = \bar{v}_s \cdot C_A, \qquad (18\text{-}10)$$

whereupon Eq. (18–7) now becomes

$$\pi = RTC_A. \qquad (18\text{-}11)$$

This is the van't Hoff equation and originally was formulated empirically on the basis of his pioneer experiments. It is a very useful approximation and suitably accurate for many purposes. Deviations of experimental measurements from the relation stated by Eq. (18–11) are not generally to be found in the fact that approximations were made in the derivation. Such deviations may be conveniently expressed in terms of a power series:

$$\pi = RTC_A + \beta C_A^2 + \gamma C_A^3 + \cdots, \qquad (18\text{--}12)$$

in which the so-called virial coefficients, β, γ, . . ., are interpretable in terms of solute molecular interactions.

It is well to note here, as was done in our consideration of the vapor pressure of solvents as a function of solute concentration (Raoult's law) that x_s and consequently the total solute mole fraction $X_A = \sum_k x_k$ is determined on the basis of all species present. With solutes such as NaCl which dissociate in solution, each ionic species must be counted as a separate solute. This being the case, C_a of Eqs. (18–11) and (18–12) must represent the total concentration. In those cases in which a membrane separates two solutions rather than a solution from a pure solvent, it is obvious that the osmotic pressure difference is obtained by the difference in concentration of all species.

The osmotic pressure referred to in this development is the total osmotic pressure based upon the total concentration to which the membrane is impermeable. Colloid osmotic pressure, in general, refers to that due to large molecules and not to small solute molecules. (See Section 18–5.) In reading the scientific literature one must be certain as to which osmotic pressure an author may be referring.

Differences in osmotic pressure, reflecting differences in the chemical potential of water, are important in biological systems in determining the movement of water across membranes. Its measurement also serves as an important tool in the study of macromolecules, i.e., in the estimation of their molecular weights and investigation of intermolecular interactions.

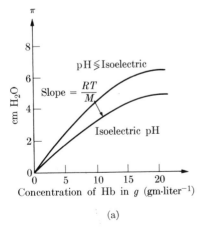
(a)

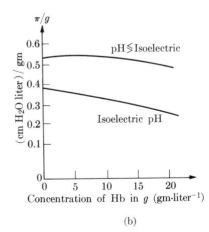
(b)

FIG. 18–1. Osmotic pressure measurements on horse hemoglobin at the isoelectric pH and at pH's greater or less than the isoelectric pH.

EQUILIBRIA ACROSS MEMBRANES

In illustration of molecular weight estimation as well as intermolecular interaction, we plot diagrammatically some data in Fig. 18–1 for horse hemoglobin under the conditions stated. In Fig. 18–1(a) the colloid osmotic pressure is plotted $vs.$ the concentration of hemoglobin measured in $\text{gm} \cdot \text{liter}^{-1}$, g. At low concentration, the experimental points would appear to be approximated by straight lines that extrapolate correctly to the origin. From Eq. (18–12) it is seen that the limiting slope at small concentrations is given by RT/M, where M is the molecular weight, since $C_a = g/M$. In this fashion, molecular weights for these large molecules may be estimated quite reliably. A more convenient plot for this purpose as well as for determining the coefficients β and γ of Eq. (18–12) is that of π/g versus g, seen in Fig. 18–1 (b). As may be ascertained, this results in the relation

$$\frac{\pi}{g} = \frac{RT}{M} + \frac{\beta g}{M^2} + \frac{\gamma g^2}{M^3} + \cdots$$

$$= \frac{RT}{M} (1 + \beta' g + \gamma' g^2 + \cdots), \tag{18–13}$$

from which it is evident that as $g \to 0$, $\pi/g \to RT/M$. Thus the ordinate intercept determines the molecular weight. From this figure we may estimate the extrapolated value of π/g to be 0.37 cm H_2O liter $\cdot$ gm^{-1}. R has a value of 0.082 liter-atm $\cdot$ $\text{degree}^{-1} \cdot \text{mole}^{-1}$, and with $T = 298°K$,

$$M = \frac{0.082 \cdot 298}{0.37} \frac{\text{atm-gm}}{\text{mole-cm } H_2O}.$$

Since 1 atm $= 760$ mm Hg and 1 mm Hg $= 1.35$ cm H_2O, we compute the molecular weight of isoelectric horse hemoglobin to be $M = 68,000$.

It is also to be noted in Fig. 18–1 that the colloid osmotic pressure appears to depend upon pH as well as upon the concentration. The explanation of this observation will be set forth in Section 18–5 where it will be seen to depend upon the fact that the molecule at other than the isoelectric point bears a net charge. Because of this net charge, one measures in actuality the colloid osmotic pressure of the protein salt and not merely the protein itself, i.e., the protein ion plus the oppositely charged counter ions.

18–3 Ionic equilibria across membranes. If a neutral solute can permeate the membrane, the equilibrium state is characterized by an equal concentration (activity) of each such solute on the two sides. If the membrane is ideally impermeable to the solute, there exists no particular relation between their concentrations on each side. However, in dealing with ionic solutes and with membranes which may be ideally semipermeable to either the cations or the anions, but not to both, some rather interesting and important relations result which have significance in considering biological membranes.

In this section we consider idealized membranes completely impermeable to charged ions of a given sign. Actually, this property is very nearly realized in certain synthetic membranes commercially fabricated from ion exchange polymers such as sulfonated polystyrene. This artificial membrane is a mesh work of cross-linked polystyrene containing a large number of sulfonic acid groups covalently bonded to the matrix. These strongly acid groups readily dissociate their protons which may then be exchanged for any other cation. Because of the high density of these covalently bonded $-SO_3^-$ groups within the structure, mobile anions from a bathing solution are repelled or excluded from entering.

Consider two solutions, I and II, of the same electrolyte solution at different concentrations separated by a membrane permeable only to the cations. The free energy of transfer of a mole of these cations, k, from I to II is then given by the electrochemical difference

$$\Delta G = \bar{\mu}_k^{II} - \bar{\mu}_k^{I}. \tag{18-14}$$

At equilibrium, of course, $\Delta G = 0$. Utilizing our expression for the electrochemical potential (Eq. 15-23), we obtain

$$\mu_k^0 + RT \ln c_k^{I} + z_k F \psi^{I} = \mu_k^0 + RT \ln c_k^{II} + z_k F \psi^{II}. \tag{18-15}$$

Solving for the electrical potential difference gives

$$\psi^{II} - \psi^{I} = \frac{RT}{z_k F} \ln \frac{c_k^{I}}{c_k^{II}}, \tag{18-16}$$

showing that the electrical potential difference is related to the logarithm of the ratio of the two concentrations. If $c_k^{I} \neq c_k^{II}$, then a potential difference must exist across the membrane. It is to be noted that for a cation exchange membrane, in which case z_k is positive, the electrical potential is higher on the more dilute side of the membrane. The situation is reversed for anion exchange membranes, for z_k is then negative.

An electrical potential difference between two regions of space, such as across our membrane, is always the result of a spatial displacement of electrical charge from a uniform distribution. If $c_k^{I} > c_k^{II}$ and $\Delta \psi = 0$, there would be a tendency for the ion k to diffuse across the membrane from I to II. However, since the ion of opposite charge is restricted from diffusing, this can occur only to the extent whereby the slight excess charge appearing in II gives rise to an electrical potential ($\Delta \psi \neq 0$) opposing further diffusion. Thus equilibrium is attained. In each phase, I and II, we still expect the law of electrical neutrality, $\sum z_k c_k = 0$, to be valid, because operationally, the difference or displacement of charge that occurs cannot be detected by any analytical means, and is manifest only as an electrical potential difference.

Equation (18–16) forms the theoretical basis of one of the commonest electrochemical measurements made, namely, that of pH. Certain glasses of specified composition, when formed into thin membranes, are virtually ideally semipermeable to H^+, being only slightly permeable to the alkali metal ions. In practice, the glass membrane divides two solutions, and it is the potential across this membrane whose magnitude is indicative of the pH. On one side is maintained a reference solution which together with its contained electrode and the glass membrane comprises the "glass electrode." This assembly is then immersed either in a solution of a standard buffer whose pH serves as a reference or in a solution whose pH it is desired to measure. Necessarily another electrode must make contact with this solution also to complete the electrical circuit, and the potential difference between the two electrodes is measured by a suitable potential measuring instrument. This reference electrode is generally of a kind that is self-contained to make it independent of the composition of the solution and makes contact with this solution at a "liquid junction." It is here that ambiguity arises in the actual measurement of pH, and it is here that there is the thermodynamic uncertainty in the very definition of pH, for this junction wherein there is mixing of two solutions of different compositions is not at equilibrium. To evaluate the electrical potential arising at this point requires nonthermodynamic considerations, which will be discussed in Section 19–6. Suffice it to say here that all the potentials arising in the circuit are constant at a given constant temperature and are not dependent upon the composition of the solutions being measured except that across the glass membrane, E_m, and that arising at the "liquid junction," E_L. Lumping all the potentials which are constants into a single term designated E_0, a measured potential between the two electrodes as illustrated in Fig. 18–2 is given by

$$E = E_0 + E_L - \frac{RT}{F} \ln a_H^{II}, \qquad (18\text{--}17)$$

where superscript II refers to the solution in which the electrodes are immersed. In its essence a pH measurement is a comparison of a measured value of E when II is unknown with a measured value of E when II consists of a standard buffer. Designating these two measurements as E^u and E^s respectively, we formulate the difference as

$$E^u - E^s = E_L^u - E_L^s + \frac{RT}{F} \ln \frac{a_H^{II_s}}{a_H^{II_u}} \qquad (18\text{--}18)$$

$$= E_L^u - E_L^s + 2.3 \frac{RT}{F} (\text{pH}_u - \text{pH}_s), \qquad (18\text{--}19)$$

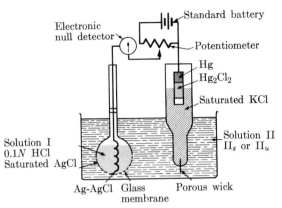

FIG. 18–2. Diagrammatic sketch illustrating the use of a semipermeable glass membrane, the "glass electrode" for the electrometric measurement of pH.

showing that this difference is directly related to the difference in pH if $E_L^u - E_L^s$ may be assumed zero. This assumption is probably a well justified one under the circumstance that a concentrated KCl solution is used, a justification which is established in Section 19–6. The coefficient $2.3RT/F$ has a value of about 0.060 volt at 25°C and therefore

$$E^u - E^s = 0.060 \ (\text{pH}_u - \text{pH}_s). \qquad (18\text{–}20)$$

In this manner, any unknown solution may be compared to some standard pH buffer solution, forming an indispensable means of measuring this important variable, pH.

18–4 The Gibbs-Donnan equilibrium. Frequent mention has been made in previous sections about a requirement of electrical neutrality which states that in a measurable volume, the number of positive charges and negative charges must be equal. If certain molecules bearing a net charge are confined to a given region, such as by a semipermeable membrane or by being covalently or otherwise linked to a structural matrix as in the case of an ion exchange resin, whereas other ionic constituents are freely mobile, then some interesting and important relations are obtained at equilibrium. These relations are a consequence of, on the one hand, the restraint imposed on the mobile ions by the "fixed" charges due to electrical attractive forces (electrical neutrality) and, on the other hand, the requirement of equality of the electrochemical potential for each of the mobile ionic substances throughout the system at equilibrium.

Let us consider two solutions, I and II, of a simple uni-univalent electrolyte, CA. Solution II contains, in addition to this simple salt, a quantity of protein salt (a salt such as the sodium proteinate or the protein hydrochloride) at concentration, c_p, the protein moiety possessing a net charge,

z_p. The two solutions are separated by a membrane permeable to solvent as well as to the simple ions, but impermeable to the protein. In this manner, the protein is confined to solution II and, bearing a net charge, can be expected to lead to an unequal distribution of the simple ions. We assume that an appropriate hydrostatic pressure difference exists such that there is equality of the chemical potential of the solvent between I and II (osmotic equilibrium). Equilibrium of the simple electrolyte, CA, is obtained when the free energy of transfer of a quantity from I to II is zero, namely,

$$CA^I \rightleftharpoons CA^{II}, \quad \Delta G = 0. \tag{18-21}$$

In terms of the chemical potential

$$\mu_{CA}^I = \mu_{CA}^{II}, \tag{18-22}$$

which, with the use of expressions like Eq. (15–19), gives

$$\mu_{CA}^{0I} + RT \ln c_C^I \cdot c_A^I = \mu_{CA}^{0II} + RT \ln c_C^{II} \cdot c_A^{II}. \tag{18-23}$$

Since $\mu_{CA}^{0I} = \mu_{CA}^{0II}$, ignoring the small effect of pressure difference on the standard potentials of salts, it follows that

$$c_C^I \cdot c_A^I = c_C^{II} \cdot c_A^{II}, \tag{18-24}$$

or

$$\frac{c_C^I}{c_C^{II}} = \frac{c_A^{II}}{c_A^I} \equiv r, \tag{18-25}$$

which defines the Gibbs-Donnan ratio, r.

In solution I, electrical neutrality requires that

$$c_C^I = c_A^I \tag{18-26}$$

and in solution II that

$$c_C^{II} = c_A^{II} - z_p c_p, \tag{18-27}$$

neglecting the contribution of H^+ and OH^- as quantitatively insignificant at reasonably neutral pH's. We divide Eq. (18–27) by c_C^I or c_A^I, which are equal according to Eq. (18–26), in order to obtain

$$\frac{c_C^{II}}{c_C^I} = \frac{c_A^{II}}{c_A^I} - \frac{z_p c_p}{c_A^I}, \tag{18-28}$$

which, with Eq. (18–25), gives

$$\frac{1}{r} = r - \frac{z_p c_p}{c_A^I}. \tag{18-29}$$

Rearranging gives

$$r^2 - \left(\frac{z_p c_p}{c_A^I}\right) r - 1 = 0. \tag{18–30}$$

This is a quadratic equation in r which may be solved in the usual manner:

$$r = \frac{z_p c_p}{2c_A^I} + \left[\left(\frac{z_p c_p}{2c_A^I}\right)^2 + 1\right]^{1/2}. \tag{18–31}$$

We select the positive root because the square root term is always larger than the first term, and had we selected the negative root, negative values for r would result, a situation physically unreal. This equation gives the ratio r in terms of the "equivalent" or charge concentration of protein, $z_p c_p$, and the electrolyte concentration in solution I.

It is evident that as $z_p c_p$ approaches zero, either by z_p going to zero at the isoelectric point or by c_p going to zero by dilution, the value of r approaches unity, as would be expected, since it indicates that electrolytes are uniformly distributed between the two solutions in the absence of any restrained charge. It is evident that the same is true for large values of c_A^I relative to $z_p c_p$. When $z_p c_p \ll c_A^I$, or rather when $(z_p c_p / 2 c_A^I)^2 \ll 1$, then the value of r is approximated by

$$r \cong 1 + \frac{z_p c_p}{2c_A^I}, \tag{18–32}$$

which is a useful approximation for many purposes.

One may deduce from the above development that if z_p is negative, $r < 1$ and thus $c_C^{II} > c_A^I < c_A^I$. That is, the presence of negatively charged protein leads to an increase in the simple cation concentration and a decrease in the simple anion concentration compared to that present in solution I. The inverse situation prevails in the case when z_p is positive. It is also evident that this nonuniform distribution as represented by $r \neq 1$ is independent of the manner in which the restrained charge is actually restrained, whether by a membrane confining it to a specific region, or by being part of the matrix of a gel or other structure.

It should be noted that the above relations were derived for the case of uni-univalent simple electrolytes. For polyvalent electrolytes the mathematics, as well as the notation, become a little more complicated. It is, nevertheless, relatively easy to show that in the general case,

$$r \equiv (c_k^I / c_k^{II})^{I/z_k}, \tag{18–33}$$

where c_k with either superscript refers to the concentration of the kth ion species whose charge is z_k. Also, it should be noted that if there is more than one electrolyte component in the system, relationships of Eq. (18–33) obtain for each species separately.

From our knowledge of the electrochemical potential and the fact that the distribution ratio r, derived above, is an equilibrium ratio, we may surmise that between the two regions, I and II, there must exist an electrical potential difference. From Eq. (18–16) we see that

$$\psi^{II} - \psi^{I} = \frac{RT}{F} \ln \left(\frac{c_k^{I}}{c_k^{II}} \right)^{1/z_k} = \frac{RT}{F} \ln r, \qquad (18\text{–}34)$$

showing that the electrical potential difference is a linear function of the logarithm of r, the Gibbs-Donnan ratio.

18–5 Colloid osmotic pressure. We noted in Fig. 18–1 that the measured osmotic pressure for hemoglobin was somewhat larger at a given concentration for the nonisoelectric molecules than for the isoelectric ones. This observation, together with our present knowledge of nonuniform distribution of small electrolytes in such cases prompts us to ask whether an explanation may not lie in a possible nonuniform distribution of ionic species on the two sides of the boundary associated with given ratios of distribution for each ionic species. Indeed, we may easily show this to be true, and for simplicity we employ the same model system as used in the previous section, namely, a simple uni-univalent electrolyte solution I and II, solution II containing, in addition, a protein salt with net charge z_p at a concentration c_p. The two solutions are separated by a membrane permeable to the simple electrolyte and solvent but impermeable to the protein. At equilibrium, the osmotic pressure is properly related to the difference in total molar concentration on each side. The total concentration in solution I is

$$C_T^{I} = c_C^{I} + c_A^{I}, \qquad (18\text{–}35)$$

and that in solution II is

$$C_T^{II} = c_C^{II} + c_A^{II} + c_p. \qquad (18\text{–}36)$$

The difference in total concentration is given by

$$\begin{aligned} \Delta C_T &= C_T^{II} - C_T^{I} \\ &= c_C^{II} + c_A^{II} + c_p - c_C^{I} - c_A^{I}. \end{aligned} \qquad (18\text{–}37)$$

Employing the equations of electrical neutrality, (18–26) and (18–27), we may substitute for c_C^{II} and c_C^{I} in Eq. (18–37) to give

$$\Delta C = 2c_A^{II} + (1 - z_p)c_p - 2c_A^{I}. \qquad (18\text{–}38)$$

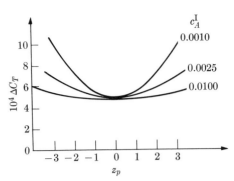

FIG. 18–3. Plot of Eq. (18–40) utilizing values of r computed from Eq. (18–31) at differing values of c_A^I as indicated, and at a constant value of $c_p = 0.0005$ molar of a hypothetical protein.

Dividing both sides by $2c_A^I$, we obtain

$$\frac{\Delta C_T}{2c_A^I} = \frac{c_A^{II}}{c_A^I} + \frac{(1 - z_p)c_p}{2c_A^I} - 1 \qquad (18\text{--}39)$$

or

$$\Delta C_T = (r - 1)2c_A^I + (1 - z_p)c_p. \qquad (18\text{--}40)$$

From Eq. (18–40) together with Eq. (18–31) for r, we may deduce the following: When $z_p = 0$, r is 1; therefore, the first term on the right-hand side of Eq. (18–40) vanishes and the last reduces to c_p, giving $\Delta C_T = c_p$, i.e., this total concentration difference is due to the protein only, for the electrolyte is uniformly distributed. When $z_p > 0$, with the protein then bearing a net positive charge (the acid side of the isoelectric point), then $r > 1$, making the first term positive, although, in the second term, c_p is multiplied by a number <1. It may be calculated that the net effect in any case is an increase in ΔC_T. The same conclusion is deducible with $z_p < 0$, the pH being on the alkaline side of the isoelectric point of the protein. The function ΔC_T, for several values of c_A^I, is plotted against z_p at a given constant value of c_p in Fig. 18–3. Here it is evident that our deductions are correct and that the measured osmotic pressure of protein in salt solution is increased on each side of the isoelectric point, due to nonuniform equilibrium distribution of total simple electrolytes. In practice, this "error" is avoided by making the measurements near the isoelectric pH and/or by employing sufficiently high salt concentrations to make r near unity.

REFERENCES

1. E. A. GUGGENHEIM, *Thermodynamics*. Interscience, New York, 1949.

2. S. GLASSTONE, *Textbook of Physical Chemistry*. D. van Nostrand, Princeton, 1946.

3. E. J. COHN and J. T. EDSALL, *Proteins, Amino Acids and Peptides*. Reinhold, New York, 1943.

4. F. H. JOHNSON, H. EYRING, and M. J. POLISSAR, *Kinetic Bases of Molecular Biology*. Wiley, New York, 1954.

5. R. HÖBER, *Physical Chemistry of Cells and Tissues*. Blakiston, Philadelphia, 1946, also Dover, New York.

CHAPTER 19

NONEQUILIBRIUM PROCESSES—DIFFUSION

19-1 INTRODUCTION
Free energy decrease in approach to equilibrium

19-2 MOLECULAR BASIS OF DIFFUSION PROCESSES
Equilibria as dynamic states
Continued random molecular motion
Energy and mass transfer

19-3 THERMODYNAMIC FORCES
Force as negative gradient of potential energy
One *vs.* three dimensions
Chemical potential gradient
Electrical potential gradient
Thermal gradients
Pressure gradients

19-4 FRICTIONAL OR RESISTIVE FORCES; VISCOSITY
Dissipation of energy as heat
Resistive force proportional to velocity
Viscosity of medium
Size and shape of moving particles
Stokes-Einstein relation for sphere
Frictional coefficient, f
Mobility, ω_i

19-5 EQUATIONS OF TRANSPORT
Velocity $\sim$ force
Flux (J) = velocity $\cdot$ concentration
Simple diffusion from chemical potential gradients
Diffusion coefficient, D_i
Fick's law of diffusion
Tabulated diffusion coefficients

19-6 DIFFUSION OF ELECTROLYTES
Electrical potential gradients associated with
    concentration gradients
General case
Case of simple uni-univalent salt
Limiting conductances
Protonic jumps
Ionic hydration
Near-equal mobility of K^+ and Cl^-, liquid junctions

287

CHAPTER 19

NONEQUILIBRIUM PROCESS—DIFFUSION

19-1 Introduction. In our discussion of physical-chemical principles involved in the function of biological systems in the Chapters 14 through 18, we have restricted ourselves to considerations of systems at equilibrium. We have dealt with equilibrium (reversible) processes and we have repeatedly exploited the criterion that for such a process at a constant temperature and pressure, the free energy change is zero; that is, $\Delta G = 0$, and T, $P = $ constant. In using this condition we found that the chemical potential function was very useful and convenient. We have also learned that these equilibrium processes are idealized processes because of the very fact that they are at equilibrium, a state requiring, in any mathematical sense, an infinite time to achieve. Real processes or "natural processes," on the other hand, are those that go on about us, that go on continually in biological systems and are always attended by a free energy decrease for the system. In this chapter we wish to exploit this fact and show how this leads us to the common laws of diffusion.

19-2 Molecular basis of diffusion processes. Equilibrium is a state attended by no further change in the system with time, together with a minimum in the free energy. However, as discussed in Section 15-3, this does not imply that molecular motions cease, nor even that reactions or processes are "frozen," but only that no *net* changes occur. In other words, equilibrium of molecular systems is a dynamic one, and there is continual molecular motion. This motion, random in nature, is related to the kinetic energy of the molecules.

As may be imagined, this random molecular motion leads to continual molecular collisions. Momentum or kinetic energy is being continually passed from one molecule to another. It is this fact alone that leads to thermal equilibration in an isolated system, or in any case permits heat conduction and transfer. It is just this random motion that, given sufficient time for an isolated system, always leads to a uniformity in the distribution of molecules in a given phase throughout its volume and a maximum in the entropy function. This random motion thus accounts for mass transfer as well. It is our problem here to formulate a quantitative description of this transfer in terms of the factors involved, i.e., factors that are representative of the average behavior of a large population of molecules. The kinetic theory of gases and liquids describing this molecular motion in terms of mechanical principles (based on mass, velocity, momentum, kinetic energy, potential energy, etc.) is an entire field unto itself. This includes the theory of Brownian motion, a very important concept in the relation to an understanding of the molecular mechanism in diffusion and transport. A brief discussion of kinetic theory especially as it pertains to chemical reactions is to be found in Sections 22–3, 22–6, and 22–7. It is difficult to do this field justice here in this brief introduction; the interested reader is referred to Hildebrand for a rather good but elementary discussion of these matters.

19–3 Thermodynamic forces. As has been pointed out in Chapters 3 and 15, a force operating through a distance represents an energy, and this may be formulated in rather general terms as

$$dE = -F_x \, dx, \qquad (19\text{--}1)$$

where dE represents an infinitesimal change in energy of the system as a result of an infinitesimal displacement, dx, at a force, F_x, operating in the x-direction. If the force and the displacement are in the same direction, say toward increasing values of x, then the energy of the system decreases, a natural process. If the force F_x is opposing the displacement, i.e., if it has a sign opposite to dx, then work must be done on the system to overcome this force, and the energy is consequently increased. The energy E is a potential energy in this formulation, and the force represents the rate of decrease in potential energy with respect to distance in that direction, as may be seen by rewriting Eq. (19–1) as

$$F_x = -\frac{dE}{dx}. \qquad (19\text{--}2)$$

The derivative dE/dx is called the gradient of E in the x-direction. Attention is directed to the example illustrated in Section 15–2. In particular the component of force in the x-direction given by Eq. (15–4) is $-2kmgx$, whereas the vertical component of force is $-mg$. In general for three-dimensional space there exists components of the force in each direction. The resultant force is the vector sum of all these components and would be properly written

$$\mathbf{F} = \mathbf{F}_x + \mathbf{F}_y + \mathbf{F}_z = \mathbf{i}F_x + \mathbf{j}F_y + \mathbf{k}F_z$$

$$= \mathbf{i}\frac{\partial E}{\partial x} + \mathbf{j}\frac{\partial E}{\partial y} + \mathbf{k}\frac{\partial E}{\partial z} = \text{grad } E, \qquad (19\text{--}3)$$

where $\mathbf{i}$, $\mathbf{j}$, and $\mathbf{k}$ are the unit vectors along the x-, y-, and z-coordinates and the last relation defines the grad operator. In this introduction we shall confine our discussion to one dimension and thereby avoid the necessity of using vector notation, realizing that those readers familiar with vector analysis will have no difficulty in translating to the more general three-dimensional case.

Consider a solution system in which, at a given initial time there exists a nonuniform distribution of a solute component in the x-direction. This nonuniformity in concentration is, of course, reflected in a nonuniformity of chemical potential of the components. Since c_i is some function of x, which we note by writing $c_i(x)$, then so must be the chemical potential. The two are related by

$$\mu_i(x) = \mu_i^0 + RT \ln c_i(x). \tag{19-4}$$

The degree to which the chemical potential of component i changes with respect to distance, i.e., its gradient, comprises a force operating on this component. We write, as in Eq. (19-2),

$$F_{ix} = -\frac{d\mu_i}{dx}. \tag{19-5}$$

In Fig. 19-1 is plotted the concentration of a solute as a function of the x-coordinate as well as its chemical potential. The slope of the chemical potential curve is, of course, $d\mu_i/dx$, which is seen by Eq. (19-5) to be negative or downward to the right. This gives a positive force to the right, and thus the force acts to decrease the potential or lower the concentration on the left. Solute will move from left to right.

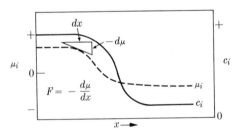

Fig. 19-1. The force is a negative gradient of the chemical potential of i whose concentration, c_i, is distributed in the x dimension as indicated. See text for discussion.

A gradient in the chemical potential of a component is only one example of a thermodynamic force. An electrical force may operate on charged ionic species to bring about translational movement. If the electrical potential is ψ, its negative gradient along the x-coordinate is $-(d\psi/dx)$; and this, operating upon a charged particle with positive charge, q, gives a force

$$F_{ex} = -q\frac{d\psi}{dx}. \tag{19-6}$$

The electrical force operating on a mole of ionic particles with charge

$z_i\mathbf{F}$ (z_i bearing the algebraic sign of the charge), is

$$F_{ex} = -z_i\mathbf{F}\,\frac{d\psi}{dx}\,. \qquad (19\text{--}7)$$

In general, then, the forces operating upon electrolytes are both chemical potential gradients and electrical potential gradients. We may write

$$F_{kx} = -\frac{d\mu_k}{dx} - z_k\mathbf{F}\,\frac{d\psi}{dx} = -\frac{d\bar{\mu}_k}{dx}\,, \qquad (19\text{--}8)$$

where the last term is seen to be the gradient of the electrochemical potential for an ionic species k.

Gradients of other potential functions or gradients of the variables proportional to these potential functions may likewise comprise thermodynamic forces. In this respect a thermal gradient $-(dT/dx)$ is a force leading to heat flow, and a pressure gradient $-(dP/dx)$ is a force which on existing in a fluid or gas leads to mass flow. Both of these gradients comprise a gradient of the Gibbs free energy in a system.

These are then some of the forces termed thermodynamic forces. They play a central role in determining the direction and rate of progress of nonequilibrium processes.

19–4 Frictional or resistive forces; viscosity. In contrast to motion in free space or vacuum, motion of molecules in a gas or liquid involves resistive or frictional forces. According to Newton's second law of motion, a body in vacuum subjected to a force experiences an acceleration, a, inversely proportional to its mass, m. Thus, $a = F/m$. However, a gas or liquid is composed of molecules. A particle moving in such a medium must cause displacement and separation of these interacting molecules. Force is required, and the net result is an expenditure of energy. In other words, when the path of a particle involves the separation of two or more molecules, work is done by the particle on these two or more molecules. This work or energy expenditure by the particle is not recovered by the particle when the two or more molecules again return to their average intermolecular distances. Instead, this work of separation is dissipated as heat characteristic of irreversible processes (see Section 15–4). This is the nature of frictional or resistive forces encountered by particles moving in a gas or liquid system, wherein the rate of energy dissipation by a moving particle is proportional to its velocity.

One speaks of this resistive force as a frictional force, and reasons that it is not only a property of the particular medium through which the particle is moving but also dependent upon the particle size and shape. The larger the size, the greater the resistance encountered. The inherent property of the medium which determines the friction force is called the viscosity and is related, in part, to the degree of molecular interaction and molecular size and shape. Ideal noninteracting molecules show no viscosity, a situation curiously enough observed in liquid helium II at 2°K. Liquids of elongated molecules are generally more viscous than those composed of comparable spherical molecules. The viscosities of some common liquids appear in Table 4–1.

Since the frictional force encountered by a particle moving in a viscous medium is proportional to the velocity of the particle, it is evident that a driving force acting on the particle cannot lead to its continual acceleration. The particle will reach a velocity such that the frictional force opposing the motion is of the same magnitude as the driving force. Therefore, given a constant driving force, the velocity of motion of a particle in a viscous medium will be a constant. This is a familiar fact to anyone who has observed a stone or spherical object falling through water; the constant driving force is, of course, that of the gravitational field. A free-falling body in air falls much more rapidly, but nevertheless it will reach a constant velocity if the fall is long enough.

Stokes, in 1850, derived a theoretical expression for the frictional force encountered by a sphere moving with a given velocity in a viscous medium. It is interesting to state the relation here, for although the derivation is rather complicated, the result is simple. It is

$$\mathbf{F}_f = -6\pi r \eta \mathbf{v}, \qquad (19\text{–}9)$$

where $\mathbf{F}_f$ is the opposing frictional force, η is the viscosity of the medium, and $\mathbf{v}$ is the velocity of the sphere having radius r. The factor $6\pi r \eta$ is the frictional coefficient, f, relating the velocity to a frictional force. This expression has been exploited in the measurement of viscosity, and in the study of macromolecules it has been used to estimate molecular radii. It may be appreciated that if the macromolecule is a sphere, estimations of its radius and its density permit an estimation of its molecular weight.

As will be more evident in the following section, it is often convenient to invert the frictional coefficient and speak instead of a mobility, ω:

$$\omega = 1/f. \qquad (19\text{–}10)$$

Since an opposing frictional force, $\mathbf{F}_f$, encountered by a steadily moving particle is equal in magnitude but opposite in direction to a driving force, $\mathbf{F}_d$, that is, $\mathbf{F}_f = \mathbf{F}_d$, we have

$$\mathbf{v} = \omega \mathbf{F}_d. \qquad (19\text{–}11)$$

The coefficient ω then may be interpreted as the velocity the particle assumes when unit driving force is acting upon it.

19–5 Equations of transport. In the foregoing two sections, we have indicated the nature of thermodynamic forces and have pointed out that the velocity of a particle in a viscous medium is proportional to the forces acting on it, the proportionality coefficient being the mobility, ω. Consider now a large number of molecules of substance, i, moving with an average velocity, $\mathbf{v}_i$, as a result of the action of some thermodynamic force $\mathbf{F}_i$. In one dimension the number of such molecules crossing an imagined plane of unit area (1 cm^2) perpendicular to the direction of motion, in unit time (1 sec) is related not only to their average velocity but also to the number present per unit volume, i.e. the concentration. Expressing the concentration in moles $\cdot$ cm^{-3}, the number of moles crossing this unit area per second is

$$J_i = c_i v_i, \tag{19–12}$$

when J_i is called the flux and has the dimensions of moles $\cdot$ cm$^{-2} \cdot$ sec^{-1}. Substituting for the velocity in terms of the force and mobility gives

$$J_i = \omega_i c_i F_i. \tag{19–13}$$

For a neutral uncharged solute component, i, we will assume that there exists only a chemical potential gradient in the one dimension, all other forces such as thermal, gravitational, and the like being absent. F_i is then given by Eq. (19–5) giving for (19–13)

$$J_i = -\omega_i c_i \frac{d\mu_i}{dx}. \tag{19–14}$$

Now μ_i bears a relation to the concentration, c_i, given by Eq. (19–4) or (15–19) valid at every point in space.* Differentiating, we obtain

$$\frac{d\mu_i}{dx} = \frac{d(\mu_i^0 + RT \ln c_i)}{dx} = \frac{RT}{c_i} \frac{dc_i}{dx}, \tag{19–15}$$

and substituting in Eq. (19–14) gives the result

$$J_i = -\omega_i RT \frac{dc_i}{dx}. \tag{19–16}$$

The quantity $\omega_i RT$ is defined as the diffusion coefficient D_i, that is $D_i = \omega_i RT$, and as may be ascertained has the dimensions of cm$^2 \cdot$ sec^{-1}. Thus

$$J_i = -D_i \frac{dc_i}{dx}, \tag{19–17}$$

---

* It should be noted that these equations for the chemical potential are independent of the particular concentration units employed since any differences are accountable in terms of the standard reference potential μ_i^0.

TABLE 19-1

APPROXIMATE DIFFUSION COEFFICIENTS OF SOME
REPRESENTATIVE COMPOUNDS IN AQUEOUS SOLUTION

Substance	Concentration	Temperature, °C	Diffusion coefficient, cm²/sec
Glycine*	Infinite dilution	20	$9.5 \cdot 10^{-6}$
Leu. Gly. Gly.	Infinite dilution	20	$4.6 \cdot 10^{-6}$
Ribonuclease	Infinite dilution	20	$10.2 \cdot 10^{-7}$
Human serum albumin	Infinite dilution	20	$6.1 \cdot 10^{-7}$
Human hemoglobin	Infinite dilution	20	$6.8 \cdot 10^{-7}$
Tobacco mosaic virus	Infinite dilution	20	$3.0 \cdot 10^{-8}$

* For a more exact value for glycine as well as an excellent description of the technique employed in measuring coefficients, the interested reader is referred to Thompson and Oncley (See Ref. 4).

an expression known as Fick's law of diffusion, first derived empirically on the basis of his experimental observations.

The diffusion coefficient, D_i, and, of course, the mobility, ω_i, are a characteristic property of the molecular species under given particular conditions. In it are contained not only the size and shape factors of the molecule, but also the properties of the medium (the viscosity) through which diffusion is occurring. There is generally some dependency of the magnitude of this coefficient on the concentration; this reflects the fact that molecular interactions exist. For this reason tabulated values of diffusion coefficients are often those obtained by extrapolation of experimental results to infinite dilution for a given solvent at a particular temperature. In Table 19-1 are tabulated such extrapolated values for a few compounds of interest. As noted in Chapter 6, the diffusion coefficients of proteins are of the order of 10^{-6} to 10^{-7} cm² · sec^{-1}, an order of magnitude or more smaller than simpler small molecules such as glycine. This reflects their differences in size.

19-6 Diffusion of electrolytes. In dealing with the motion of electrolytes, we must recognize that they are electrically charged species. Other than this, there is no fundamental distinction to be considered in their diffusion. We assume a system in which the only forces present are electrochemical potential gradients. From Eqs. (19-14) and (15-23), we may write for the flux of the kth ionic species:

$$J_k = -\omega_k c_k \frac{d\bar{\mu}_k}{dx} = -\omega_k c_k \left[\frac{d\mu_k}{dx} + z_k F \frac{d\psi}{dx} \right]. \qquad (19\text{-}20)$$

Differentiating the chemical potential term as before, we obtain

$$J_k = -\omega_k c_k \left[\frac{RT}{c_k} \frac{dc_k}{dx} + z_k F \frac{d\psi}{dx} \right]. \qquad (19\text{-}21)$$

Rearranging gives

$$J_k = -\omega_k RT \left[\frac{dc_k}{dx} + \frac{z_c c_k F}{RT} \frac{d\psi}{dx} \right], \qquad (19\text{-}22)$$

which shows that the flux of an ionic species is determined by both its concentration gradient and an electrical potential gradient. The electrical potential gradient may exist purely as a result of diffusion of the electrolyte or it may be imposed on the system from an external source with the use of appropriate electrodes.

For the case of free diffusion of an electrolyte not subjected to an externally imposed electrical potential field, there can be no electric current flow, i.e. no net charge flow, for otherwise charges would accumulate in one part of the system. Stated mathematically, this means that for a binary electrolyte,

$$z_+ J_+ + z_- J_- = 0 \qquad \text{(for all values of } x\text{)}, \qquad (19\text{-}23)$$

or for a mixture of electrolytes,

$$\sum z_k J_k = 0 \qquad \text{(for all values of } x\text{)}. \qquad (19\text{-}24)$$

For simplicity, let us consider the binary electrolyte. Using Eqs. (19–22) and (19–23), we may write

$$z_+ \omega_+ \frac{dc_+}{dx} + \frac{\omega_+ z_+^2 c_+ F}{RT} \frac{d\psi}{dx} + z_- \omega_- \frac{dc_-}{dx} + \frac{\omega_- z_-^2 c_- F}{RT} \frac{d\psi}{dx} = 0. \qquad (19\text{-}25)$$

We may recall that for a binary electrolyte, the concentration, c_k, of each ionic species is related to the salt concentration, c, by $c_k = \nu_k c$ where ν_k is the stoichiometric number of the ion. Since the ν's are constants, we have $dc_k = \nu_k \, dc$. Substituting these relations in Eq. (19–25) and rearranging to solve for $d\psi/dk$, one obtains

$$\frac{d\psi}{dx} = \frac{RT}{F} \left[\frac{z_+ \nu_+ \omega_+ + z_- \nu_- \omega_-}{z_+^2 \nu_+ \omega_+ + z_-^2 \nu_- \omega_-} \right] \frac{1}{c} \frac{dc}{dx} \qquad (19\text{-}26)$$

or

$$\frac{d\psi}{dx} = \frac{RT}{F} \left[\frac{z_+ \nu_+ \omega_+ + z_- \nu_- \omega_-}{z_+^2 \nu_+ \omega_+ + z_-^2 \nu_- \omega_-} \right] \frac{d \ln c}{dx}. \qquad (19\text{-}27)$$

TABLE 19–2

LIMITING CONDUCTANCES OF SOME IONS IN
AQUEOUS SOLUTION AT 25°C*

Ion	λ_0	Ion	λ_0	Ion	λ_0
H^+	349.8	Be^{2+}	45	OH^-	198.6
Li^+	38.7	Mg^{2+}	53.0	F^-	55.4
Na^+	50.1	Ca^{2+}	59.5	Cl^-	76.4
K^+	73.5	Sr^{2+}	59.4	Br^-	78.1
Rb^+	77.8	Ba^{2+}	63.6	I^-	76.8
Cs^+	77.2			Acetate$^-$	40.9
				SO_4^{2-}	80.0

* Taken as compiled by Robinson and Stokes (see Ref. 1, p. 452).

These equations show that in general, one expects some electrical potential gradient to be associated with the simple diffusion of an electrolyte. Only if the coefficient in brackets were zero, namely if

$$z_+\nu_+\omega_+ + z_-\nu_-\omega_- = 0, \qquad (19\text{--}28)$$

would there be no potential gradient associated with a concentration gradient.

For a simple uni-univalent electrolyte where $z_+ = 1$, $z_- = -1$, and $\nu_+ = \nu_- = 1$, Eq. (19–27) reduces to

$$\frac{d\psi}{dx} = -\frac{RT}{F}\left[\frac{\omega_+ - \omega_-}{\omega_+ + \omega_-}\right]\frac{d\ln c}{dx}. \qquad (19\text{--}29)$$

Here one may more easily ascertain the following: If the mobility of the cation ω_+ is larger than that of the anion ω_-, that is, $\omega_+ > \omega_-$, then the resulting electrical potential gradient has the opposite sign of the concentration gradient or, in other words, opposes the motion of the cation. If $\omega_- > \omega_+$, then the resulting electrical potential gradient has the same sign as the concentration gradient and tends to oppose the motion of the anion. In effect, what exists in a diffusing system is a slight displacement of charge; the more mobile charge leads the less mobile by a slight amount just sufficient enough to give rise to the potential gradient observed. The diffusion of cation and anion are coupled together in this fashion by their electrical attraction for each other or manifestly through the electrical potential gradient; the more mobile leads and the resultant electrical potential gradient acts as an additional force on the less mobile.

An idea of the relative mobilities of some common ions of biological importance may be gained from the data collected in Table 19–2. Here are tabulated the limiting equivalent conductances of these ions, the limiting equivalent conductance being directly proportional to the mobility of the ion in infinitely dilute solutions. Conductance is an electrical unit, the reciprocal of resistance, and has therefore the dimensions of ohm^{-1}. (An ohm is a joule $\cdot$ sec $\cdot$ $coul^{-2}$.) The specific conductance, the conductance of a cube of the solution one centimeter on each side, would then have the dimensions of $ohm^{-1} \cdot cm^{-1}$. The equivalent conductance, λ (the word "equivalent" refers to a gram equivalent of charge), is the specific conductance per gram equivalent per cubic centimeter, and thus λ has the dimensions of $cm^{-2} \cdot ohm^{-1} \cdot equiv^{-1}$. The word "limiting" of limiting conductance λ_0 refers to the fact that the data obtained on dilute solutions has been extrapolated to infinite dilution where, due to the absence of interionic interactions, the individual ions would behave ideally. The relation between mobility and equivalent conductance of an ion may be deduced to be

$$\omega_i = \frac{N}{10^7 F^2} \frac{\lambda_i}{|z_i|} , \qquad (19\text{--}30)$$

where N is Avogadro's number and $|z_i|$ refers to the absolute value of z_i (the magnitude, disregarding sign).

It is to be noted from Table 19–2 that the proton, H^+, has an unusually large conductance relative to other cations. This fact relates to the structure of water itself discussed in Chapter 4, and is due to the fact that water is extensively structured by hydrogen bridges. The individual protons subject to an electrical field migrate from one oxygen center to an adjacent one, a hydrogen bond distance away. Another proton on this newly created H_3O^+ moves to the next H_2O, creating an adjacent H_3O^+ and leaving an H_2O. This process continues across the hydrogen bonded water structure. It is illustrated schematically in Fig. 4–9. This protonic jump, accounting for the high conductance of H^+, is quite analogous to electron conductance in metals.

Also to be noted on the data of Table 19–2 is the progression of mobilities or conductances shown by the alkali metal ions. Li^+, being the first in the series and the smallest, has the lowest conductance. This is contrary to what we might have expected from our discussion of the relation of size to mobility. From the Stokes relation, mobility is inversely related to the particle radius, $\omega_i = 1/6\pi\eta r_i$. This, together with Eq. (19–30), gives

$$r_i = \frac{10^7 F^2}{6\pi N} \frac{|z_i|}{\eta^0 \lambda_i^0} , \qquad (19\text{--}31)$$

where r_i is now given in centimeters, and the superscript zeros refer to the condition of infinite dilution. Carrying out the calculation for Li^+, Na^+, and K^+, we obtain values of 2.37, 1.83, and 1.25 Angstrom units respectively. Although there are serious questions concerning the applicability of the Stokes relation at these dimensions (see Chapter 6 of Ref. 1) since the assumption of a solvent continuum is hardly justified, the relative values are perhaps indicative of the actual state. These results may be accounted for in terms of ion-water interaction to give a hydrated ion. The smaller unsoluted ions have a greater electric field intensity at their surface to attract the water dipoles and therefore have a more stable, more extensive "shell" of hydration.

Finally, we have noted in Eq. (19–29) that a potential gradient resulting from the diffusion of a simple electrolyte is dependent in part upon the difference in mobility of cation and anion. This potential gradient vanishes if the mobilities of the two charged species are equal. In Table 19–2 we note that the limiting conductances of K^+ and Cl^- are very nearly the same. It is for this reason that solutions of KCl (saturated solutions) are often used to form "liquid junctions" of the type mentioned in our discussion of the measurement of pH in Chapter 18. At such junctions the mobilities of K^+ and Cl^- dominate, they being the principle ions present. Thus electrical potentials across such junctions would be expected to be small.

References

1. R. A. Robinson and R. H. Stokes, *Electrolyte Solutions*. Butterworths, London, 1955.

2. E. J. Cohn and J. T. Edsall, *Proteins, Amino Acids and Peptides*. Reinhold, New York, 1943.

3. H. Neurath and K. Bailey, Eds., *The Proteins*, Vol. IB. Academic Press, New York, 1953.

4. T. E. Thompson and J. L. Oncley, "A Method for Calculating Differential Diffusion Coefficients in Two Component Systems: Application to Glycine-Water and Bovine Mercaptalbumin-Buffer Systems," *J. Am. Chem. Soc.* **83**, 2425 (1961).

5. J. H. Hildebrand, *Introduction to Molecular Kinetic Theory*. Reinhold, New York, 1963.

CHAPTER 20

TRANSPORT PHENOMENA IN BIOLOGICAL SYSTEMS

I. SIMPLE TRANSPORT

CHAPTER 20

TRANSPORT PHENOMENA IN BIOLOGICAL SYSTEMS

I. SIMPLE TRANSPORT

20–1 Introduction. In the previous chapter, we have developed some of the concepts and relations of simple diffusion, indicating the nature of thermodynamic forces and the associated fluxes. We have also discussed the nature of viscous forces which give rise to frictional coefficients or mobilities. In the present chapter, we apply these same principles and concepts to biological systems where diffusion processes are continually occurring as an integral part of biological function. For instance, O_2 must diffuse from the external environment of a cell into the interior and reach those sites where it undergoes chemical reaction. Similarly, CO_2 is produced within the cell as an end product of metabolic reactions and must be eliminated. Chemical compounds produced by a particular reaction in one locus must diffuse to other loci for further reaction. Although diffusion may not contribute significantly as an important quantitative time delay in that distances involved are small, it nevertheless is important for an understanding of overall cellular dynamics. Much more investigation is needed in this regard before a final assessment of the relative importance of these diffusion processes can be made.

More important in any discussion of transport in biological systems pertains to the recognition of the many compartments involved, separated, of course, by discrete boundaries or membranes. We have outlined some of these membrane concepts heretofore, especially in Chapters 1, 13, and 18. We have alluded to the "semipermeable" characteristics of biological membranes, characteristics which in the real nonideal situation have important bearing on the transport properties. With our development of the transport equations we are in a position to discuss these nonideal boundaries instead of limiting ourselves to those ideal kinds in which a chemical component or species *is* or *is not* penetrable. We may now deal with rates of penetrability or permeability.

Biological membranes that limit the cell are important contributors to cellular function. The cell is a delicate piece of metabolic machinery capable of utilizing chemical energy for its great variety of purposes. The functioning state of this machinery is very dependent upon the immediate environment, that is, the chemical composition of the cytoplasm. The

cell membrane, by virtue of its semipermeable characteristics as well as
its more direct participation in transport functions, acts as an important
guard to the cellular environment. In this respect it is important to develop an understanding of the influence of the bounding membranes on
the passage of solutes as well as on the solvent itself, water.

20–2 Simple transport across membranes; neutral, uncharged solutes.
In our considerations of simple diffusion of neutral uncharged molecules
in solvent systems, we have outlined the concepts of a diffusion flux, J_i,
representing the number of moles of a substance i that cross a plane of
unit area in unit time, that is moles $\cdot$ cm^{-2} $\cdot$ sec^{-1}. We have related J_i
to a thermodynamic force consisting of the negative of a potential gradient,
that is $-\partial\mu_i/\partial x$ at this plane, the relation involving a mobility term ω_i as
well as a concentration term c_i. In dealing with membranes, we may apply
the exact same considerations, although for simplicity of consideration a
few approximations are generally made. In the first place, the chemical
potential of a diffusing constituent or its related concentration is, in
general, not known and is not a quantity subject to easy experimental
measurement within the membrane phase itself. In that biological membranes, cellular and subcellular boundaries, are only of the order of 100 A
thick, indeed there is some question as to whether one may even properly
speak of a concentration.* The solution phases bounding the membrane
on each side are experimentally accessible and therefore our equations
should, for convenience, refer to these. In this regard, therefore, with thin
membranes we may be quite justified in simply considering our infinitesimal quantities $d\mu_i$ and dx_i as noninfinitesimal increments of $\Delta\mu_i$ and
Δx. The delta operation is thus a difference between the values at the
two sides, that is,

$$\Delta\mu_i = \mu_i(x + \Delta x) - \mu_i(x),$$

where Δx would represent the thickness of the membrane. The force acting upon a constituent i, across the membrane, would then be $-\Delta\mu_i/\Delta x$
or, expressed in terms of the concentrations on sides 1 and 2,

$$\frac{\Delta\mu_i}{\Delta x} = \frac{RT}{\Delta x}\ln\frac{c_{i_2}}{c_{i_1}} \cong \frac{RT}{\bar{c}_i}\frac{\Delta c_i}{\Delta x}, \tag{20–1}$$

where $\bar{c}_i$ must obviously represent some sort of mean concentration over
this interval Δx. With this approximation we may then write, for the flux

---

* In treating the thermodynamics of surfaces, interfaces between phases,
one does speak of a surface excess concentration, Γ_s. Thus the Gibbs free energy
of a surface phase is equal to $\Sigma\Gamma_s\, d\mu_s$ analogous to $\Sigma n_i\, d\mu_i$ for a volume phase at
constant T and P. See Höber.

of i across unit area of a membrane m, the equation

$$J_i^m = -\omega_i^m \bar{c}_i^m \frac{\Delta \mu_i}{\Delta x} = -\frac{\omega_i^m \bar{c}_i^m RT}{\bar{c}_i} \frac{\Delta c_i}{\Delta x}, \qquad (20\text{-}2)$$

where ω_i^m is the mobility of substance i within the membrane and $\bar{c}_i^m$ is some mean concentration of i within the membrane phase; $\bar{c}_i$ must refer to some mean concentration over the interval Δx derived from the solution concentrations, and would not in general equal $\bar{c}_i^m$. We must therefore make simplifying assumptions. The most obvious one would be to assume that the membrane offers by far the greatest resistance to diffusion and therefore at each bounding surface there exists an equilibrium distribution of the concentrations between solution phase and membrane phase. If this is so, we may write a relation $c_i^m = k_i c_i$ in a fashion analogous to Henry's law (see Section 16–2). Applying this to the mean concentrations we may rewrite (20–2) as

$$J_i^m = -\omega_i^m k_i RT \frac{\Delta c_i}{\Delta x} = -\Omega_i^m RT \frac{\Delta c_i}{\Delta x}, \qquad (20\text{-}3)$$

where Ω_i^m defined as $\omega_i^m k_i$ is a modified mobility containing an equilibrium distribution coefficient term.

In stating Eq. (20–2), we have also made another implicit assumption not obvious from the above discussion. To arrive at this result properly, we should have integrated J_i over the thickness of the membrane Δx, namely

$$J_i^m = \frac{1}{\Delta x} \int_0^{\Delta x} J_i \, dx = -\frac{1}{\Delta x} \int_0^{\Delta x} \omega_i^m RT \frac{dc_i^m}{dx} \, dx. \qquad (20\text{-}4)$$

To do so we must first know J_i as a function of x for the first integral and dc_i^m/dx as a function of x in the second integral, assuming ω_i^m is a constant. In the absence of such detailed knowledge we are forced to assume that J_i is independent of x, an assumption known as a steady-state assumption. It is so called because if J_i does not vary with x, then this implies that none of i is accumulating in any region within 0 to x, and therefore the concentration is invariant with time in any region. With this assumption, J_i may be removed from the integrand, and integration would give simply

$$\frac{1}{\Delta x} J_i^m \Delta x = J_i^m.$$

The further assumption that dc_i^m/dx is independent of x, for the second integral states that c_i^m varies linearly with x; i.e., a linear concentration gradient exists. Integration then gives $\omega_i^m RT (\Delta c_i^m / \Delta x)$.

For the most part the above refinements to our considerations of simple diffusion or transport across membrane need not give us much concern.

We recognize more simply that the flux of a constituent across a thin membrane phase is proportional to the concentration difference divided by the thickness Δx, the proportionality coefficient being a mobility term Ω_i^m within the membrane phase. We may even simplify a step further, for more often than not the thickness Δx is not a quantity that can be given a precise value or meaning for many biological boundaries. It is convenient therefore to lump this term together with RT into Ω_i^m and define a permeability coefficient as $p_i^m = \Omega_i^m RT / \Delta x$, simplifying Eq. (20–3) to

$$J_i^m = -p_i^m \, \Delta c_i. \qquad (20\text{–}5)$$

Finally, since J_i^m is on the basis of unit area (1 cm^2) and often the area is indeterminate and we may be primarily interested in a total flux across an entire membrane bounding a cell, we may multiply both sides of (20–5) by the area and define a new permeability coefficient as $P_i^m = p_i^m A_m$, where A_m is the area. In summary we may say that the total net flux of a neutral uncharged constituent across a membrane is, to a good approximation, proportional to the concentration difference across this membrane, the proportionality coefficient being a permeability coefficient.

20–3 Unidirectional fluxes. We might well imagine that the net flux of a constituent across a membrane is the result of a difference between two unidirectional fluxes proceeding simultaneously, since after all, diffusion is a process involving extensive random molecular motions and collisions. We may, therefore, quite formally divide the net flux accordingly, indicating the direction by subscripts, 12 or 21, 12 being the flux from solution 1 to solution 2, and 21 the opposite. We write

$$J_i = J_{i_{12}} - J_{i_{21}} = -p_i^m (c_{i_2} - c_{i_1}) = -p_i^m (\Delta c_i). \qquad (20\text{–}6)$$

The flux of i from 1 to 2, $J_{i_{12}}$ involves molecules of i originating in 1 and should be rationally proportional only to the number per unit volume in solution 1, that is, c_{i_1}. The flux of i from 2 to 1, $J_{i_{21}}$, involves molecules of i, which originate in 2 and therefore should be proportional to c_{i_2}. Thus we may write

$$J_{i_{12}} = p_i^m c_{i_1},$$

$$\qquad (20\text{–}7)$$

$$J_{i_{21}} = p_i^m c_{i_2}.$$

Now we must recognize that this division of the flux into two unidirectional fluxes is a purely artificial device unless we can in some manner distinguish operationally the side on which the molecules originate. If there is no way that this information is to be had, then the formal division is unnecessary and meaningless, for the individual fluxes are not operational quantities. However, if there were some means of labeling those molecules on side 1 which distinguished them from those present on side 2, but otherwise did not alter their behavior, Eqs. (20–7) become meaningful. This condition is almost ideally realizable if one employs isotopic labeling, either with a stable or, more conveniently, with a radioactive isotope. We imagine that at the start of an experimental observation we charge side 1 with a given known density of iostopic label of constituent i, so that the percent of label or specific activity† is known. Side 2 may then be successively sampled and the isotopic content measured to obtain a concentration of isotope as a function of time.

This information, together with the volume of side 2, permits a calculation of the amount of isotope appearing in side 2 as a function of time. If we may assume that in the initial short periods of observation, dilution of isotope into solution 2 is so large that loss by return flux may be neglected, then the rate of gain of the amount of isotope in solution 2 is proportional to the flux $J_{k_{12}}$, the proportionality being the specific activity factor of the label on side 1. Stated more mathematically, we may designate our isotope concentration in solution 1 as c_i^* (e.g. as counts per cm^3) and then the specific activity may be defined as $\alpha_{i_1} = c_{i_1}^*/c_{i_1}$ with c_{i_1}, for example, in units of moles $\cdot$ cm^{-3}. The rate of isotopic flux from 1 to 2 is $J_{i_{12}}^* = J_{i_{12}}\alpha_{i_1}$, and this is equal to the rate of appearance in solution 2, namely, $V_2(dc_{i_2}^*/dt)$, where V_2 is the volume of side 2 and $dc_{i_2}^*/dt$ is the time rate of change in concentration of isotope. Then from Equation (20–7), we have

$$V_2 \frac{dc_{i_2}^*}{dt} = J_{i_{12}}^* = J_{i_{12}}\alpha_{i_1} = p_i^m c_{i_1}\alpha_{i_1} \qquad (20\text{–}8)$$

or

$$J_{i_{12}}^* = p_i^m c_{i_1}^*, \qquad (20\text{–}9)$$

which merely states that the isotopic flux from 1 to 2 is proportional to the isotopic concentration in solution 1.

Experimentally, the periods of observation are kept short enough that $c_{i_2}^*$ is always small in comparison to $c_{i_1}^*$, and therefore the back flux term, given by a relation analogous to (20–9) with change in subscript, is negligible. Also, we assume that the period of observation is small enough to allow $c_{i_1}^*$ to be considered constant; that is, its percentage change is negligible. The flux from 2 to 1, $J_{i_{21}}$, is generally measured in a separate experiment by reversing the conditions, but one may employ a double-labeling technique when feasible to measure the flux in both directions simultaneously. Alternately, a unidirectional flux measurement

---

† Specific activity may be designated in a variety of ways according to the units employed. As an example, we may choose to designate the specific activity as radioactive counts per mole of constituent i.

and a simultaneous net flux measurement would provide the equivalent information as deducible from Eq. (20–6).

The use of isotopes has been indispensable in the investigation of membrane permeability. Since their availability, the concepts of many biological membrane phenomena have undergone marked revision.

20–4 Diffusion of ions across membranes. In considering the diffusion of charged ionic species across membranes, we may advance the same arguments as we have with neutral solutes, although, in general, we must add the additional thermodynamic force of the electrical potential difference. Without attempting to be mathematically rigorous, but only intuitively reasonable, we write as before, but include a potential term:

$$J_k^m = -\Omega_k^m RT \left(\frac{\Delta c_k}{\Delta x} + \frac{z_k \bar{c}_k F}{RT} \frac{\Delta \psi}{\Delta x} \right). \tag{20–10}$$

Again the Ω_k^m contains implicitly a distribution coefficient for the constituent k between solution and membrane phase; Δc_i represents the difference in solution phase concentrations, and $\bar{c}_i$ is some mean value of these solution phase concentrations. Again, steady-state assumptions regarding independence of concentration with time within the membrane phase, as well as the assumption regarding a linear concentration gradient in the region $0 \to \Delta x$, have been made. We have also assumed in addition, a linear potential gradient in this region.

Again we may combine the $\Omega_k^m RT/\Delta x$ coefficient into a single permeability coefficient per unit area, p_k^m, to give

$$J_k^m = -p_k^m \left(\Delta c_k + \frac{z_k \bar{c}_k F}{RT} \Delta \psi \right). \tag{20–11}$$

Equation (20–11) is valid for each ion species, k, diffusing across a membrane; the diffusion results from a concentration difference as well as a potential difference. Let us examine this equation by considering two types of membranes.

(a) If we have a membrane which is ideally permeable only to one species of ion, say the kth, then without an external electrical connection no electric current can flow due to the restrictions on electrical neutrality in any region. Thus $J_k = 0$ with the result that we may solve for the potential difference to obtain

$$\Delta \psi = - \frac{RT}{z_k F} \frac{\Delta c_k}{\bar{c}_k} \tag{20–12}$$

or more exactly from integration

$$\Delta \psi = \psi_2 - \psi_1 = - \frac{RT}{z_k F} \ln \frac{c_{k_2}}{c_{k_1}}. \tag{20–13}$$

This equation is identical to one derived in considering equilibrium of ions across semipermeable membranes (see Section 18–3). The condition we imposed here, by assuming a membrane permeable only to k and setting $J_k = 0$, is indeed an equilibrium condition.

(b) If, on the other hand, we have a membrane permeable to a variety of ions present, each with its own permeability coefficient, the condition of zero electric current flow is

$$\sum_{k=1}^{s} z_k J_k = -\sum_{k=1}^{s} z_k p_k^m \, \Delta c_k - \frac{F}{RT} \sum_{k=1}^{s} z_k^2 \bar{c}_k \, \Delta \psi = 0. \quad (20\text{–}14)$$

Solving for $\Delta \psi$, we obtain

$$\Delta \psi = -\frac{RT}{F} \frac{\sum_{k=1}^{s} z_k p_k^m \, \Delta c_k}{\sum_{k=1}^{s} z_k^2 \bar{c}_k}, \quad (20\text{–}15)$$

a more formidable appearing expression but certainly more realistic for biological membranes. It applies within the framework of the assumptions and approximations made, but may be simplified for the usual biological membranes. Relative to the few that predominate, many of the ionic permeabilities or concentrations are very small. As a result the summation needs to be carried out over only the principle ions whose permeabilities or "conductances" across the membrane are significant.

For instance, it is well appreciated that over reasonable ranges of concentration, the membrane potential of resting nerve and muscle is very nearly given by an expression of (20–13) applied to K^+; this implies, of course, that the permeability coefficient of this ion is dominant relative to any other. However, in the excited state of impulse transmission, changes occur in the membrane so that the "conductances" of both K^+ and Na^+ are important, and reaches a transient point wherein the Na^+ conductance is much greater than that for K^+. At this point the potential difference is approximated by an expression of (20–13) applied to Na^+. These changes in the membrane characteristics, occurring with considerable rapidity, are a subject of intensive investigation at present and comprise one of the central problems of biology, paramount to an understanding of nerve impulse propagation. It is the relations of the kind we have been considering that have provided at least a basis for "understanding" these membrane problems, but it is ultimately the relation between a transport mechanism, the coefficients p_k^m and membrane structure that must be resolved before a complete understanding will be possible.

Equation (20–11) describes the relations pertaining to the *net* flux of an ion. As with other solutes, it is often experimentally desirable to measure the fluxes with isotopes to determine the unidirectional flux. This may be done in a fashion precisely the same as that described for neutral solutes, but the equation describing the theoretical results to be expected are, of course, different due to the influence of the electrical potential. Most simply one may consider a relation precisely analogous to those of Eq. (20–7) or that of Eq. (20–9) but with the concentration replaced by a new type of concentration designated an electrochemical concentration. From our knowledge of the electrochemical potential defined by Eq. (15–23), we may write quite formally

$$\bar{\mu}_k - \mu_k^0 = RT \ln c_k + z_k F \psi = RT \ln \bar{\theta}_k + z_k F \psi^0, \qquad (20–16)$$

and in this way define an electrochemical concentration, $\bar{\theta}_k$ for the kth ionic species; ψ^0 is some arbitrary reference potential. In that $\ln e^y = y$ we then have

$$\bar{\theta}_k = c_k e^{[z_k F(\psi - \psi^0)]/RT}, \qquad (20–17)$$

and from our reasoning above together with Eq. (20–9) we obtain

$$J_{k_{12}} = p_k^m \bar{\theta}_{k_1}^* = p_k^m c_{k_1}^* e^{[z_k F(\psi - \psi^0)]/RT}. \qquad (20–18)$$

This equation indicates that the isotopic flux from solution 1 to 2 is proportional not to the concentration of isotope c_{k_1} in 1 but to this concentration multiplied by an exponential quantity containing the potential in the region of solution 1 relative to some standard potential. It may be immediately appreciated that this equation *per se* is rather ridiculous because of the standard potential ψ^0, which, as far as relation (20–16) is concerned, is quite arbitrary. It points out that the potential in a region is in actuality an unmeasurable quantity by itself. Only electrical potential differences are operationally meaningful. However, if we take only the flux ratio

$$\frac{J_{k_{12}}}{J_{k_{21}}} = \frac{c_1 e^{z_k F(\psi_1 - \psi^0)/RT}}{c_2 e^{z_k F(\psi_2 - \psi^0)/RT}} = \frac{c_1}{c_2} e^{-z_k F(\psi_2 - \psi_1)/RT}, \qquad (20–19)$$

we note that ψ^0 cancels out, therefore this ratio is theoretically sound, containing only the potential difference across the membrane, $\psi_2 - \psi_1$. This equation, derived by both Ussing and Linderholm (see Refs. 1 and 2), has proved very useful in the study of transport across membranes, for it states that if the unidirectional flux ratio experimentally measured is equal to that calculated from the expression on the right, the flux may be entirely accounted for in terms of simple diffusion based upon a concentration and electrical potential difference.

Departures from this predicted result must be explained on the basis of the existence of other forces, notably the existence of "active" transport systems. For this reason, the equation has assumed particular importance in establishing a criterion for establishing experimentally the existence of "active" transport and occasionally serving as a definition for active transport processes *per se*. However, it may be readily shown that a flow

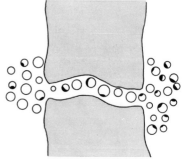

FIG. 20-1. Single-file diffusion
through a membrane hole.

of solvent, carrying with it by viscous drag a quantity of solute, results in
a flux ratio not given by Eq. (20–19). Ussing (Ref. 1) has extended the
simple theory to include such forces. Nevertheless, it may also be shown
that other mechanism of diffusion still do not conform to this relation.
For example, the single file migration of molecules through a narrow
channel illustrated in Fig. 20–1 gives an isotopic flux ratio which is that of
Eq. (20–19) with the right-hand member raised to some power. The
power depends on the number of molecules or ions the channel contains in
file. (See Ref. 3.) Such factors as these, therefore, which require mechanistic explanations, make Eq. (20–19) a rather ambiguous basis for
formulating a definition of "active" transport. We will consider the entire
subject of active transport in some detail in Section 21–3.

We may illustrate the application of Eq. (20–19) with some selected data
taken from the published work of Johnsen, Levi, and Ussing (Ref. 4) and
collected in Table 20–1. The data is offered as evidence that across the
isolated frog-skin preparation, chloride ion passage is dependent upon only

TABLE 20–1

CHLORIDE FLUXES ACROSS THE FROG SKIN AT VARIOUS
ELECTRICAL POTENTIAL DIFFERENCES
(OBSERVATIONS MADE IN FOUR-HOUR PERIODS)

$\dfrac{c_1{}^*}{c_2}$	$\psi_2 - \psi_1$, mv	J_{12}, μ equiv $\cdot$ cm^{-2} $\cdot$ hr^{-1}	J_{21}, μ equiv $\cdot$ cm^{-2} $\cdot$ hr^{-1}	J_{12}/J_{21}	$\dfrac{c_1}{c_2} e^{[F(\psi_2 - \psi_1)]/RT}$
0.1	87	0.578	0.151	3.85	3.22
0.1	94	0.291	0.069	4.24	3.78
0.1	86	0.254	0.065	3.90	2.93
0.1	93	0.201	0.052	3.86	3.80
0.1	72	†0.159	0.098	1.62	1.61
0.1	100	‡0.376	0.073	5.2	4.9

* Side 1 is the "outside" of the skin; Side 2 is the "inside" of the skin.
† Acetylcholine present.
‡ Neurohypophyseal hormone present.

its concentration and the electrical forces present when net water movement (and mucous gland secretion) is absent. It is seen that the ratio of the unidirectional fluxes measured isotopically bears respectible agreement to the ratio computed from the concentration ratio and electrical potential differences.

20–5 Transport of water across membranes. Most biological membranes are permeable to water as well as to certain solutes, neutral or charged. They differ widely in their mechanical properties. Some membranes are relatively rigid such as the glomerular membranes and are thus able to support an actual hydrostatic pressure difference. Others are only very slightly rigid, such as the red cell envelope; and still others, such as the cell membranes of amoebae, appear to possess no rigidity whatsoever, and are therefore able to support little or no mechanical pressure. These latter types are by far the most common cellular boundaries for animal cells and for subcellular particles such as mitochondria and nuclei. In plant cells we find rigid supporting cellulose matrixes against which thin cellular membranes may be supported. Thus these are able to withstand considerable hydrostatic pressure in one direction but not the other. Water being the principle constituent of living cells, it is important to understand some of the principles involved in its movement, although only the simple essentials will be developed here.

For simplicity of development let us consider that we have an ideal semipermeable membrane of the kind discussed in Section 18–2. The forces acting on the solvent, water in this case, may be visualized as differences in the chemical potential arising from hydrostatic pressure difference and solute concentration (water concentration) differences across the membrane. The force may be written as

$$F_s = -\frac{\Delta \mu_s}{\Delta x} = -\frac{\Delta \mu_s^0}{\Delta x} - RT \frac{\Delta \ln x_s}{\Delta x}. \qquad (20\text{–}20)$$

According to our development for osmotic pressure, the first term of the right-hand side is related to the hydrostatic pressure by

$$\frac{\Delta \mu^0}{\Delta x} = \bar{v}_s \frac{\Delta p}{\Delta x}, \qquad (20\text{–}21)$$

where $\bar{v}_s$ is, as before, the partial molar volume of solvent. The second term is related to the osmotic pressure by the relation

$$RT \frac{\Delta \ln x_s}{\Delta x} = -\bar{v}_s \frac{\Delta \pi}{\Delta x}. \qquad (20\text{–}22)$$

With these relations, Eq. (20–22) may be rewritten as

$$F_s = -\bar{v}_s \left[\frac{\Delta P}{\Delta x} - \frac{\Delta \pi}{\Delta x} \right],\tag{20–23}$$

and since by the van't Hoff approximation $\Delta \pi = RT\,\Delta C_t$, where C_t refers to the total concentration difference of solutes to which the membrane is impermeable, we have

$$F_s = -\bar{v}_s \left[\frac{\Delta P}{\Delta x} - RT\,\frac{\Delta C_t}{\Delta x} \right].\tag{20–24}$$

The average velocity of solvent molecules as a result of this force, F_s, is then $v_s = F_s \Omega_s^m$, and the flux per unit area is this velocity times the concentration, i.e., number of molecules per unit of volume moving with this average velocity. We write

$$J_s^m = -\Omega_s^m \cdot c_s \cdot F_s = -\Omega_s^m \bar{v}_s \cdot c_s \left[\frac{\Delta P}{\Delta x} - RT\,\frac{\Delta C_t}{\Delta x} \right],\tag{20–25}$$

giving the flux in units, for example, of moles $\cdot$ cm^{-2} $\cdot$ sec^{-1}. We note that the product $\bar{v}_s \cdot c_s$ (volume per mole $\cdot$ mole per unit volume) is about unity for the solvent of dilute solutions. Defining our permeability coefficient as $\Omega_s^m / \Delta x$, we obtain

$$J_s^m = -p_s^m(\Delta P - RT\,\Delta C_t).\tag{20–26}$$

This states that the flux of a solvent such as water across a membrane is proportional to both a mechanical pressure difference and a solute concentration difference (osmotic pressure difference). If $J_s^m = 0$, i.e. no net flux exists and p_s^m is not zero, then we find that $\Delta P = RT\Delta C_t$. This mechanical or hydrostatic pressure is just the osmotic pressure as we have previously developed, for indeed the condition, $J_s^m = 0$, is an equilibrium condition for solvent provided $p_s^m \neq 0$.

This derivation has been made for membranes that are ideally semipermeable to the dissolved solutes, a situation not often completely realized in real biological systems. More often than not, solutes are able to diffuse through the membrane to some degree, but perhaps slower than solvent itself, due to the difference in molecular size. We can imagine a situation in which the membrane is perfectly freely permeable to solute as well as solvent, i.e., it freely passes the solution. At this extreme, we would certainly not expect the osmotic term to be effective as a force in causing solvent flux, and thus it must vanish. An intermediate situation is that in which the solute molecules are somewhat restricted in their passage across the membrane relative to solvent. Under such circumstances, the osmotic concentration term would not be fully manifest as a force but only partially effective. It is only in an ideally semipermeable membrane of the type assumed in the derivation of osmotic pressure that the osmotic concentration term would be fully manifest as a force on the solvent. To take account of the nonideality of the semipermeable characteristics of real membrane, we may introduce a correction coefficient for the osmotic term giving it the symbol, σ_m, and thus rewrite Eq. (20–26) as

$$J_s^m = -p_s^m(\Delta P - \sigma_m RT \, \Delta C_t). \qquad (20\text{--}27)$$

Introduced in this fashion, σ_m is an empirical coefficient pertaining to the effectiveness of the membrane as an osmotic barrier. It may be reasoned that a coefficient value of unity denotes perfect semipermeable properties of the membrane to the solvent, whereas a value of zero would indicate a barrier completely and equally permeable to solutes and solvent. In actuality this coefficient may be given a theoretical basis related to the relative frictional coefficients of solute to solvent, solute to membrane, and solvent to membrane. For further reading see the papers of Staverman (Ref. 5) and Kedem and Katchalsky (Ref. 6).

20–6 The permeability coefficient and membrane structure. Before proceeding to other than the simple diffusion processes considered in this chapter, it would be well to discuss briefly some of the factors relating the permeability coefficient p_i^m to concepts of biological membrane structure. According to our definition, we recognize that this coefficient is composed of a number of presumed constants. It is made up of an inherent mobility, ω_i^m, of a constituent in the membrane phase; it contains a solubility or partition coefficient, k_i, of the constituent in the membrane phase, which is, of course, the relative solubility of the constituent in the bounding solution phases *vs.* the membrane phase itself; it contains a factor relating to the functional thickness of the membrane, Δx; and finally, it contains the factor, RT. Thus

$$p_i^m = \frac{\omega_i^m k_i RT}{\Delta x}, \qquad (20\text{--}28)$$

and if we had included the effective area to give an overall permeability coefficient, then our definition is

$$P_i^m = \frac{\omega_i^m k_i RTA}{\Delta x}. \qquad (20\text{--}29)$$

The first of these factors, ω_i^m, depends upon both the nature and properties of the membrane as well as upon the individual properties of the diffusing molecular species themselves. Our concepts of biological membranes are crude and lack sufficient detail to discuss precise mechanisms. On the one hand, we may well imagine a tightly structured membrane composed of lipid and proteins in some closely packed array. The lipids would tend to

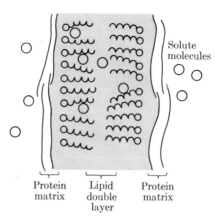

Fig. 20–2. Example of a tightly structured biological membrane.

align their alaphatic chains or phenanthrene rings in a parallel fashion, perpendicular to the membrane surface. This packing would be stabilized by a meshwork of protein. Such a picture is diagrammatically sketched in Fig. 20–2. If the membrane is of this structure, lacking "holes," we must consider diffusion across this boundary as involving perhaps an actual solution of a molecular species from the solvent into the membrane phase, followed by subsequent diffusion through this rather viscous semi-solid. Such being the case, we might expect the mobility term, ω_i^m, to be rather small. However, for certain types of molecules, the distribution coefficient between the aqueous solution and membrane phase may be rather favorable so that the actual concentration of some diffusing molecular species, i, would be rather high in the membrane phase, thus compensating for the unfavorable mobility. Molecules possessing this favorable distribution coefficient would be those that are rather "lipid soluble."

Indeed, the correlation between the so-called lipophilic nature of molecules, and their rate of penetration across cellular membranes is good. A plot of the ratio of solubility of such molecules in oil to their solubility in water vs. a measured permeability coefficient into *Chara* cells is seen in Fig. 20–3. Many exceptions to this relation do exist, however, which indicates that our concepts should not be too simple-minded. In fact, on this basis, one might expect that the hydrophilic substances such as the ionic constituents and amino acids are very poorly permeable, whereas in actuality they are often quite rapidly penetrating. These latter observations suggest perhaps a membrane which rather than being a tightly structured lipid-protein laminate might be rather loosely structured such as to provide a number of actual aqueous channels or pores through the barrier. An attempt is made to picture this in Fig. 20–4. Through these channels we may readily visualize diffusion of solutes small enough

Fig. 20–3. Correlation between permeability coefficients of various substances in *Chara* cells and their oil/water distribution ratios. [Data from E. J. Harris, *Transport and Accumulation in Biological Systems,* Academic Press, New York, 1960.]

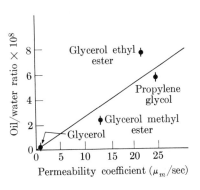

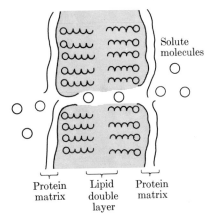

Fig. 20–4. An example of a loosely structured biological membrane with holes.

Protein matrix   Lipid double layer   Protein matrix

to be accommodated or that "fit," as well as flow of water. In addition, to account for certain observations, one may postulate that the channels be structured with certain constituents bearing ionic charges of a given sign, giving the pores an ion exchange character and leading to a degree of charge selectivity of electrolyte permeation.

The many observations of permeability are such that it is difficult to postulate the membrane structure as falling into any single category. Instead, our concepts are one of composite structure. The molecular mechanisms of diffusion are then composites of a number of different schemes, all occurring simultaneously in parallel and in series. The detailed mechanisms are, of course, complicated; and still, with this simplified picture, many observations cannot be adequately accounted for. This is especially true concerning the often observed high degree of selectivity and specificity shown towards certain molecular constituents in their passage across membranal structures. Also, there is nothing in the membrane structure, as here outlined, which would account for the frequent observation that many molecular constituents can be transported from a low concentration to a higher concentration. Possible mechanisms which may account for these observations are outlined in the following chapter, and their principles are discussed in Section 21–6.

REFERENCES

1. H. H. Ussing and K. Zerahn, "Active Transport of Sodium as the Source of Electric Current in the Short-Circuited Isolated Frog Skin," *Acta Physiol. Scand.* **23,** 110 (1951).

2. H. Linderholm, "Active Transport of Ions Through Frog Skin With Special Reference to the Action of Certain Diuretics," *Acta Physiol. Scand.,* **27,** 97 (1952).

3. A. L. Hodgkin and R. D. Keynes, "Active Transport of Cations in Giant Axons from Sepia and Loligo," *J. Physiol.* **128,** 61 (1955).

4. V. K. Johnsen, H. Levi, and H. H. Ussing, "The Mode of Passage of Chloride Ions Through the Isolated Frog Skin," *Acta Physiol. Scand.* **25,** 150 (1952).

5. A. J. Staverman, "The Theory of Measurement of Osmotic Pressure," *Recueil.* **70,** 344 (1951).

6. O. Kedem and A. Katchalsky, "A Physical Interpretation of the Phenomenological Coefficients of Membrane Permeability," *J. Gen. Physiol.* **45,** 143 (1961).

CHAPTER 21

TRANSPORT PHENOMENA IN BIOLOGICAL SYSTEMS

II. TRANSPORT BY CHEMICAL ASSOCIATION—ACTIVE TRANSPORT

CHAPTER 21

TRANSPORT PHENOMENA IN BIOLOGICAL SYSTEMS

II. TRANSPORT BY CHEMICAL ASSOCIATION—
ACTIVE TRANSPORT

21-1 Introduction. In the previous chapter, we have considered the essentials of transport by simple diffusion that occurs across membranes. We have attempted to derive an understanding of the various forces involved and some possible mechanisms. Nowhere in the discussion of these principles, however, did we provide for an adequate explanation to account for the great specificity and selectivity so frequently observed in transport across biological membranes.

We have noted that differences in the algebraic sign of ionic charges could be distinguished to a degree by postulating ion exchange type membranes. This would hardly serve as a means of distinguishing selectively such similar ions as Na^+ and K^+. Furthermore, nowhere in the discussion did we provide for an explanation to account for the observations that certain constituents may be transported in a direction opposite to that which would be expected on the basis of the forces involved in simple diffusion. For instance, it is well known that muscle and nerve cells and, in fact, most animal cells contain a low cytoplasmic concentration of Na^+, whereas the concentration in the immediate extracellular environment is of the order of tenfold larger. From isotopic tracer studies, the membrane is observed to be permeable to a degree to not only Na^+ but also other ions, and therefore one is forced to the conclusion that if Na^+ does diffuse inwardly as a consequence of the natural forces present, it must also be removed by some other process in order that the low cytoplasmic concentration be maintained.

More or less the same may be said concerning the K^+, although here the concentration ratio is the inverse of that of Na^+, the cytoplasmic K^+ concentration being more than tenfold greater than the extracellular concentration. Taking into account the electrical potential difference that exists across these cellular boundaries which is of the order of 100 millivolts, extracellular phase positive with respect to the cytoplasmic, suggests perhaps that the K^+ distribution may be nearly that of equilibrium. These observations and relations are perhaps clarified with an illustrative example pictured and calculated in Fig. 21-1 assuming some representative values for the concentrations and electrical potential difference.

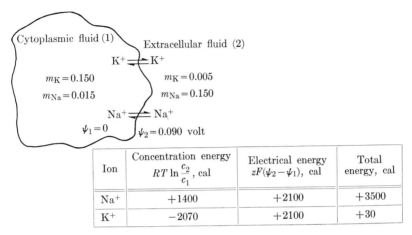

Ion	Concentration energy $RT \ln \frac{c_2}{c_1}$, cal	Electrical energy $zF(\psi_2 - \psi_1)$, cal	Total energy, cal
Na+	+1400	+2100	+3500
K+	−2070	+2100	+30

Fig. 21–1. A sketch and some numerical values illustrating a more or less typical ionic distribution pattern for Na+ and K+ and an electrical potential difference. The table shows the energies involved in transfer of a mole of either ion from cytoplasm (1) to extracellular fluid (2), computed in calories per mole. The m's denote the molal concentrations, i.e., moles per kilogram of H_2O.

In addition to these electrolyte distributions, it should also be pointed out that many constituents such as glucose and certain of the amino acids are often found to be at a higher cytoplasmic concentration than in the extracellular environment. Once again, one must postulate some sort of mechanism that will account for and explain these findings.

Another problem to be considered and for which an explanation must be sought is that involving water permeation. It should be recognized that there are many cytoplasmic constituents to which cellular membranes are not appreciably permeable. Among these are the cellular proteins and many of the compounds that are involved in the elaborate cellular metabolic machinery. Although the state of these constituents in the cytoplasm, whether free or bound, is not in general known, there is reason to believe that they are in large part free and therefore would exert an osmotic influence. As we have indicated, animal cellular membranes cannot support much hydrostatic pressure difference, and therefore we must look to some mechanism which may control the total solute concentration to prevent swelling or shrinking of the cells due to osmotic differences.

21–2 Transport by chemical association. In order to achieve the considerable degree of specificity often seen in chemical interaction, it is necessary to postulate a close association of the interacting species. The closer the molecules are to each other, the greater is the degree of specificity.

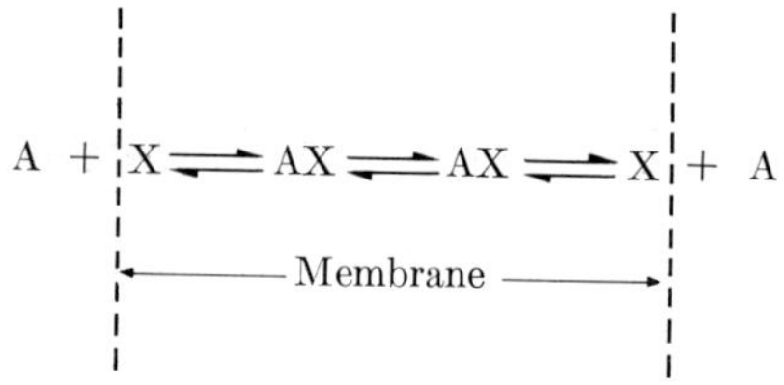

$$A + \overset{}{X} \rightleftharpoons AX \rightleftharpoons AX \rightleftharpoons X + A$$

FIG. 21-2. Diagrammatic sketch of transport by chemical association. See text for discussion.

Specificity of interaction is lacking at large distances, because at large distances intermolecular forces are weak and there is very little to distinguish one kind of molecule from another. To account for the high degree of specificity frequently observed in biological transport systems, it is convenient to postulate a chemical constituent existent in the membrane phase which shows chemical affinity for the species transported. The chemical affinity is of such a degree that actual association may occur and diffusion of the resulting complex would result. We may illustrate this in a diagrammatic sketch seen in Fig. 21-2, in which X refers to such a membrane constituent and has the property of associating with the molecule or ion designated, A, that is, A becomes bound by X. We may easily imagine that X is confined to the membrane phase by virtue perhaps of its properties and may even have a fair degree of mobility within this phase. We may also imagine that A itself has a poor distribution coefficient in the membrane phase, and therefore there is likely to be very little free A (unassociated A) present. We may presume that the affinity of X for A may be described in terms of an equilibrium constant, for if the chemical reaction is rapid relative to the diffusion process, the reaction would always be near equilibrium. In this manner, X may be envisaged as a "carrier" of A across the membrane.

With the above considerations, we may describe the transport somewhat more quantitatively. Let us assume that the total concentration of X, made up of free X and AX, is a constant at each membrane surface ignoring for the present without justification any volume considerations of a surface phase. Thus

$$C_{T_1} = c_{X_1} + c_{AX_1} \quad \text{and} \quad C_{T_2} = c_{X_2} + c_{AX_2}, \quad (21\text{-}1)$$

where the subscript numbers refer to the two surfaces 1 and 2. We may write the equilibrium constant as

$$K = \frac{c_A \cdot c_X}{c_{AX}}; \quad (21\text{-}2)$$

there is one such relation for each surface although the constants are presumed the same. We then apply our diffusion equations to the complex AX. For simplicity, let us assume that it is a neutral, uncharged complex and we may then neglect any electrical potential difference as a force. The flux of AX per unit area is then given as

$$J_{AX} = -p^m_{AX} \Delta c_{AX} \qquad (21\text{-}3)$$

taken from Eq. (20-5). Our problem is then to express Δc_{AX} in terms of c_{A_1} and c_{A_2}, the experimentally measurable quantities in the solution phases. We do this with Eqs. (21-1) and (21-2), for in each surface we have

$$K \cdot c_{AX} = c_A \cdot c_X = c_A[C_T - c_{AX}], \qquad (21\text{-}4)$$

which on rearrangement gives

$$c_{AX} = \frac{c_A \cdot C_T}{c_A + K}. \qquad (21\text{-}5)$$

We obtain therefore from Eq. (21-3), the following equation:

$$J_{AX} = -p^m_{AX}\left[\frac{c_{A_2} \cdot C_{T_2}}{c_{A_2} + K} - \frac{c_{A_1} \cdot C_{T_1}}{c_{A_1} + K}\right], \qquad (21\text{-}6)$$

which describes the transport of A by association with X. This is obviously somewhat more complicated than simple diffusion and shows some unusual properties.

Let us simplify Eq. (21-6) by making $c_{A_2} = 0$. We then evaluate how the flux varies with variations of c_{A_1}. In effect, we are removing the back flux quantity of the net flux, J_{AX}, so that the net flux becomes equal to the flux $J_{AX_{12}}$. This situation could also prevail in isotopic measurements, as previously discussed in Section 20-3, limiting the isotope to Side 1 at the start of the period of experimental observation. The result is

$$J_{AX} = p^m_{AX} \frac{C_{T_1} \cdot c_{A_1}}{c_{A_1} + K}. \qquad (21\text{-}7)$$

Analyzing this relation, we first establish that as c_{A_1} goes to zero, so does J_{AX}, which is to be expected. However, as c_{A_1} becomes very large, much larger than K, we may ignore K in the denominator relative to c_{A_1}, and

$$J_{AX} = p^m_{AX} \cdot C_T; \qquad (21\text{-}8)$$

J_{AX} thus approaches a constant at high concentration of A in 1, and is thereby independent of c_{A_1}. The system is said to become saturated at these large values. When $c_{A_1} = K$, J_{AX} is one half this maximum value, suggesting a means of ascertaining experimentally the value of K. Equation (21-7) is representative of a general class of equations known as rectangular hyperbolas. It exhibits characteristic features which will be dis-

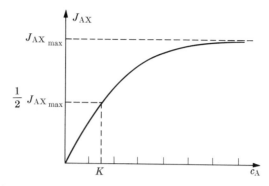

FIG. 21–3. A plot of Eq. (21–7) with J_{AX} vs. c_A. At large values of c_A, J_{AX} approaches $p_{AX}^m C_T$ asymptotically. When $J_{AX} = \frac{1}{2} p_{AX}^m C_T$, $c_A = K$.

cussed more fully in Chapter 23. Its graphic form is seen in Fig. 21–3, where J_{AX_1} is plotted vs. c_{A_1}. Here it is evident that J_{AX_1} reaches a limiting maximal value asymptotically at large values of c_{A_1}. Also indicated in the figure is the half-maximum value of J_{AX_1} occurring at the point where $c_A = K$.

Admittedly, this model of associated transport is crude and probably represents considerable oversimplification of actuality. Nevertheless, it does account in principle for a variety of observed phenomena. It has the distinct advantage of simplicity of concept, and is quite general in form.

As has been indicated, biological membranes exhibit, in general, a relatively high degree of selectivity toward many substances. In such cases, these substances portray saturation in their permeation across these membranes at higher concentrations, a fact nicely accounted for by this model. Furthermore, as one may intuitively reason, compounds that resemble each other and are present together may possibly compete for the same "carrier" molecule X, and thereby compete in their diffusion across the cell boundary. Competition among similar chemical compounds is indeed a phenomenon often observed.

It may be evident that on the one hand the concept of transport by chemical association developed in the foregoing merges with that which stresses the importance of actual solution of a constituent in the membrane phase, i.e., a favorable type of partition coefficient. This is so because the dissolution of a constitution by a "good" solvent implies a relatively high degree of positive solute-solvent interaction, that is, what may be called solvation. In this respect, then, the substance X is considered solvent. In general, however, one tends to associate with solvation a somewhat lower degree of specificity than that of an individual chemical reaction describable in terms of a definite equilibrium constant.

On the other hand, it is not necessary in our model to explicitly identify the carrier X as an actual molecule. Instead, we may consider it as a "site" of transport and that a membrane possesses a limited number of these "sites" where diffusion or transport may occur. These sites could conceivably represent some special "holes" which, having an affinity for the constituent that is diffusing, becomes occupied during the actual passage of this constituent. Again, this concept would tend to provide an upper limit to a flux but a high specificity is difficult to imagine without considering some type of true chemical association. Postulates have been made suggesting that the hole or "pore" dimensions lend specificity.

In any case, the transport by association as outlined, accounting in principle for a number of observations, has not yet been experimentally demonstrated and proved in any natural biological systems. Substances such as X have yet to be identified. At the present time, this is an area of active research. At this point it should be noted that transport by chemical association alone fails to account for transport in a direction contrary to that expected on the basis of concentration differences and electrical potential differences. Clearly, more elaborate mechanisms must be envisaged.

21–3 Active transport or metabolically coupled transport. In postulating a mechanism which could carry out transport and result in accumulation against concentration and electrical potential differences, it is not difficult to extend our concepts of transport by association outlined in the previous section. We retain all our postulates concerning substance X, except that rather than consider it to be some stable membrane constituent, present in some fixed concentration, we consider it a more dynamic constituent capable of undergoing chemical change which alters its affinity for the substance being transported. Thus, if we were to provide a source of X on one membrane surface, that is, if it were generated by some chemical reaction at this surface, and if we were to provide a sink for it at the other surface where it is destroyed by chemical reaction, then we have the necessary conditions for actively transporting A.

For purposes of being more definite, we may visualize the scheme seen in Fig. 21–4. Here we indicate the formation of X at surface 1 from a substance Y by some presumed chemical conversion, the details of which are unnecessary for explanations of the principles involved. However, it must be assumed that Y does not have the property of reversible association with any such constituent as A, as does X. The substance A becomes associated with X as before, X being continually supplied by conversion from Y; AX diffuses from surface 1 to surface 2, where dissociation into A and X may occur. This dissociation is favored by the fact that c_{X_2} is kept low by another chemical reaction occurring at this surface, a reaction converting X back to Y. Now, since Y is being continually formed at surface 2,

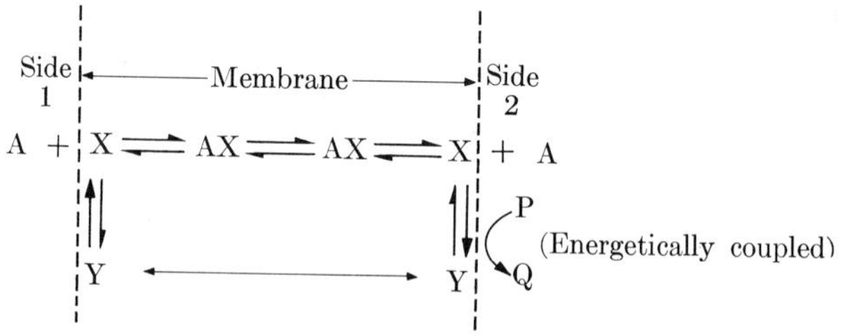

FIG. 21–4. Transport by chemical association with X. The process is energetically coupled to cellular metabolism to lead to active transport of substance A from side 1 to 2.

it would here have a higher concentration than at surface 1, where it is being converted to X, so that diffusion of Y from surface 2 to 1 would occur, supplying in this manner a source for X at surface 1.

It is quite evident from energetic considerations that accumulation of A in solution 2 from a lower concentration in solution 1 would not result unless either the conversion of X to Y on surface 2 or Y to X on surface 1 were coupled to some other "driving" chemical reaction. It is necessary that energy be put into this cyclic system for the work of transporting A against a concentration difference to be performed. To proceed naturally, each step of the cycle must involve a free energy decrease as discussed in Chapter 15. This is, of course, impossible in a cyclic system unless at one step energy is supplied from outside the cycle. (See Chapter 23 for a discussion of coupled chemical reactions.) Thus we may visualize that the reaction converting X to Y is "driven" by a coupled reaction forming a part of the metabolic machinery. For instance, if the conditions are such that X being converted to Y involves a free energy per mole, ΔG_{XY}, and that another reaction, P being converted to Q, involves a free energy per mole, ΔG_{PQ}, then it is conceivable that the reaction

$$X + P \rightleftharpoons Y + Q, \qquad \Delta G = \Delta G_{XY} + \Delta G_{PQ}, \qquad (21\text{–}9)$$

would proceed naturally from left to right if $\Delta G < 0$. In this manner we visualized the cyclic transporting system to be energetically coupled with some energy yeilding metabolic reaction. The system is able to transport A from 1 to 2 against a concentration difference if ΔG of Eq. (21–9) is less than 0.

We may note that in principle it would make no difference on which surface the energetic coupling were made, that is, whether it involved $X \rightarrow Y$ or $Y \rightarrow X$ or even both. It is required, however, that there be a spatial separation of these two reactions. It is obvious that the system would be ineffective as an effective transport mechanism for A if, in the scheme of Fig. 21–4, Y were to be reconverted to X at surface 2. For this reason, we must stipulate that the chemical reaction which is nonenergetically coupled be one which, though possessing the necessary free energy to proceed in a forward direction, requires a catalyst. Such a catalyst is, of course, in biological systems, an enzyme. Similarly, an enzymatic catalysis of the conversion of X to Y at surface 2 would ensure its localization to this surface. Employing enzymes in this manner, in our scheme, we have no difficulty in concept to spacially separate these two chemical reactions, source for X and sink for X, to either side of a membranal boundary. We locate the appropriate enzyme at the appropriate surface.

We have outlined a scheme which will, in principle, carry out the accumulative transport of a constituent. It is to be emphasized, however, that such schemata have yet to be demonstrated in biological systems by any direct isolation procedure. Evidence for their existence to date is purely circumstantial, the validity of the evidence resting largely on how well the dynamic behavior of such a model scheme analyzed theoretically conforms to experimental observation. For this reason, we will undertake here a simple analysis of this type of model transport scheme.

First, we may reason that the flux of A from side 1 to 2 will bear the same sort of relation to the concentration of A as we have derived for transport by chemical association alone. Indeed, when the cycle is actively working, the concentration of X may be kept vanishingly small in the region of surface 2 so that c_{AX_2} is, likewise, so small that it may be ignored. Thus, Eq. (21–3) simplifies to

$$J_{AX} = p_{AX}^m c_{AX_1}, \qquad c_{AX_2} = 0, \qquad (21\text{–}10)$$

and c_{AX_1} is given as a function of c_{A_1} by Eq. (21–5), whereupon the result is identical to Eq. (21–7). Thus, the net transport by this metabolically coupled system should exhibit the same type of kinetics as illustrated in Fig. 21–3, i.e., saturation kinetics with a rectangular hyperbolic relation between net flux and concentration of A in solution 1. This is indeed a good approximation for all experimental observations made to date on transport of molecules that are dependent on metabolically coupled reactions, a fact which lends support but does not prove the essential correctness of the model. With this assumption of c_{X_2} being held at a very low concentration, the back flux would be negligible and thus the net flux would be expected to be independent of c_{A_2}. The maximum flux observable is again asymptotically approached at large c_{A_1}, and its actual value is dependent upon the total quantity of X available and upon the permeability of the complex p_{AX}^m. Furthermore, in a given steady-state situation, there may be a dependence of the transport flux of A (or rather AX) upon the individual reaction velocities of Y being converted to X or even $X + P \rightarrow Y + Q$, and upon the return of Y from 2 to 1 by diffusion. In actual fact, when these considerations become quantitatively significant, it implies that C_T becomes a function of the flux rate and the hyperbolic relation developed above would not be valid. For our purpose, we recognize this possibility, but need not consider it analytically or quantitatively.

It is of some interest to consider the factors that determine the maximum concentration difference against which the substance A may be transported. This maximum represents, of course, the maximum work that the cyclic system may perform, a maximum which may be computed if we were to consider the system to come to an equilibrium, for then we may compute the reversible thermodynamic work. Under these conditions J_{AX} goes to zero because the energy required is just that available. If we write for each reaction of the cycle the free energy change per mole and then sum these, we obtain the overall change. Thus,

$$\mu_{A_1} + \mu_{X_1} = \mu_{AX_1},$$
$$\mu_{AX_1} = \mu_{AX_2},$$
$$\mu_{AX_2} = \mu_{A_2} + \mu_{X_2},$$
$$\mu_{X_2} + \mu_P = \mu_{Y_2} + \mu_Q, \qquad (21\text{--}11)$$
$$\mu_{Y_2} = \mu_{Y_1},$$
$$\mu_{Y_1} = \mu_{X_1},$$

and the overall change is

$$\mu_{A_1} + \mu_P = \mu_{A_2} + \mu_Q. \qquad (21\text{--}12)$$

In other words, by rearrangement and by employing the relation expressing the chemical potential in terms of a concentration (Eq. 15–19), we have

$$\mu_P - \mu_Q = \mu_{A_2} - \mu_{A_1} = RT \ln \frac{c_{A_2}}{c_{A_1}}, \qquad (21\text{--}13)$$

which states that the maximum concentration ratio against which A may be transported depends entirely on the metabolic energy difference available in P being converted to Q, a fact which, of course, is intuitively logical. The point of zero transport in case of a metabolically coupled process is then not at the point where c_{A_1} becomes zero as in diffusion by chemical association, but at a point where c_{A_1} is low enough that insufficient energy is available from metabolic sources (P → Q) to perform the work of transport.

Although there is no direct evidence to prove the contention, there is much circumstantial evidence that the reaction of $P \to Q$ is one involving "high energy phosphate" compounds such as ATP → ADP + P, a reaction very commonly encountered in biochemistry. The standard free energy, ΔG^0, of this reaction is of the order of -7500 cal/mole^{-1}. The concentrations of the reactants and products of this reaction in cytoplasm may be such as to give an actual free energy of reaction of the order of 2000 to 3000 cal · mole^{-1}. Such being the case,

$$\log \frac{c_{A_2}}{c_{A_1}} = \frac{3000}{2.3RT} = 2.1, \qquad T = 38°C, \qquad (21\text{-}14)$$

giving a ratio

$$\frac{c_{A_2}}{c_{A_1}} \cong 100. \qquad (21\text{-}15)$$

It is evident therefore that transport may occur against a hundredfold difference in concentration.

In recent years there has accumulated additional circumstantial evidence which suggests that ATP and a specific associated enzyme, whose activity requires the presence of Na^+ and K^+, do participate rather directly in the transport process. However, the mechanism is still conjectural especially insofar as some evidence suggests that a number of molecules (4-8) of a substance such as Na^+ may be transported per mole of ATP utilized.

21-4 Characteristics of active transport. We may summarize some of the typical properties of active transport in biological systems. These properties are useful experimentally in judging whether a given observed flux is the result of an active transport system or not. It is to be emphasized, however, that the total observed transport of a substance across a biological membrane is not the result of any single mechanism but, as previously indicated in Chapter 20, is, in general, the result of several mechanisms occurring simultaneously. The same may be said when active transport exists, for in parallel there must be simple diffusion processes. Indeed, under true steady-state conditions, when all the concentrations, both cytoplasmic and extracellular, are time independent, the net "passive" diffusion flux is equal to the net active flux against this concentration difference. Experimentally any measurement of flux by isotopic or other means is a measure of all the fluxes combined unless, of course, the conditions may be imposed which specifically interfere with a particular mechanism without disturbing transport by any other mechanism.

Typical of active transport systems are the following characteristics.

(a) The net flux generally bears some nonlinear relation to the concentration of the constituent transported. This nonlinear relation is usually hyperbolic in form as illustrated in Fig. 21-3, and shows an asymptotically approached maximum flux independent of concentration of the transported constituent at high concentrations. This is in distinct contrast to that of the usual simple diffusion or permeability, but is also seen in those cases of transport by specific chemical association indicated in Section 21-2. The typical hyperbolic relation is clearly evident in the relation between

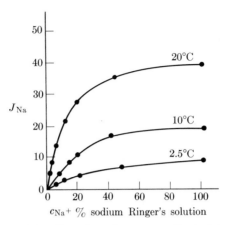

FIG. 21-5. Net flux of sodium ion, J_{Na}, across the isolated frog skin (*Rana pipiens*) as a function of sodium ion concentration c_{Na} bathing the external surface. The flux is seen to diminish with a decrease in temperature. Modified from Snell and Leeman [Ref. 3].

net Na^+ transport and concentration of Na^+ bathing the external surface of a frog skin seen in Fig. 21-5.

(b) The flux of an active transport system must be clearly dependent upon a metabolic source of energy, coupled to metabolism by chemical reactions. Therefore, interference with metabolism should lead to an observable decrease in flux. A simple means of interference is to lower the temperature to greatly decrease metabolic reaction rates. (See Chapters 22 and 23.) This is seen in Fig. 21-5, which shows a marked decrease in flux of Na^+ with decrease in temperature to 2.5°C. In many systems it is also readily demonstrable that inhibition of metabolism by chemical means, using metabolic inhibitors, leads to inhibition of active transport. The effect of temperature is of some considerable importance in the storage of erythrocytes where active transport systems exist that determine the sodium and potassium composition. In the cold, metabolism is virtually stopped and as a consequence active transport ceases. However, simple permeation by diffusion, not directly metabolically dependent, continues. With time, therefore, there is a continuing potassium loss and sodium gain by the cell to approach an equilibrium distribution with the plasma environment.

(c) The flux of an active transport system is generally against an existing concentration difference, taking a constituent from a low concentration and accumulating it at a higher concentration. This is opposite to that of free permeation by simple diffusion processes. However, in principle, active transport systems could operate to facilitate the passively occurring permeation mechanisms.

(d) As a consequence of C, the ratios of the two unidirectional fluxes observed for systems exhibiting active transport depart from that calculated considering simple diffusion forces. Namely, the unidirectional flux ratio is not given by

$$\frac{J_{A_{12}}}{J_{A_{21}}} = \frac{c_{A_1}}{c_{A_2}} e^{-z_A F \Delta\psi / RT} , \qquad (21\text{–}16)$$

and departure from this relation may be taken as evidence for the existence of an active transport system.

(e) Active transport systems generally exhibit a degree of competition for transport of structurally or functionally similar molecules or ions. For instance, in the frog skin, lithium ion appears to be actively transported in competition with sodium ion and in the erythrocyte, rubidium is transported in competition with K^+. In ascites tumor cells and in intestinal mucosa, many of the different amino acids appear to utilize the same active transport system and thus compete with each other.

(f) Finally, active transport systems generally have a greater dependency on temperature *per se* than do passive permeation mechanisms. This may be rightfully attributable to their coupling to metabolic reactions and to the fact that chemical reactions are directly involved. Chemical reactions, in general, show a larger temperature coefficient than do simple diffusion processes.

REFERENCES

1. E. J. HARRIS, *Transport and Accumulation in Biological Systems.* Academic Press, New York, 1960.

2. "Active Transport and Secretion," *Symposium Soc. Exp. Biol.*, Vol. VIII (1954).

3. F. M. SNELL and C. P. LEEMAN, "Temperature Coefficients of the Sodium Transport System of Isolated Frog Skin," *Biochem. Biophys. Acta.* **25,** 311 (1957).

4. A. LEAF, "Respiration and Active Sodium Transport of Isolated Toad Bladder," *J. Biol. Chem.* **234,** 1625 (1959).

5. H. H. CLARKE, Ed., *Ion Transport Across Membranes.* Academic Press, New York, 1954.

6. Q. R. MURPHY, Ed., *Metabolic Aspects of Transport Across Cell Membranes.* Univ. of Wisconsin Press, Madison, 1957.

7. A. KLEINZELLER and A. KOTYK, *Membrane Transport and Metabolism,* Proceedings of a Symposium held in Prague. Academic Press, New York, 1960.

8. F. M. SNELL, and W. K. NOELL, Eds., *Transcellular Membrane Potentials and Ionic Fluxes.* Gordon and Breach, New York, 1964.

CHAPTER 22

KINETICS OF CHEMICAL REACTIONS

I. SIMPLE REACTION MECHANISMS

CHAPTER 22

KINETICS OF CHEMICAL REACTIONS

I. SIMPLE REACTION MECHANISM

22–1 Introduction. In Chapters 14–18 the various principles involved in considering the equilibrium of chemical and physical systems have been discussed. In these discussions we have stated that a reaction proceeding naturally always involves a free energy decrease at a given constant temperature and pressure. An equilibrium state is one in which further infinitesimal changes are attended by zero free energy change. In discussing chemical reactions we did not, however, discuss the rates of chemical reactions nor give note to any of the factors that make some reactions proceed very rapidly and others proceed exceedingly slowly. Thermodynamics, as we have developed it, is not concerned with the rates of processes. Thermodynamic considerations alone cannot be utilized to make predictions concerning rates. As we have indicated in Chapter 15, such considerations only determine whether or not a given process *may* proceed naturally. In our discussion of simple diffusion and transport processes, however, we did show that the rates of these processes, namely the fluxes, are indeed proportional to free energy decreases in a spatial direction (negative gradients in the chemical potentials) or, in the case of membranes, proportional to free energy differences across these structures. Are the rates of chemical reactions then expected to be proportional to the decrease in energy attending the reaction process? The answer is in the affirmative, but the proportionality relation is rather limited and valid only when such reactions are very near equilibrium.

Rather than limiting our discussion of reaction rates to only those systems close to equilibrium, we will employ a kinetic description of chemical reactions. This is an approach based on probability considerations. It describes the behavior of chemical reactions in terms of the concentrations of the reactants and products, together with certain empirical coefficients, the *rate coefficients*. It is outside the scope of this book to include much discussion on the theoretical interpretation in molecular terms of these rate coefficients. It is here that kinetic theory assumes a level of sophistication relegated to a more advanced treatment than is possible in this introduction.

We will treat in this chapter the more simple reaction systems and describe what is meant by *molecularity* of a reaction and its *kinetic order*. We will point out the relation to equilibrium and also discuss that aspect of a reaction which pertains to its temperature dependence and the relation of this to the concept of *activation energy*. In the following chapter, we consider some of the special properties of enzyme catalyzed reactions.

22–2 Molecularity and kinetic order of chemical reactions. The transformations of chemical substances in even the simplest of chemical reactions is generally complex. Electron orbital shifts occur, and mean interatomic distances become altered, all in a very complex manner. However, we are not concerned with the details at the electronic level but primarily with the mechanism at the molecular level, that is, whether the reaction is an intramolecular rearrangement and thus involves only molecules of the one kind or involves combinations of two molecules or more. This level of mechanistic consideration is termed the *molecularity* of a reaction. Thus, one may have a *monomolecular* reaction, which may be written

$$A \rightleftharpoons P. \qquad (22\text{-}1)$$

The substance A is considered as the reactant and by convention is written on the left, whereas the substance P is the product and is written on the right. This particular reaction is monomolecular both in the forward direction (from left to right) and in the reverse direction (from right to left).

A *bimolecular* reaction mechanism may be written

$$A + B \rightleftharpoons P, \qquad (22\text{-}2)$$

which in the forward direction is bimolecular but in the reverse direction is monomolecular. Or we may write

$$A + B \rightleftharpoons P + Q, \qquad (22\text{-}3)$$

in which the reaction mechanism in both directions is bimolecular. It is recognized that we may have a bimolecular reaction in which either A and B or P and Q are the same substance. In such instances, we may write, for example,

$$2A \rightleftharpoons P. \qquad (22\text{-}4)$$

It is apparent that we may extend our considerations to higher molecularity such as the trimolecular reaction

$$A + B + C \rightleftharpoons P. \qquad (22\text{-}5)$$

It is intuitively apparent that for chemical change to occur which involves two or more molecules, the molecules must be in juxtaposition (i.e., they must collide), so that electronic shifts and bond rearrangements may be realized. The simultaneous collision of three bodies might reasonably be expected to be very infrequent, depending on how stringent the condition of simultaneity. Indeed, it is generally found that reactions with an overall molecularity greater than bimolecular proceed in a stepwise manner, involving a number of successive bimolecular encounters. For instance, the reaction (22–5) may proceed according to the following scheme:

$$A + B \rightleftharpoons AB, \quad AB + C \rightleftharpoons P, \tag{22-6}$$

involving therefore a sequence of reaction steps, none of which is greater than bimolecular.

Examples of truly monomolecular mechanisms as indicated in Eq. (22–1) are not very common. However, the mutarotation of α, D-glucopyranose to β, D-glucopyranose via the intermediate open structure as illustrated in Fig. 11–4 is a suitable example. The radioactive decay of unstable isotopes mentioned in Chapter 2 provides another example, although such transformations do not proceed in reverse.

Bimolecular mechanisms are by far the most common. In biological systems water is often one of the reactant constituents, such as in all hydrolytic reactions. Many of these were noted and discussed in Chapters 5 and 11. Also all reactions involving proton exchanges, i.e. acid-base reactions, are bimolecular in character in that in aqueous systems water is involved as indicated in Eq. (17–2).

Although the molecularity of a chemical reaction refers to the number of molecules involved in the particular molecular transformation and is related therefore to the stoichiometry of the reaction, it *does not indicate* the particular kinetic behavior of the reaction system. The kinetic behavior refers to the form of mathematical equation which describes the time course of a reaction system stating the dependence of the rate of the reaction on the variables of the system. Under given conditions, these variables are generally the concentrations of the constituents involved. The particular form of dependence of the reaction rate on the concentration of the reactants is referred to as the *order* of the reaction and several orders are to be recognized. Thus, one may find first-order, second-order, and possibly higher-order reactions, as well as zero-order. The kinetic order is determined only in part by the molecularity of a reaction. It is determined principally by the particular conditions that prevail. The distinction between molecularity and kinetic order is an important one, and although it may appear somewhat subtle at the moment, it will become clearer as the mathematical relations are developed.

22–3 The kinetic equations. The kinetic equations describing the behavior of chemical reactions are based upon certain probability considerations. We need not at this point elaborate but will defer much of our discussion to Section 22–6. At this point we wish to recognize only that these probability factors are related to the probabilities of, for example, intramolecular rearrangement or nuclear disintegration as may occur in a monomolecular reaction, or are related to the probability of molecular encounters as in the case of a bimolecular reaction.

Consider first the simple reaction represented in Eq. (22–1). In such a transformation it is reasonable to suppose that each molecule has an inherent probability in a given interval of time of undergoing change. For a population of such molecules, therefore, the number of transformations occurring per unit time, say from $A \rightarrow P$, should be proportional to the number of A molecules present at that time. Then in a given volume element, the reaction velocity or flux per unit volume, given the symbol J and having the dimensions of moles $\cdot$ sec$^{-1} \cdot$ cm^{-3}, would be proportional to the concentration. This is true for each "direction" of transformation, $A \rightarrow P$ and $P \rightarrow A$. Designating the proportionality coefficients, k_1 and k_{-1}, we may write

$$J_1 = k_1 c_A \quad \text{and} \quad J_{-1} = k_{-1} c_P, \qquad (22\text{–}7)$$

where the subscripts to the J's imply the direction of transformation. The net flux from left to right, J_n, is then given as

$$J_n = J_1 - J_{-1} = k_1 c_A - k_{-1} c_P, \qquad (22\text{–}8)$$

which expresses the net flux as a difference in the two unidirectional fluxes.

This is quite analogous to the treatment of transport fluxes given in Section 20–3. It is evident that both kinetic coefficients, k_1 and k_{-1}, have the dimension of sec^{-1}. These coefficients are related to the inherent probabilities of transformation of the respective constituents in the reaction and are assumed to be constant at any given temperature, an assumption well justified by a wealth of experimental data.

Consider next the chemical reaction represented in Eq. (22–2). As has been indicated, in order for reaction or transformation to occur between the two reactants A and B, they must necessarily collide. This is not to suggest that a collision is sufficient to bring about a reaction, for factors relating to the molecular energies and particular orientation of the molecules at the time of collision as well as other factors are involved. Suffice it to say that under given constant conditions it is reasonable to suppose that a constant fraction of the collisions between molecules A and B are effective in that they result in a transformation.

The probability of finding a molecule of the kind A in a particular small region in space is proportional to its concentration. The same may be said for a molecule of kind B. Since these are independent probabilities, the combined probability of finding one of A and one of B at the same time in the same region of space, i.e., a collision, is the product of the individual probabilities. Thus, the frequency of collision, the number occurring per unit time, is proportional to the product of the two concentrations. The kinetic equations are then

$$J_1 = k_1 c_A \cdot c_B \quad \text{and} \quad J_{-1} = k_{-1} c_P, \tag{22-9}$$

with a net flux given by

$$J_n = J_1 = J_{-1} = k_1 c_A \cdot c_B - k_{-1} c_P. \tag{22-10}$$

This equation is obviously similar to Eq. (22-8), but differs in that there appears a term containing the product of concentration, i.e., concentration is in the power of two, and the equation is second order. The dimension of k_1 is now $cm^3 \cdot mole^{-1} \cdot sec^{-1}$, and it is a second-order rate coefficient. In this particular example k_{-1} is a first-order rate coefficient.

By now it should be apparent how the kinetic equations are formulated. We may proceed to write for (22-3),

$$J_n = k_1 c_A \cdot c_B - k_{-1} c_P \cdot c_Q, \tag{22-11}$$

for reaction (22-4),

$$J_n = k_1 c_A^2 - k_{-1} c_P, \tag{22-12}$$

and for reaction (22-5),

$$J_n = k_1 c_A \cdot c_B \cdot c_C - k_{-1} c_P. \tag{22-13}$$

In a reaction system the kinetic order of the reaction is determined by its particular behavior in time. For instance, does J in the time course of the reaction depend upon the first power of the concentration as it may vary during the progress of the reaction? If so, then the reaction kinetics are said to be of *first order*. If J depends on the second power of the concentration variable, then it is said to be of *second order*. If, on the other hand, J is independent of any concentration variable, the reaction is then said to be of *zero order*. It may be evident that the kinetic order may be as large as the molecularity of a reaction but it need not be as large. For instance, it is not difficult to imagine a bimolecular hydrolytic reaction occurring in dilute aqueous solution. One of the reactants is thus water, whose mole concentration during the course of the reaction would undergo negligible change. Kinetically the reaction proceeds as though it were first order, showing a dependency upon the first power of the concentration of the reactant being hydrolyzed. One recognizes then that the reaction is first order with respect to the concentration of this particular substance. This matter is discussed further in the following section.

We will discuss next the integrated forms of the kinetic equations. This is desirable because in any experiment designed to study kinetic processes, it is not the reaction velocity, J, that is measured but instead the concentrations of reactants or products as a function of time. From these data,

J is computed and the rate coefficients determined. These concentrations may be measured in a variety of ways depending upon the particular experiment. One may, for example, remove small samples from the reaction mixture at periodic intervals and carry out a chemical analysis; or one may observe the reaction mixture continuously, utilizing a spectrophotometric means of estimating the concentration of one of the constituents. In any case it is a concentration variable that must be assessed; and it is the integrated equations that express the concentrations as a function of time.

22–4 Integration of the kinetic equations. It is to be recognized that the kinetic equations given in the foregoing are, speaking mathematically, differential equations in that the reaction flux is proportional to the time rate of change of the concentrations of the reactants or products. In other words, we have for Eq. (22–8),

$$J_n = -\frac{dc_A}{dt} = +\frac{dc_P}{dt}, \qquad (22\text{–}14)$$

for Eq. (22–10),

$$J_n = -\frac{dc_A}{dt} = -\frac{dc_B}{dt} = +\frac{dc_P}{dt}, \qquad (22\text{–}15)$$

and for Eq. (22–12),

$$J_n = -\frac{1}{2}\frac{dc_A}{dt} = +\frac{dc_P}{dt}. \qquad (22\text{–}16)$$

These relations are valid, of course, only if the reaction systems are closed ones, i.e., none of the concentrations of the constituents involved are being altered by other reactions involving the same chemical substance.

In the study of reaction kinetics, as was pointed out in the previous section, it is not the reaction velocity J that is measured, but instead the concentrations of reactants or products as a function of time. In this respect, therefore, it is desirable to integrate the differential kinetic equations to express the concentration variables as a function of time. However, before this may be done, it is necessary to reduce the differential kinetic equations to contain only one variable and time rather than the several concentration variables of reactants and products. In closed single-reaction systems, this is always possible in that conservation of mass expressed by the stoichiometry of the reaction provides the necessary relations among the concentration variables.

We illustrate how this is done utilizing the simplest chemical reaction, Eq. (22–1), whose kinetic equation is given by Eq. (22–8). Combining Eqs. (22–8) and (22–14), we have

$$-\frac{dc_A}{dt} = k_1 c_A - k_{-1} c_P, \qquad (22\text{–}17)$$

which is a differential equation in two variables, c_A and c_P. In a closed system, however, it is to be recognized that

$$c_A + c_P = C^0 = \text{constant},\qquad(22\text{–}18)$$

where C^0 is obviously the total concentration. It is now evident that Eqs. (22–17) and (22–18) may be combined to eliminate one of the concentration variables, say, c_P, resulting in

$$-\frac{dc_A}{dt} = (k_1 + k_{-1})c_A - k_{-1}C^0.\qquad(22\text{–}19)$$

This can now be rearranged and integrated. We write

$$\int_{c_A^0}^{c_A} \frac{dc_A}{c_A - [k_{-1}/(k_1 + k_{-1})]C^0} = -\int_0^t (k_1 + k_{-1})\,dt,\qquad(22\text{–}20)$$

where the integration limits indicate that at $t = 0, c_A = c_A^0$, the so-called initial condition, and that at some time, t, the concentration will be c_A. Both integrands are of standard form (see table of integrals in Appendix), and carrying out the integration, we obtain

$$\ln \frac{c_A - [k_{-1}/(k_1 + k_{-1})]C^0}{c_A^0 - [k_{-1}/(k_1 + k_{-1})]C^0} = -(k_1 + k_{-1})t.\qquad(22\text{–}21)$$

This equation describes the concentration, c_A, as a function of time from given initial conditions $c_A = c_A^0$ and $c_P = c_P^0 = C^0 - c_A^0$ to any time thereafter. Of course, as t approaches ∞ the system approaches equilibrium. Accordingly, the numerator of the logarithmic term approaches zero, and we have

$$c_A^e = \frac{k_{-1}}{k_1 + k_{-1}} C^0 = \frac{k_{-1}}{k_1 + k_{-1}} (c_A^e + c_P^e)\qquad(22\text{–}22)$$

or

$$\frac{c_P^e}{c_A^e} = \frac{k_1}{k_{-1}}\qquad(22\text{–}23)$$

as the relation between the reactant and product concentration at equilibrium. We will discuss more fully the relations between the kinetic equations and equilibrium in Section 22–5.

Equation (22–21) is a little more complicated than need be considered if one were able to choose appropriate experimental conditions such that the back reaction flux, J_{-1}, were negligible in comparison to the forward flux, J_1. As may be readily seen, this condition prevails at the very start of the reaction if the product concentrations at this time are zero. For instance, in the present example, $J_{-1} = k_{-1}c_P$. By neglecting J_{-1} and confining our attention to reaction systems where this is indeed a valid assumption, our differential equation simplifies to

$$-\frac{dc_A}{dt} = k_1 c_A, \tag{22-24}$$

which on rearrangement gives

$$\frac{dc_A}{c_A} = d \ln c_A = -k_1\, dt. \tag{22-25}$$

Integration (see Appendix) between appropriate limits gives

$$\int_{c_A^0}^{c_A} d \ln c_A = -k_1 \int_0^t dt = \ln \frac{c_A}{c_A^0} = -k_1 t, \tag{22-26}$$

a form considerably less opaque than Eq. (22-21) but valid, of course, only under conditions such that the backward reaction flux, J_{-1}, can be neglected. This can, in general, be readily achieved, and certainly in the case of radioisotope decay, the reverse reaction always remains zero. A plot of Eq. (22-26) appears in Fig. 22-1, and it is evident that the logarithm of c_A decreases linearly with time. It is a characteristic of this equation that the time required for c_A to decrease to a given fraction of its initial value is independent of the actual initial value and is determined solely by the value of k_1. In the case of isotopic decay, it has become conventional to speak of the "half-life," which is the time required for the concentration (or amount) to be reduced to one-half of an original concentration (or amount). It may be deduced that this $t_{1/2}$ is related to k_1 by

$$t_{1/2} = \frac{2.303 \log 2}{k_1} = \frac{0.694}{k_1}. \tag{22-27}$$

The foregoing has indicated how in the simplest reaction system one can obtain from the differential kinetic equations, expressing the reaction flux

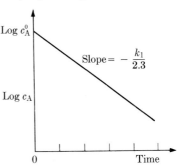

Fig. 22-1.   Diagram illustrating the first-order reaction kinetics of radioactive isotopic disintegration. (See Eq. 24-10.) At $t = 0$, the concentration is c_A^0. Concentration and time are in arbitrary units.

as a function of concentrations, an integrated form expressing the concentrations as a function of time. The resultant form in which the logarithm of the concentration (or the difference between the concentration and a constant) varies linearly with time is that known as first-order kinetics.

Higher-order kinetics are somewhat more complicated, but for certain kinetic systems, integration of the differential equations may be achieved in a straightforward manner. We illustrate now with the bimolecular reaction scheme of Eq. (22–3), the kinetic equation which is given by Eq. (22–10). Combining this with Eq. (22–15) gives the differential equation in the three concentration variables:

$$-\frac{dc_A}{dt} = k_1 c_A c_B - k_{-1} c_P. \tag{22–28}$$

The concentration variables are, however, not all independent, for the chemical stoichiometry specifies that a change in one is associated with a concomitant change in the others. There is a conservation of mass provided the reaction system is closed to the environment. If we let the symbol ξ represent the increase in c_P in mole units, then it represents also the decrease in both c_A and c_B in mole units. We may write then

$$c_P = c_P^0 + \xi, \qquad c_A = c_A^0 - \xi, \qquad c_B = c_B^0 - \xi, \tag{22–29}$$

whereupon Eq. (22–28) may be rewritten in terms of the one variable, ξ, and the initial concentrations:

$$\frac{d\xi}{dt} = k_1(c_A^0 - \xi)(c_B^0 - \xi) - k_{-1}(c_P^0 + \xi). \tag{22–30}$$

This may be rearranged into standard form and integrated. We write

$$\int_0^\xi \frac{d\xi}{\xi^2 + \beta\xi + \gamma} = \int_0^t k_1 \, dt. \tag{22–31}$$

with $\beta = -[c_A^0 + c_B^0 + (k_{-1}/k_1)]$, $\gamma = c_A^0 c_B^0 - (k_{-1}/k_1)c_P^0$. It is to be noted that at $t = 0$, $\xi = 0$. Integration gives (see Appendix)

$$\ln \frac{(2\xi + \beta - \delta)(\beta + \delta)}{(2\xi + \beta + \delta)(\beta - \delta)} = \delta k_1 t, \tag{22–32}$$

with $\delta = \sqrt{\beta^2 - 4\gamma}$. This result expresses the variable ξ as a function of time. It is a rather cumbersome expression, but again simplification may be obtained by proper choice of experimental conditions. In this respect, only initial rates need be considered. This is tantamount to assuming that $c_P k_{-1}$ during the period of observation is sufficiently small to be

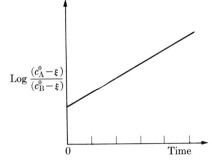

Fig. 22-2. The initial reaction flux for the second-order bimolecular forward reaction of $A + B \rightarrow P$, neglecting the reverse reaction, $P \rightarrow A + B$. See text.

justifiably neglected. Under these circumstances, Eq. (22–32) reduces to

$$\ln \frac{(c_A^0 - \xi)c_B^0}{(c_A^0 - \xi)c_A^0} = (c_A^0 - c_B^0)k_1 t, \tag{22–33}$$

as may be verified. Plots of the function $\log [(c_A^0 - \xi)/(c_B^0 - \xi)]$ vs. time are seen in Fig. 22–2 and, as Eq. (22–33) indicates, results in a straight line with an intercept of $t = 0$ of $\log c_A^0/c_B^0$. The slope of the line is $(c_A^0 - c_B^0)k_1/2.3$, from which the coefficient k_1 may be evaluated.

It is apparent in Eq. (22–33) that if $c_A^0 = c_B^0$, the equation is indeterminate in that both sides are zero. However, if one lets $c_A^0 = c_B^0$ in the original differential equation, Eq. (22–28), then retaining the assumption that $k_{-1}c_P$ may be neglected in studying the initial reaction velocity, considerable simplification ensues. Integration then gives

$$\frac{2}{c_A^0 + c_B^0 - 2\xi} - \frac{2}{c_A^0 + c_B^0} = k_1 t \tag{22–34}$$

or, since $c_A^0 = c_B^0$ and $c_A^0 - \xi = c_A$,

$$\frac{1}{c_A} - \frac{1}{c_A^0} = k_1 t. \tag{22–35}$$

Here it is evident that a plot of $1/c_A$ vs. t results in a straight line as seen in Fig. 22–3. The slope of the line has a value of k_1. Except for a factor of two in the slope, which results from the stoichiometry involved, the above result is identical to that we would have obtained on integrating the differential equation describing reaction (22–4), which is given by combining Eqs. (22–12) and (22–16), and neglecting J_{-1}.

The foregoing has indicated how we may proceed to integrate differential equations of higher molecularity, and in illustration we have utilized a bimolecular example. The resultant equations, (22–32), which is generally valid, and (22–33) and (22–35), which are valid under restricted experi-

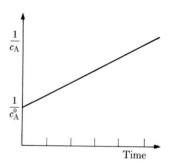

FIG. 22–3. Plot of the integrated form of a second-order bimolecular reaction. Equation (22–34) represents the transformation, $A + B \to P$ with the conditions that $c_A^0 = c_B^0$.

mental conditions, express the concentration of each chemical substance through a parametric variable ξ as a function of time. These are the equations characteristic of second-order kinetics.

At this juncture, it should be pointed out that very often the experimental conditions may be so chosen that a bimolecular reaction is described by first-order kinetics. We see in Eq. (22–28) or Eq. (22–30) that if one of the reactants, A or B, has a much larger concentration than the other, for instance $c_B \gg c_A$, then for all practical purposes c_B may be considered a constant during the course of the reaction, for $c_B^0 - \xi$ remains virtually constant if c_B^0 is $\gg \xi$. Again, neglecting the reverse reaction flux, we find that Eq. (22–28) may be written

$$-\frac{dc_A}{dt} = (k_1 c_B)c_A \cong (k_1 c_B^0)c_A, \qquad (22\text{–}36)$$

which is identical in form to Eq. (22–24). The coefficient may now be considered to be $k_1 c_B^0$. The integrated form has been illustrated in Fig. 22–1.

As has been previously noted, in many reactions of biological interest, one of the reactants is water, which is usually present in much greater molar concentration than any solute species entering into a reaction. The result is that even though such reactions are bimolecular, they follow first-order kinetics, the reaction flux being dependent upon the solute reactant concentration. As an example, we may consider the hydrolysis reaction of sucrose (see Chapter 11) which may be written

$$\text{Sucrose} + \text{H}_2\text{O} \rightleftharpoons \text{Glucose} + \text{Fructose}. \qquad (22\text{–}37)$$

This reaction is conveniently followed experimentally by changes in optical rotation. In Fig. 22–4 are plotted some concentration changes as a function of time at three different temperatures. The slope of the plots is equal to $-55.4\, k_1/2.3 = -24.0\, k_1$, and it is evident that k_1 must be larger with increasing temperature.

The foregoing discussion on the integrated forms of the kinetic equations may be summarized by stating that it is these particular mathematical re-

Fig. 22–4. Reaction kinetics for the acid hydrolysis of sucrose at several different temperatures. The c_S is the concentration of sucrose at time t, c_S^0 is the initial concentration. The slope is -24.0 k_1, and k_1 computes to be $0.75 \cdot 10^{-6}$ at 15°C, $3.42 \cdot 10^{-6}$ at 25°C, and $14.2 \cdot 10^{-6}$ at 35°C. Dimensions are liter sec^{-1} mole^{-1}.

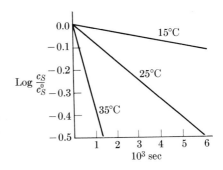

lations together with the graphic plots of experimental data that are used to assess the kinetic order of a chemical reaction. However, as has been indicated, there are certain circumstances under which a chemical reaction may be found to proceed with a constant velocity or reaction flux quite independent of the apparent reactant concentration. Such a reaction bears analogy to the saturation kinetics discussed in Chapter 21 dealing with transport by chemical association (Section 21–2) and active transport (Section 21–4). For such kinetic behavior we speak of zero-order kinetics, and as may be expected, it is most often encountered in catalyzed reactions. A limited amount of catalyst in the presence of a relatively high concentration of reactant becomes "saturated" and reaction thus proceeds at a constant rate. This will be discussed in greater detail in our consideration of enzyme kinetics in the following chapter.

22–5 Kinetic equations and the law of mass action. It is of some interest that the law of mass action derived its name from the kinds of kinetic considerations discussed in the foregoing paragraphs. We have noted that the flux of a chemical reaction, the reaction velocity, forward and reverse, is proportional to the mass of reactant and product respectively. Thus, the action is mass dependent. Let us examine the kinetic equations at equilibrium. It has been previously noted that in our simple monomolecular reaction system [see Eq. (22–23)] as time approaches infinity, a point where equilibrium is to be expected, the ratio of product and reactant concentration is a constant equal to the ratio of the forward and reverse rate constants.

It is evident that at equilibrium, the two "unidirectional" reaction fluxes J_1 and J_{-1}, become equal so that the net reaction flux, J_n, vanishes. Alternatively, it is evident that at equilibrium the time derivatives of all the concentration variables must also vanish. Examining the kinetic equations with these considerations in mind we obtain, for example, for Eq. (22–11),

$$k_1 c_A^e \cdot c_B^e - k_{-1} c_P^e \cdot c_Q^e = 0. \tag{22–38}$$

This may be rearranged to give

$$\frac{c_P^e c_Q^e}{c_A^e c_B^e} = \frac{k_{-1}}{k_1} = K.$$ (22-39)

As before, the superscript e on the concentrations denote that these are equilibrium concentrations. The K, a ratio of rate constants, is the ordinary equilibrium constant, identical to that derived from chemical reactions at equilibrium through consideration of the energy changes (Eq. 16-33). In the present example the stoichiometric coefficients are all unity.

In our thermodynamic considerations of chemical equilibrium, we noted that in order for relations such as Eq. (16-33) to be strictly valid, the concentrations must be in actuality the effective concentrations or activities. This, of course, implies that with use of physical concentrations at equilibrium the relations do not result in a true constant, but instead K would be expected to vary as conditions may be altered. Consequently, since $k_1/k_{-1} = K$, one would also expect that the kinetic coefficients themselves are not strictly constants at a given temperature and pressure, but may vary somewhat with the concentrations under different conditions.

22-6 Temperature coefficients of chemical reactions; activation energy.
It has long been noted that the rates of chemical reactions increase with an increase in temperature. Arrhenius (1887) made an extensive study of this and found that in general the thermal dependence of the reaction flux could be described by the following empirical equation:

$$\log k_i = -A_i \left(\frac{1}{T}\right) + \text{constant},$$ (22-40)

where A_i is the proportionality constant referring to a particular rate coefficient k_i. This relation, known as the Arrhenius equation, has been found valid for a large number of chemical reactions, at least over limited ranges of temperature variation. Also the equation may now be given a sound theoretical basis in which A_i is interpreted as being proportional to an "activation energy." The activation energy, E_i^*, is the energy that a mole of reactant molecules must acquire in order to react, i.e., the amount of energy that a substance must possess in order to undergo transformation. E_i^* is related to the empirical quantity A_i by $E_i^* = RA_i$, where R is the gas constant.

In a population of molecules at a given temperature, not all individual molecules have the same energy, but rather there is a certain distribution of energies as pictured in Fig. 14-1. At a given instant, some molecules have very little kinetic energy, whereas others may have large velocities

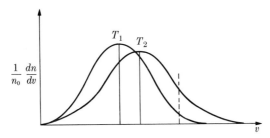

$$\frac{1}{n_0}\frac{dn}{dv}$$

FIG. 22–5. Normal distribution of molecular velocities of a gas at two temperatures, T_1 and T_2, $T_2 T_1$. The n_0 represents the total number of molecules and dn/n_0 is that fraction possessing a velocity in the range of v to $v + dv$. The area under each curve has a value of unity.

and thus a large amount of kinetic energy. Similar statements may be made concerning the vibrational energy that is associated with stretching or bending of covalent bonds. If we were to plot the fractional number of total molecules, dn/n_0, having velocities in the range between v and $v + dv$, we might obtain curves much like those portrayed in Fig. 22–5. In this figure, curves are drawn for two different temperatures. The mean energy is, of course, related to the temperature and shifts slightly upward with an increase in temperature. However, there is also a broadening and flattening of the curve. The areas under the curves are the same, since the ordinate represents a fractional quantity. Such curves are a normal distribution and are described mathematically by the relation

$$\frac{1}{n_0}\frac{dn}{dv} = \frac{mv}{kT}\,e^{-mv^2/2kT}; \qquad (22\text{–}41)$$

$\frac{1}{2}mv^2$ is the kinetic energy of the molecule, which we may designate as ϵ, and k is R/N, where R is the gas constant and N is Avogadro's number. The change in kinetic energy, $d\epsilon$, for a change in velocity, dv, is $d\epsilon = mv\,dv$; substituting in Eq. (22–41), we obtain

$$\frac{1}{n_0}\,dn = \frac{1}{kT}\,e^{-\epsilon/kT}\,d\epsilon. \qquad (22\text{–}42)$$

We ask then what fraction of all the molecules present has an energy greater than some prescribed value of ϵ when the fraction dn/n_0 has an energy in the range ϵ to $\epsilon + d\epsilon$.

To ascertain this we must integrate under the distribution curve, determining the area under that portion from some given energy ϵ upward to ∞. Thus, we write

$$\int_0^n \frac{dn}{n_0} = \frac{1}{kT}\int_\epsilon^\infty e^{-\epsilon/kT}\,d\epsilon. \qquad (22\text{–}43)$$

These integrations may be easily performed (see Appendix) with the result that

$$\frac{n}{n_0} = e^{-\epsilon/kT}, \tag{22-44}$$

which states that n out of the total n_0 molecules present would be expected to have an energy of ϵ or greater. This is the famous Maxwell-Boltzmann equation and pertains to the equilibrium distribution of molecular energies. We multiply numerator and denominator of the exponent by Avogadro's number to put the energy in units per mole; and taking logarithms of both sides, we obtain

$$\ln \frac{n}{n_0} = -\frac{E}{RT}. \tag{22-45}$$

Comparing Eq. (22-45) with Eq. (22-40), together with the definition of E^*, we note that n/n_0 varies in a fashion identical to that of k_i, the particular rate coefficient. In this respect we deduce, therefore, that the activation energy, E_i^*, is to be interpreted as that energy which individual molecules must possess (per mole) in order to react. We note in Fig. 22-5 that for a relative small change in a mean kinetic energy (velocity in this case), the area under the curves to the right of the vertical dashed line is greatly different, and thus greatly alters the fraction of molecules possessing at least this amount of energy. The reaction velocity would be altered accordingly.

From the data of Fig. 22-4 relating to the hydrolysis of sucrose at three different temperatures, we may calculate the energy of activation, E^*. Equation (22-45) or Eq. (22-40) are applicable at each temperature, and the difference for any two temperatures takes the form

$$\ln k_1' - \ln k_1 = -\frac{E^*}{R}\left(\frac{1}{T'} - \frac{1}{T}\right) = -\frac{E^*}{R}\frac{T - T'}{TT'}. \tag{22-46}$$

Substituting the appropriate values for k_1' at temperature T' and k_1 at T, one may solve for E^* to obtain $E^* = 26{,}000$ cal · mole^{-1}. For this value for E^* it is interesting to calculate the increase in the fractional number of molecules possessing an energy of this value or greater. At 15°C,

$$\frac{n}{n_0} = e^{-26{,}000/(R \cdot 288)} = 2 \cdot 10^{-20}, \tag{22-47}$$

while at 25°C,

$$\frac{n}{n_0} = e^{-26{,}000/(R \cdot 298)} = 1 \cdot 10^{-19}. \tag{22-48}$$

It is evident, therefore, that for an increase of only 10°C in the temperature there are $(1 \cdot 10^{-19}/2 \cdot 10^{-20}) = 5$ times as many molecules possessing energy equal to or greater than the activation energy of 26,000 cal · mole^{-1}. One is also impressed by the very small fraction of molecules that at any

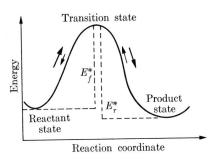

Fig. 22-6. Diagram illustrating the hypothetical transition state as an energy barrier in going from reactants to products along the reaction coordinate.

instant possess this amount of energy. One may calculate that in a liter of a 0.01 molar solution containing $6.02 \cdot 10^{21}$ sucrose molecules, roughly 10 molecules would have the requisite energy at any instant to react with water at 15°C.

22-7 Transition-state theory of reaction kinetics. In the foregoing sections we have, on frequent occasions, spoken of reactions in terms of molecular collision and intrinsic probability of molecular breakdown. Attempts have been made (notably by Eyring and his colleagues) to refine these relatively crude pictures of reaction mechanisms in terms of a concept of a transition-state hypothesis. Although much of the detail in this theory is more sophisticated than necessary in the context of our discussion, a brief outline and some interpretative conclusions are perhaps warranted for the interested student.

In essence this theory postulates the existence of a transition state through which reacting molecules must pass, prior to forming the product or products of the reaction. This transition state is a molecular configuration that has an average energy greater than that of the average energy of the reactants by an amount about equal to the activation energy. We may visualize this in the sketch of Fig. 22-6, in which the hump represents an "energy barrier" in the passage of molecules from the reactant state to the product state. The transition state at the top is, however, a state occupied by a certain small number of molecules. Some of these "activated molecules" may return to the reactant state, while others continue on to become products. The rate of the reaction is proportional to the number of molecules in this transition state at any instant. The problem resolves itself, then, into computing this number and the proportionality constant. This computation involves quantum mechanical considerations with the result that the specific rate coefficient, k_1, with which we are dealing, is related to a steady-state constant, K^* (analogous to an equilibrium constant), as follows:

$$k_i = \gamma kT/h \; K^*, \tag{22-49}$$

where k is the Boltzmann constant, R/N, as before, and h is Planck's constant $(6.54 \cdot 10^{-27}$ erg sec); T is the absolute temperature, and γ is a coefficient which represents the relative probability of a molecule in the transition state proceeding to form products or reverting to reactants.

With no attempt to justify, we may write the usual thermodynamic relations for K^*, treating it as an equilibrium constant. Thus,

$$\Delta G_0^* = -RT \ln K^* \tag{22-50}$$

is the standard Gibbs free energy change associated with formation of the transition-state molecules. Substituting from Eq. (22–49) and recalling the definitions (see Chapter 14), we may write

$$\Delta G_0^* = T \Delta S_0^* - \Delta H_0^* = -RT \ln \frac{hk_i}{\gamma kT}, \tag{22-51}$$

where ΔS_0^* and ΔH_0^* are the standard entropy and enthalpy changes associated with the formation of the transition-state molecules. In exponential form this becomes

$$k_i = \frac{\gamma kT}{h} e^{\Delta S_0^*/R} \cdot e^{-\Delta H_0^*/RT}, \tag{22-52}$$

which we compare with Eq. (22–44) written in terms of activation energy per mole

$$\frac{n}{n_0} = e^{-E^*/RT}. \tag{22-53}$$

We have previously stated that k_i is proportional to n/n_0, and if we therefore identify E^* with ΔH_0^* (actually $E^* - RT = \Delta H_0^*$), we see that the coefficient of this proportionality is $(\gamma kT/h)e^{\Delta S_0^*/R}$. The factor $\gamma kT/h$ has the dimensions of sec^{-1} and therefore is a frequency which may be interpreted in terms of frequency of collision. The factor $e^{\Delta S_0^*/R}$ is, of course, dimensionless, but involving the entropy, it may be interpreted in terms of the effectiveness of the molecular collision, together with possible steric factors involved.

These brief considerations of the transition state do not do justice to an elegant theoretical development in a very difficult area. The interested reader is referred to standard texts on this matter.

REFERENCES

1. F. H. JOHNSON, H. EYRING, and M. J. POLLISAR, *Kinetic Basis of Molecular Biology.* Wiley, New York, 1954.

2. S. GLASSTONE, K. J. LAIDLER, and H. EYRING, *The Theory of Rate Processes.* McGraw-Hill, New York, 1941.

3. K. J. LAIDLER, *Chemical Kinetics of Enzyme Action.* Oxford Press, 1958.

CHAPTER 23

KINETICS OF CHEMICAL REACTIONS

II. ENZYMATIC REACTIONS

CHAPTER 23

KINETICS OF CHEMICAL REACTIONS

II. ENZYMATIC REACTIONS

23-1 Introduction. In the previous chapter the essence of simple chemical reaction systems was presented and discussed. However, most chemical reactions occurring in biological systems, at least those reactions that are not purely ionic in character, depend upon particular biological catalysts, the enzymes. In general, it is true that reactions involving ionic associations and dissociations, such as proton exchanges, are very rapid in their approach to equilibrium, but reactions that involve the formation and rupture of covalent linkages are extremely slow under the ordinary conditions represented by the biological internal environment. Take, for example, the hydrolysis of sucrose, mentioned in the previous chapter (see Fig. 22-4). In this hydrolysis the pH of the medium is about 1. At pH 6 to 8, however, a condition more representative of the biological cytoplasmic and extracellular environment, the rate of hydrolysis is imperceptible unless catalyzed. Catalysis is then a particular mechanism whereby the rate of a reaction may be enhanced.

Enzymes are biological catalysts and, as indicated before, are proteins (see Chapters 6 and 7). For the most part, therefore, they are true macromolecules and possess the characteristics generally associated with such structures. In particular, it is well to remind the reader that they are polyampholytes, bearing both positive and negative charges whose distributions and numbers are sensitively determined by the pH of the solution. Their solubility characteristics are determined in large part by their particular amino acid compositions, some being freely soluble and free in cytoplasm, and others being closely associated with structural components of the cell and subcellular particles. Their structures are complicated and subject to relatively easy conformational changes termed *denaturation*, especially if the temperature is too high. Functionally, therefore, they are quite thermally labile.

Only a portion of an enzyme molecule appears to be directly concerned with its functional properties as a catalyst. This has led to the concept of an enzymatic site on such molecules, a site whose particular characteristics may lend great specificity to its catalytic properties, catalyzing only a particular reaction or class of reactions. This site may be composed entirely of amino acid residues, or it may contain other types of functional groups such as certain metals, Fe^{2+} or Fe^{3+}, porphyrin residues, or many temporarily linked compounds. Often the word *holoenzyme* is applied to the complete entity, and *apoenzyme* to the protein portion alone.

In this chapter we are interested in developing some concepts of the mechanisms of action of these specific catalysts. We cannot discuss much in the way of molecular mechanisms, for not only is little known concerning this, but what is known is limited to certain model enzymatic systems. We are more interested in the general characteristics of kinetic behavior and how these pertain to a general molecular mechanism. This chapter will serve only as a brief introduction to an area in which a vast amount of investigation has been made and is still being made.

23–2 The intermediate compound; enzyme-substrate complex. One may well argue that catalytic effects necessarily involve short-range forces, especially if a high degree of specificity is seen. It is also reasonable to suppose that enzymes function by imposing a temporary reduction in bond stability, a bond strain, in such a manner that electron orbital shifts are more likely to occur, resulting in the chemical transformation or chemical reaction. It is not difficult to visualize, therefore, the possibility that in the process of enzymatic catalysis, a close association between a particular reactant and enzyme occurs, an association having perhaps sufficient stability to be experimentally identifiable. Indeed, this so-called intermediate compound was postulated for enzyme reactions by Michaelis and Menten in 1913 in explanation of the kinetic behavior observed. However, it existed only as a postulate, well founded on circumstantial evidence, until Stern provided some spectroscopic evidence. More recently, Chance (see Ref. 4) unequivocally demonstrated with rapid spectrophotometric techniques, the existence of an enzyme-substrate complex with a particular enzyme, peroxidase. Many other complexes have since been demonstrated and the concept of an intermediate complex in enzymatic catalysis is an integral feature in mechanistic considerations of enzyme action.

We visualize the intermediate compound, then, as being a molecular association between a particular reactant and a particular enzyme to form a complex. The complex may have any degree of stability and, once formed, it may again dissociate to give back the original reactant and enzyme, or if no other reactant is involved in the overall chemical reaction, the complex may acquire sufficient energy to result in a chemical transformation generating the product of the reaction. The product may also have some degree of association with the enzyme. We may write for an enzyme E and a reactant substrate S the following chemical equation:

$$S + E \rightleftharpoons ES \rightleftharpoons ES^* \rightleftharpoons EP^* \rightleftharpoons P + E, \qquad (23\text{--}1)$$

in which ES represents the enzyme-substrate complex, the intermediate compound.   In terms of transition-state theory, this complex becomes activated to ES^* and hence may pass on along the reaction coordinate to give the product of the reaction and return the enzyme unchanged.   The enzyme thus cycles through the reaction system, functioning repetitively with many substrate molecules.   The overall reaction is nothing more than

$$S \rightleftharpoons P, \qquad\qquad (23\text{–}2)$$

and since no net energy is imparted to the system by the presence of enzyme, it is deduced that an enzyme can have no effect on the usual concentration relation between S and P at equilibrium.   The enzyme then affects only the rate of a reaction in its approach to an equilibrium, but not the equilibrium relations themselves.

Before discussing the kinetics involved in a scheme such as Eq. (23–1), one may ask how catalysis effects a change in rate if it does not put energy into the system.   Covalent bonds represent, in general, stable electron orbital configurations (see Chapter 3).   However, an enzyme may conceivably provide a surface of multipoint attachment for a particular substrate molecule in the vicinity of a particular bond.   One may then imagine that this multipoint attachment is such that the bond is strained from its usual configuration and is thus possibly weakened.   We attempt to picture this in Fig. 23–1, utilizing the hydrolysis of urea as catalyzed by the enzyme urease as an example.   Urea is a planar molecule, and by hypothesizing hydrogen-bonding groups on the enzyme at appropriate locations, a rotation of the amino groups of urea out of the planar configuration could be achieved, thus inducing a strain.   Such a strain would subject the molecule to more ready attack by H_2O in that the electron orbitals would not

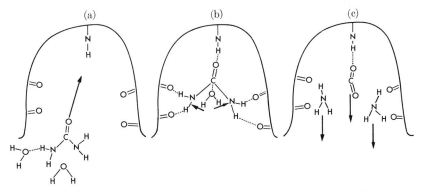

FIG. 23–1.   (a) Sketch of a possible arrangement of hydrogen bonding groups on a urease molecule.   (b) In complexing with urea, bond strain in the planar structure is induced, thus permitting (c) easier attack by colliding H_2O molecules.

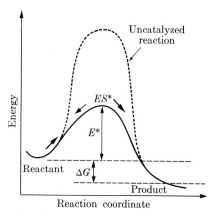

FIG 23–2. Sketch indicating the energy profile along the reaction coordinate for a catalyzed reaction (solid line) and uncatalyzed reaction (broken line).

be in their most stable configuration. This relatively simple-minded scheme has some good theoretical foundations and provides, to some extent, a means of visualizing, in concept, enzymatic action. The resultant effect of bond strain is a decrease in the activation energy of a reaction, which was discussed in the previous chapter. This decrease in activation energy, a principal feature of all catalyzed reactions, has the effect of greatly increasing the probability that chemical reaction will occur. Less energy above the mean molecular energy need be acquired to attain the transition state. In view of the normal spread in the distribution of molecular energies about some mean, the transition state becomes more accessible.

We sketch an energy profile along a reaction coordinate in Fig. 23–2. Activation energies for some reactions, catalyzed and uncatalyzed, are seen in Table 23–1.

TABLE 23–1

ACTIVATION ENERGIES ON SOME REACTIONS

Reaction	Catalyst	Activation energy, cals · mole^{-1}
Sucrose → glucose and fructose	H_3O^+	26,000
	Invertase	11,500
$H_2O_2 \rightarrow H_2O + \frac{1}{2}O_2$	None	18,000
	Colloidal platinum	11,700
	Liver catalase	5,500

23-3 Michaelis-Menten enzyme kinetics. In order to simplify discussion of the kinetics involved in enzymatically catalyzed reactions, we should like first to reduce our proposed schema of possible steps to its bare essentials. We will ignore distinctions between an enzyme-substrate complex, an enzyme-product complex, and any possible transition states of these, lumping them together as a single ES complex. We also will assume that the product concentration will always be negligible and will thus remove from our consideration reverse reaction fluxes. With these simplifications, we rewrite Eq. (23-1) as

$$S + E \underset{k_{-1}}{\overset{k_1}{\rightleftarrows}} ES \overset{k_2}{\rightarrow} E + P, \qquad (23\text{-}3)$$

where we have inserted the kinetic coefficients by the appropriate arrows. We have purposely omitted a k_{-2} since it need not enter our considerations, having made the assumption that the product concentration will be negligible. We assume we have a system in which, for our period of observation, the total quantity (or concentration) of enzyme remains unchanged, that is,

$$C_T = c_E + c_{ES} = \text{constant.} \qquad (23\text{-}4)$$

We recognize that the flux through the reaction at any time is given by the rate of appearance of product and that according to our discussions in Section 22-2, we may write this flux as

$$J = \frac{dc_P}{dt} = k_2 c_{ES}. \qquad (23\text{-}5)$$

Thus, J is proportional to the concentration of enzyme-substrate complex. Our problem is then to express this concentration in terms of the experimentally assessable variables, C_T and c_S. To do this, we may write the usual differential kinetic expression for the change in the concentration of ES with time. This gives

$$\frac{dc_{ES}}{dt} = k_1 c_S c_E - (k_{-1} + k_2) c_{ES}, \qquad (23\text{-}6)$$

the first term giving the rate of production by combination of E and S, and the second describing the total rate of breakdown either into the original reactant and enzyme or into the product, P, and enzyme.

Experimentally, if we were to employ reasonably large concentrations of S and our reaction flux measurement were made by observing, in some sufficiently sensitive manner, the rate of appearance of P, then a measurable amount of product could appear without a significant change in c_S. Under such circumstances it would appear reasonable that $dc_{ES}/dt \cong 0$;

i.e., a virtual steady state with respect to c_{ES} would exist. Equation (23–6) then becomes

$$k_1 c_S \cdot c_E = (k_{-1} + k_2)c_{ES}. \tag{23–7}$$

With Eq. (23–4), this equation may be solved for c_{ES} to give

$$c_{ES} = \frac{C_T c_S}{K_m + c_S}, \qquad K_m \equiv \frac{k_{-1} + k_2}{k_1}, \tag{23–8}$$

where K_m is now a steady-state dissociation constant of the enzyme-substrate complex defined in terms of the individual rate coefficients and is the Michaelis-Menten constant. Combining Eqs. (23–8) and (23–5), we immediately have our final result of

$$J = \frac{k_2 C_T \cdot c_S}{K_m + c_S}, \tag{23–9}$$

describing the velocity or reaction flux in terms of the concentration of substrate, kinetic constants, and the total enzyme concentration.

We note the similarity of this relation to that derived for transport by chemical association and that derived for active transport. Indeed, the model from which the mathematics is formulated is very much the same and involves the same principle of recycling one of the constituents through the mechanism. This equation was first derived to describe enzymatic kinetics by Michaelis and Menten, and represents a very important contribution to our understanding of enzymatic behavior.

In context of this discussion, we again examine some of the characteristics of this mathematical relation describing enzymatic reaction flux. We first note that as c_S becomes very large such that $c_S \gg K_m$, we may neglect K_m in the denominator, whence

$$J = k_2 C_T \equiv J_{max} \qquad (c_S \gg K_m). \tag{23–10}$$

In other words, at large values of c_S approaching infinity, all of the enzyme is in the ES form; and since the maximum value of c_{ES} is actually C_T, the flux is at a maximum and the system exhibits zero-order kinetics. We may rewrite Eq. (23–9) using Eq. (23–10) to obtain

$$J = \frac{J_{max} c_S}{K_m + c_S}. \tag{23–11}$$

Examining this equation we note that

$$J = \frac{J_{max}}{2} \qquad (c_S = K_m), \tag{23–12}$$

stating that half-maximum flux occurs when the concentration of substrate is the value of the steady-state constant. This provides a possible means of estimating K_m from experiment.

At very low values of c_S, such that $c_S \ll K$, we may neglect c_S in the denominator of Eq. (25–11), giving

$$J = \frac{J_{\max}}{K_m} c_S \qquad (c_S \ll K). \qquad (23\text{–}13)$$

This indicates that at very low concentrations of substrate, the reaction flux is directly proportional to the concentration; in other words, the system behaves as a monomolecular reaction, following first-order kinetics. In passing from first-order kinetics at low c_S to zero-order kinetics at high values of c_S, the behavior in between cannot be described in terms of kinetic order. These principal points of interest relating to the characteristics of Eq. (25–11), a rectangular hyperbola, are summarized in Fig. 23–3.

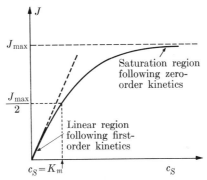

Fig. 23–3. Plot of Eq. (23–11) illustrating some of the principal characteristics of the rectangular hyperbolic relation.

Curvilinear relations such as those we have been dealing with are generally somewhat inconvenient to handle in fitting experimental results into a theoretical description. It is difficult, for instance, to estimate the asymptote, $J_{\max}$, and consequently the value of K_m from $J_{\max}/2$. In 1934, Lineweaver and Burk applied to this problem a general property of hyperbolas; namely, by changing the variables to their reciprocals, a hyperbola becomes a straight line. Taking Eq. (23–11) and inverting, we obtain

$$\frac{1}{J} = \frac{K_m}{J_{\max}} \frac{1}{c_S} + \frac{1}{J_{\max}}, \qquad (23\text{–}14)$$

which is, of course, an equation of a straight line in the variables $1/J$ and $1/c_S$. The slope is $K_m/J_{\max}$ and the intercept at $1/c_S = 0$, is $1/J_{\max}$.

Since it is a straight line, the intercept can easily be obtained by extrapolation. The curve of Fig. 23–3 is replotted in this form in Fig. 23–4. It is to be noted that we may further extend our extrapolation to the negative axis of $1/c_S$, where $1/J = 0$. From Eq. (23–14) we note that here $K_m = -c_S$, and thus both K_m and $J_{\max}$ may be easily determined from the experimental data by graphical means.

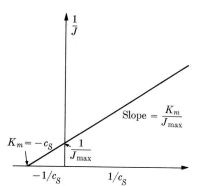

FIG. 23–4. The reciprocal plot of Lineweaver and Burk given in Eq. (23–14).

Since the above method weighs rather heavily the data obtained at high concentrations of S in making an extrapolation and often in this region data are least accurate, we may alternatively obtain an equation by multiplying both sides of Eq. (23–14) by c_S. This results in

$$\frac{c_S}{J} = \frac{K_m}{J_{\max}} + \frac{1}{J_{\max}} c_S, \qquad (23\text{–}15)$$

and also gives a straight line in the variables c_S/J and c_S. The significance of the two intercepts is easily established.

The foregoing considerations of enzymatic kinetics represents a degree of simplification over real situations but has comprised an invaluable aid in guiding experimental work. We must emphasize that a principal assumption made was that of a steady state in regard to the concentration of the enzyme-substrate complex, a valid assumption under properly chosen conditions. A general time course description of the reaction flux without this or an equivalent assumption is mathematically impossible. The differential equations describing the changes of concentration with time are nonlinear and a general solution does not exist. For this reason, nonsteady-state mathematical solutions are often obtained by analog and digital computer techniques.

23–4 Inhibition of enzyme function. Enzymes, in general, tend to show a large degree of specificity with respect to the reaction they catalyze. Some enzymes are specific for certain bond types. For instance, some esterases catalyze the hydrolysis of ester linkages, showing little heed to particular molecules involved in the ester, and certain peptidases catalyze the hydrolysis of peptide groups. At the other extreme, there are enzymes that are absolutely specific toward one particular substrate, such as urease, mentioned above. In the bond or group specific case, one would normally expect that if there were more than one possible substrate or reactant present in a chemical system, the enzyme would catalyze all possible kinds, each of which would mutually compete for availability of the active site and thus act as mutual inhibitors. Also it is conceivable that certain molecules may have an affinity for the active site of particular enzymes but are not themselves substrates since they do not undergo chemical change. Such molecules may bear a close structural configurational relation to the true substrate of a particular enzyme and may be bound in a reversible manner at the active site, thus comprising an enzyme-inhibitor complex. Furthermore, it is not difficult to imagine an enzyme which, by association with some other molecule not necessarily directly at the active site, may nevertheless experience conformational changes in the active site sufficient to make it nonfunctional.

As has been suggested in Chapter 7, the active site of an enzyme may involve several groups which in the primary structure represent points remote from each other, but which because of the particular folding of the peptide chain determining the tertiary structure are brought into proximity. Such tertiary structures may be labile,* and it is not difficult to envisage that reaction of the enzyme molecule with certain chemical substances may distort or actually disrupt to some degree the active site. Such reacting substances are then inhibitors.

In this section, we elaborate upon a simple model scheme that provides a description of the various mechanisms of inhibition. This description distinguishes between the extremes in inhibitory behavior, purely competitive and purely noncompetitive, and also recognizes the occurrence of mixed inhibitors of all degrees. In deriving the expressions for inhibition, we consider the following three chemical equations:

$$E + S \underset{k_{-1}}{\overset{k_1}{\rightleftharpoons}} ES \overset{k_2}{\rightarrow} E + P, \tag{23–3}$$

$$E + I \underset{l_{-1}}{\overset{l_1}{\rightleftharpoons}} EI \overset{(l_2)}{\rightarrow} E + Q, \tag{23–16}$$

$$ES + I \underset{m_{-1}}{\overset{m_1}{\rightleftharpoons}} ESI \overset{(m_2)}{\rightarrow} E + P + Q. \tag{23–17}$$

The first of these is that considered in deriving the Michaelis-Menten

---

* It is an observed fact that the functional activity of many enzymes isolated and stored is better preserved when in the presence of their particular substrates.

kinetics of the previous section. The second equation allows for the reversible association of enzyme with a molecule I, which with $l_2 = 0$ acts as a pure inhibitor of the enzyme but which with $l_2 \neq 0$ acts as an alternate substrate being catalytically transformed to a product, Q. The third equation recognizes the possibility that I may combine with the enzyme molecule even though S is already associated at the active site. If such occurs and $m_2 = 0$, then ESI is an inactive noncatalytic form of E, a condition representing enzymatic inhibition. Those cases in which $m_2 \neq 0$, but in which k_2 and l_2 are both zero, are examples wherein both substrates, S and I, are required for enzymatic activity and will be considered in the following section.

These three chemical equations are visualized as occurring simultaneously, and the problem at hand is to ascertain the effect of varying concentrations of I upon the initial reaction flux and altering the dependency of the initial reaction flux upon the concentrations of S. As in the previous section, we neglect any reverse reaction flux by letting k_{-2}, l_{-2}, and m_{-2} be zero. We again assume virtual steady-state conditions in c_{ES}, c_{EI}, and c_{EIS}, and write the equations:

$$\frac{c_E \cdot c_S}{c_{ES}} = \frac{k_{-1} + k_2}{k_1} = K_m, \tag{23-18}$$

$$\frac{c_E \cdot c_I}{c_{EI}} = \frac{l_{-1} + (l_2)}{l_1} = L, \tag{23-19}$$

$$\frac{c_{ES} \cdot c_I}{c_{ESI}} = \frac{m_{-1} + (m_2)}{m_1} = M, \tag{23-20}$$

where the parentheses on the kinetic coefficients l_2 and m_2 indicate that they may be zero, in which case L and M are equilibrium constants rather than steady-state constants. As previously indicated, we take $m_2 = 0$ for our discussion in this section. The expression for conservation of total enzyme is

$$C_T = c_E + c_{ES} + c_{EI} + c_{ESI}. \tag{23-21}$$

These four equations are sufficient to express c_{ES} in terms of c_S and c_I, the experimental variables. The result which is easily verified is

$$c_{ES} = \left(\frac{M}{M + c_I}\right) \frac{C_T \cdot c_S}{K_m \left(\frac{L + c_I}{M + c_I}\right) \frac{M}{L} + c_S}. \tag{23-22}$$

By introducing a new parameter which relates the magnitudes of L and M and is defined by

$$\alpha \equiv \frac{L}{M} \tag{23-23}$$

and recognizing that $J = k_2 c_{ES}$, Eq. (23–22) is altered to give

$$J = \left(\frac{L}{L + \alpha c_I}\right) \frac{k_2 C_T \cdot c_S}{K_m \left(\dfrac{L + c_I}{L + \alpha c_I}\right) + c_S} . \qquad (23\text{–}24)$$

The significance of the parameter α will now be made clear. If α approaches zero ($\alpha \to 0$) and L is not zero, then M approaches infinity, which is tantamount to saying that the complex ESI is nonexistent. In other words, under the condition that $\alpha = 0$, the enzyme may associate to form a complex with either S or I but not both. This is easily visualized in terms of a competition for the active site. Equation (23–24) reduces to the expression

$$J = \frac{k_2 C_T c_S}{K_m \left(\dfrac{L + c_I}{L}\right) + c_S} , \qquad (23\text{–}25)$$

representing the case of enzyme inhibition which is purely competitive; I competes with S for the active site. As may be deduced this is true whether I itself is a catalytically transformable substrate or not. If I is a substrate, both S and I are mutually competitive inhibitors.

Equation (23–25) is to be compared with the uninhibited case, Eq. (23–11). We note that the only difference is that here K_m is multiplied by the factor in parentheses,

$$\left(\frac{L + c_I}{L}\right) .$$

When $c_I = 0$, the equations become identical, as indeed they must. We may deduce that $J_{\max}$ is the same as before, since at large values of c_S, i.e., when

$$c_S \gg K_m \left(\frac{L + c_I}{L}\right) ,$$

this latter term may be neglected in the denominator and $k_2 C_T$ is still $J_{\max}$ in the numerator. Thus,

$$J = \frac{J_{\max} c_S}{K_m \left(\dfrac{L + c_I}{L}\right) + c_S} . \qquad (23\text{–}26)$$

We therefore are in a position to deduce that the only effect a competitive inhibitor has upon the flux is an effect of multiplying K_m by the factor $(L + c_I)/L$ as stated above. At a given constant concentration of inhibitor I, the same form of flux variation with concentration of substrate S exists.

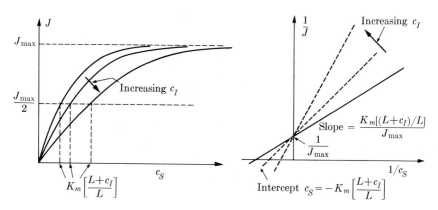

FIG. 23–5. Plot of Eq. (23–26) illustrating the effect of a purely competitive inhibitor on reaction flux.

FIG. 23–6. Reciprocal plots illustrating the effect of varying concentrations of a competitive inhibitor.

Increasing c_I shifts the $J_{\max}/2$ point to the right, as shown in Fig. 23–5. In reciprocal plots, competitive inhibition results in an increased slope of the line without change in the $1/J$-axis intercept but with change in the $(1/c_S)$-axis intercept, it being closer to the origin. We illustrate this in Fig. 23–6, representing classical competitive inhibition.

We next examine the circumstances in which $\alpha \to 1$. From the definition this indicates that $L = M$, a condition which states that the substance I will associate with enzyme with equal affinity whether or not E is complexed with S. If by virtue of this association EI and ESI are inactive catalytically, that is, if $l_2 = m_2 = 0$, then I acts as an inhibitor of the enzyme for S. However, in this case there is no competition between S and I and the resultant effect represents that of purely noncompetitive inhibition. Equation (23–24) reduces to

$$ J = \frac{\left(\dfrac{L}{L + c_I}\right) k_2 C_T c_S}{K_m + c_S} . \qquad (23\text{–}27)$$

We note here that it is not K_m that becomes modified with varying values of c_I, but instead $J_{\max}$ becomes

$$ \left(\frac{L}{L + c_I}\right) k_2 C_T . $$

On plotting J vs. c_S for a given constant value of c_I, we find that $J_{\max}$ decreases with increasing values of c_I. This is to be noted in Fig. 23–7. In reciprocal coordinates the curves are replotted in Fig. 23–8.

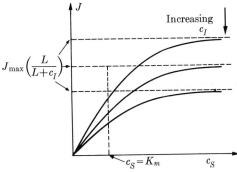

FIG. 23–7. Effect of a pure noncompetitive inhibition on an enzyme catalyzed reaction.

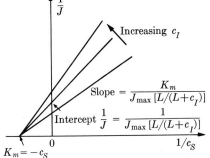

FIG. 23–8. Effect of a pure noncompetitive inhibitor, illustrated on the reciprocal plot.

We have thus far in our discussion of enzymatic inhibitions considered the two "extreme" circumstances in which $\alpha = 0$, representing pure competitive inhibition, and $\alpha = 1$, representing pure noncompetitive inhibition. It is easily imaginable that in actuality α may take on intermediate values between 0 and 1 and in fact values greater than 1, all of which would thus represent mixed forms of inhibition. In the study of enzyme kinetics, all varieties of the inhibitions are observable in particular situations and indeed some forms of behavior may be observed which are not explicable in terms of these simple schemata. For interpretation of these observations a variety of special model mechanisms have been devised which need not be considered in this introduction. Suffice it to say that forms of inhibition outlined in the foregoing paragraphs may provide the cell with a means of regulating its metabolic function. Certainly it provides a means of modifying cellular function artificially, for these forms of inhibition are just those that explain the function of various antimetabolites such as the sulfonomides.

23–5 Activation of enzyme function; coupled reactions. Often it is observed in the study of enzymatically catalyzed reactions that the velocity of the reaction is sensitively determined by the presence of some constituent other than the substrate itself. In the absence of such a constituent which itself does not become chemically transformed, catalytic activity of the enzyme is either zero or very nearly zero. Metal ions, especially the divalent ions such as Ca^{2+} and Mg^{2+} or Mn^{2+}, often are found to play this role. Presumably these ions serve as an ionic bridge, stabilizing the enzyme-substrate complex in those instances when both active site and substrate molecule bear a negative charge. These kinds of constituents are termed activators.

On the other hand, it is the function of many enzymes to catalyze a reaction between two chemical substances as, for instance, in all group transfer reactions. Obviously, in these cases both kinds of molecules, the group donor substance and the group acceptor, must be present for catalytic activity to be manifest. The particular kinetic behavior is determined by the concentration of both as well as that of the enzyme itself. In biochemical literature, it is the frequent practice to designate one of these substances as a substrate and the other as a coenzyme. The designation "coenzyme" arises because of the requirement of the enzyme for this molecule and the fact that these molecules often serve several enzymatic systems, being in effect cyclically involved. However, not infrequently the distinction between which is substrate and which is coenzyme is not clear, and the word "cosubstrate" may be preferred.

In this section we develop some of the simpler kinetic properties of these enzymatic systems which involve either activators or dual substrates. This is done in a manner analogous to that of the foregoing section in that we consider a similar set of chemical equations. We rewrite these as

$$E + S \underset{k_{-1}}{\overset{k_1}{\rightleftharpoons}} ES,$$

$$E + A \underset{l_{-1}}{\overset{l_1}{\rightleftharpoons}} EA,$$

$$ES + A \underset{m_{-1}}{\overset{m_1}{\rightleftharpoons}} ESA \overset{m_2}{\rightarrow} E + P + Q, \qquad (23\text{–}28)$$

where it is clear that A refers to an activator molecule or perhaps a coenzyme or cosubstrate. It is to be noted that here $k_2 = l_2 = 0$, whereas $m_2 \neq 0$. The equilibrium or steady-state equations for each of these reactions may be written

$$\frac{c_E \cdot c_S}{c_{ES}} = \frac{k_{-1}}{k_1} = K, \qquad (23\text{–}29)$$

$$\frac{c_E \cdot c_A}{c_{EA}} = \frac{l_{-1}}{l} = L, \qquad (23\text{–}30)$$

$$\frac{c_{ES} \cdot c_A}{c_{ESA}} = \frac{m_{-1} + m_2}{m_1} = M. \qquad (23\text{–}31)$$

The conservation of total enzyme concentration is, as before,

$$C_T = c_E + c_{ES} + c_{EA} + c_{ESA}, \qquad (23\text{–}32)$$

whence these four equations may be appropriately combined and solved for c_{ESA}. In the steady state, $J = m_2 c_{ESA}$, and thus the result is

$$J = \frac{m_2 C_T c_S c_A}{N(L + c_A) + c_S(M + c_A)} = \frac{m_2 C_T c_S c_A}{M(K + c_S) + c_A(N + c_S)}, \qquad (23\text{–}33)$$

with $N = KM/L$. As is to be expected these equations are quite symmetrical in c_S and c_A.

Considering A as an activator or cosubstrate we note that $J = 0$ when $c_A = 0$; but at any constant value of $c_A \neq 0$, J is the usual rectangular hyperbolic function in c_S, although both the asymptotic maximum velocity and the half-maximum value of c_S (equivalent to the previously discussed K_m) are functions of c_A. It may be seen on rearranging Eq. (23–33) that

$$J_{\max} = \left(\frac{c_A}{M + c_A}\right) m_2 C_T, \qquad (23\text{–}34)$$

and the $J_{\max}/2$ point occurs when

$$c_S = N\left(\frac{L + c_A}{M + c_A}\right). \qquad (23\text{–}35)$$

Thus, $J_{\max}$ increases with increasing c_A as is reasonable, but the $J_{\max}/2$ point may either increase or decrease with increasing c_A, depending on the relative values of L and M. In illustration and for comparison with the previously derived equations of enzymatic inhibition, we plot Eq. (23–33) in Fig. 23–9, utilizing the reciprocal coordinates $1/J$ and $1/c_S$. In this case, $L/M > 1$.

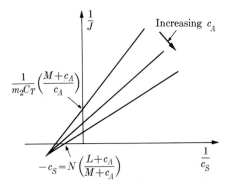

FIG. 23–9. Reciprocal plots illustrating the effect of varying concentrations of an enzyme activator or coenzyme (cosubstrate).

This mechanism outlined in the foregoing development suggests an additional means whereby the cell may regulate its metabolic function. More importantly the mechanism provides clearly a means of coupling of chemical reactions, referring, of course, to the substrate-cosubstrate case in which the overall reaction would be

$$S + A \underset{E}{\rightleftharpoons} P + Q. \tag{23-36}$$

The energetics of this coupling were discussed in some detail in Section 16–4, but here a mechanism involving a single enzyme is suggested. It is quite reasonable that such a mechanism may indeed be extremely efficient in group transfer reactions, provided, of course, that for this enzyme k_2 and l_2 are both zero. These conditions may not always prevail, or there may be other enzymes present catalyzing the individual reactions and resulting therefore in less efficient transfer.

23–6 Environmental influences on enzyme activity. Since enzymes are proteins and proteins are large molecular weight substances, $15,000 \rightarrow 10^6$, there would appear to be large portions of enzyme molecules which do not directly relate to the active site. One may well suppose that this additional structure is concerned with stabilizing the active site, determining characteristics of the enzyme in solution, and involving it in structural location within the cytoplasmic structures. We examine two relatively nonspecific environmental influences on enzymatic function.

(a) *Effect of temperature.* As has been pointed out in Chapter 7, proteins are in general thermally labile in the sense that the tertiary structure may rather easily undergo configurational changes, termed denaturation. In that these changes are greatly enhanced with an increase in temperature, thermal denaturation is a common phenomena. As has been suggested, the active site of enzymes may often involve the tertiary structure and consequently enzymes are themselves subject to thermal inactivation. Increasing the temperature increases the rate of chemical reactions, including enzyme catalyzed reactions. However, increase in temperature also increases the rate of thermal inactivation. The net observed effect is then a combination of these two effects. In actuality, denaturation of proteins occurs slowly at temperatures of biological systems and one may assume that in the living cell there is slow inactivation of enzymes both by this means as well as proteolytic degradation. The loss is, of course, balanced by continuing synthesis, and thus the cell is provided with another means for regulation and control of metabolic reactions.

(b) *Effect of* pH. Hydrogen ions in the environment of an enzyme are principal determinants of the net charge on enzyme molecules and the charge distribution. Thus changes in pH often have a profound influence on enzymatic activity. Ionic groups may be intimately involved in enzyme-

Fig. 23–10. Fractional quantities of the active forms of a hypothetical active site containing $E — RH^+$ and hypothetical substrate $S — R^-$ as a function of pH. Maximum activity would be expected to occur at the pH of intersection of the two curves where $c_{S-R^-} \cdot c_{E-RH^+}$ is a maximum, and thus ES complex concentration is a maximum.

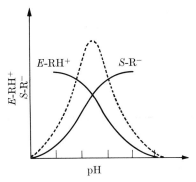

substrate complex formation at the active site, i.e., by "salt linkage" (ionic bonds). Thus the charge state of the enzyme as well as that of the substrate is often important in determining enzymatic activity. In the absence of destructive denaturation, occurring at extremes of pH, one would, in general, except some sort of optimal value of pH for maximum catalytic activity, especially those enzyme systems involving ionic bonds at the active site.

We may illustrate how such an optimum would arise in a purely hypothetical fashion by postulating the following proton dissociation reactions to occur for an active site and its substrate:

$$\text{Active site: } E\text{-}RH^+ \rightleftharpoons E\text{-}R + H^+,$$
$$\text{Substrate: }\quad S\text{-}RH \rightleftharpoons S\text{-}R^- + H^+. \qquad (23\text{--}34)$$

We assume that the enzyme-substrate complex involves $E\text{-}RH^+$ and $S\text{-}R^-$. In altering the pH, both groups are titrated, and we plot the fraction of the total enzyme and substrate that are in their active form $vs.$ pH. This is seen in Fig. 23–10. We note that there is a point where the two curves intersect, representing the point where the product of the concentrations would be a maximum and therefore also a point where the maximum amount of enzyme-substrate complex would exist under given conditions. We would expect the relative enzymatic activity to be represented approximately by the broken curve. This represents, in general, the manner in which pH of the environment may influence enzymatic activity.

23–7 Reaction sequences and control mechanism. In the foregoing sections of the chapter, we have discussed the simple elementary principles involved in the kinetic behavior of enzymatically catalyzed systems. Models of reaction mechanism have been used as a basis for the kinetic formulations, but assumptions and simplifications were necessary. The results provide some insight into enzymatic function and have been invaluable in the study of isolated enzymatic systems for which the restricted experimental conditions may be attained. However, these conditions may not exist in the living cell. In the first place a typical cell contains thousands of different enzymes and the maze of chemical reactions occurring simultaneously is indeed complex. The chemical reactions and their accompanying enzymes are not isolated entities but occur in interconnecting sequences, the sum total of which contributes toward making the cell a living system. These sequences, extensively worked out by the biochemists, take a variety of forms. Some occur in what may be a straight chain:

$$A \rightleftharpoons B \rightarrow C \rightarrow \cdots P; \tag{23-37}$$

others may be branched as in

$$\tag{23-38}$$

Cyclic sequences of transformation are common:

$$\tag{23-39}$$

and may take in only a few transformations of ten or more. Involved combinations of these are easily imaginable. The kinetics of such systems may or may not be understood in terms of the simple mechanisms developed in the foregoing. In the case of reactions catalyzed by the soluble enzymes contained in the cytoplasmic water perhaps some degree of homogeneity exists as in a test tube; but even this is doubtful in view of the complex membranous endoplasmic reticulum that may provide cytoplasmic streaming and flow patterns, thereby adding a complexity difficult at best to assess. Many of the enzymes involved in these sequences appear to be intimately associated with the structural elements themselves, as in the mitochondria and on the reticulum. In the mitochondria they appear to occur in ordered arrays, and it is quite possible that the proper enzymes occur spatially in the proper order of the reaction sequence. The consequences of such an arrangement for kinetic behavior is not fully appreciated but is a subject of considerable interest.

The normal living cell is a well-regulated functioning unit. Its metabolic reactions proceed smoothly at a rate which is remarkably adaptable to the demands made. What are some of the factors involved?

The quantities or concentrations of the various enzymes present are obviously one factor. As has been indicated in Chapter 11, there appears to be a qualitative one-to-one relation between particular genes and particular enzymes, whereby genetic determinants are manifest through enzymatic effectors. In this respect a particular genetic defect may become evident by the absence of a particular enzyme. Such defects are termed metabolic errors, and a large number have been both artificially produced and have come to be recognized as occurring naturally. This may account qualitatively but not quantitatively for metabolic control. However, it is a known fact that enzymatic activity of a cell varies and adapts to such stimuli as increased substrate concentration. Little is known at the present time of actual mechanisms leading to increased synthesis of enzyme, but undoubtedly these represent an important means of functional regulation, giving a dynamic quality of control in the differential rates of synthesis and destruction.

We have indicated in prior sections that enzymatic inhibition and activation by specific chemical constituents may well exist as a mechanism for inherent regulation of cellular metabolism and function. Direct evidence for this, however, is not extensive, although mass-law considerations, as they pertain to competition for substrate and coenzyme, are probably of utmost importance.

In a cyclic sequence it may be reasoned that the concentrations of the cycled substrate would exert an effect on the overall rates of the processes. Such a substrate behaves much like a catalyst, and the kinetics of the cycle, although dynamically more complicated than the simple two-step cycle of an enzyme reaction, would be under steady-state conditions similar to that exhibited by an enzyme. Consequently, side reactions generating or removing these substrates exert a degree of control and regulation to the sequence.

Finally, it is of some interest to question the type of control and regulation that one may associate with the structurally arrayed and ordered enzymes. Here it is conceivable that small alterations in the structural relations at each sequential step would have a profound overall influence on rate.

It is not possible in this brief introduction to discuss in detail all factors involved in metabolic regulation and control, nor indeed are all the factors known or understood. Suffice it to add that the significance of the high degree of microscopic organization seen in living systems, together with the implication this may have on microscopic compartmentalization and channelling of cytoplasmic fluid, is not fully appreciated. Our current views and knowledge of reaction kinetics and diffusive passage of substances in and about the cell are probably much too simplified and naive to ultimately account for the actual processes, whose integrated total is a living system.

REFERENCES

1. L. MICHAELIS and M. L. MENTEN, "Die Kinetik der Invertinwirkung," *Biochem. Z.* **49**, 33 (1913).

2. H. LINEWEAVER and D. BURK, "The Determination of Enzyme Dissociation Constants," *J. Am. Chem. Soc.* **56**, 658 (1934).

3. K. G. STERN, "On the Mechanism of Enzyme Action," *J. Biol. Chem.* **114**, 473 (1936).

4. B. CHANCE, "The Kinetics of the Enzyme-Substrate Compound of Peroxidase," *J. Biol. Chem.* **151**, 553 (1943).

5. P. D. BOYER, H. LARDY, and K. MYRBACK, Eds., *The Enzymes*, 2nd Ed., Vols. I–IV. Academic Press, New York, 1959.

6. G. E. W. WOLSTENHOLME and C. M. O'CONNOR, Eds., *Regulation of Cell Metabolism*, Ciba Foundation Symposium. Little, Brown, Boston, 1959.

APPENDIX

I. ALGEBRA

A. Laws of exponents:

1. $a^m a^n = a^{m+n}$,

2. $(ab)^m = a^m b^m$,

3. $a^{m/n} = \sqrt[n]{a^m}$,

4. $a^m/a^n = a^{m-n}$ $(a \neq 0)$,

5. $a^0 = 1$,

6. $a^{-m} = \dfrac{1}{a^m}$.

B. Proportionality:

If y is proportional to x in a functional relation, then $y = kx$, where k is the proportionality constant.

C. Quadratic formula:

The roots of the equation $ax^2 + bx + c = 0$, $a \neq 0$, are given by

$$x = \frac{-b \pm \sqrt{b^2 - 4ac}}{2a} = -\frac{b}{2a} \pm \sqrt{\left(\frac{b}{2a}\right)^2 - \frac{c}{a}}.$$

D. Sum (Σ) and product (Π) notation:

$$\sum_{i=m}^{m+n} x_i \equiv x_m + x_{m+1} + \cdots + x_{m+n};$$

$$\prod_{i=m}^{m+n} y_i \equiv y_m \cdot y_{m+1} \cdots y_{m+n}.$$

II. STATISTICS

A. Symbol definitions:

1. $n_i \equiv$ number of events, objects, etc., in class i, i being one of M classes, that is, $i = 1, 2, \ldots M$.

$$\sum_{i=1}^{M} n_i \equiv N = \text{total number in all classes.}$$

2. $f_i \equiv \dfrac{n_i}{\sum n_i} = \dfrac{n_i}{N} = $ fractional number in class i.

$$\sum_{i=1}^{M} f_i = 1.$$

369

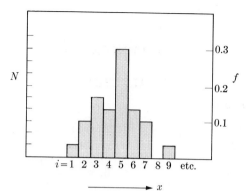

FIGURE 1A

3. $x_i \equiv$ value associated with the class i.

B. Mean:

$$\bar{x} = \frac{\sum n_i x_i}{\sum n_i} = \sum f_i x_i.$$

C. Root mean square:

$$\text{rms} = \sqrt{\frac{\sum n_i x_i^2}{\sum n_i}} = \sqrt{\sum f_i x_i^2}.$$

D. Mode:

Value of class i, (x_i), having maximum f_i or n_i.

E. Median:

Value of class i, (x_i), with

$$\sum_{j=1}^{i} f_j = 0.5 = \sum_{j=i}^{M} f_j.$$

F. Moments of distribution:

1. First moment about value A:

$$\gamma_1(A) = \frac{\sum n_i (x_i - A)}{\sum n_i} = \sum f_i (x_i - A) = \overline{(x - A)} = \bar{x} - A.$$

If $A = \bar{x}$, then $\gamma_1(\bar{x}) = 0$, that is,

$$\sum f_i (x_i - \bar{x}) = \overline{(x - \bar{x})} = \bar{x} - \bar{x} = 0.$$

2. Second moment about value A:

$$\gamma_2(A) = \frac{\sum n_i (x_i - A)^2}{\sum n_i} = \sum f_i (x_i - A)^2 = \overline{(x - A)^2}$$

$$= \overline{x^2 - 2Ax + A^2} = \overline{x^2} - 2A\bar{x} + A^2.$$

If $A = \bar{x}$, then $\gamma_2(\bar{x}) = \overline{x^2} - \bar{x}^2 = $ variance of value of x.
If $A = 0$, then $\gamma_2(0) = \sum f_i x_1^2 = \overline{x^2} = (\text{rms})^2$.

G. Standard deviation:

$$\sigma = \sqrt{[\sum n_i (x_i - \bar{x})^2]/\sum n_i} = \sqrt{\sum f_i (x_i - \bar{x})^2} = \sqrt{\gamma_2(\bar{x})}.$$

H. Probable error:

P. E. $= 0.6745\sigma.$

III. TRIGONOMETRY

A. Definitions of trigonometric functions:

In a right triangle (Fig. 2A),

$\sin \alpha = A/C,$

$\cos \alpha = B/C,$

$\tan \alpha = A/B = \dfrac{\sin \alpha}{\cos \alpha}.$

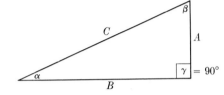

FIGURE 2A

B. Identities:

$$\sin(-\alpha) = -\sin \alpha, \qquad \cos(-\alpha) = \cos \alpha, \qquad \sin^2 \alpha + \cos^2 \alpha = 1.$$

IV. ANALYTIC GEOMETRY

A. Equation of a straight line (Fig. 3A):

$y - y_1 = m(x - x_1);$
$m =$ slope; line passes through
point $(x_1, y_1).$

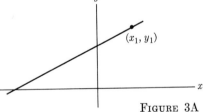

FIGURE 3A

B. Equation of circle (Fig. 4A):

$(x - x_1)^2 + (y - y_1)^2 = R^2.$
Center is at point (x_1, y_1). Radius is R.

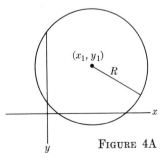

FIGURE 4A

C. Equation of parabola:

$(y - y_1)^2 = F(x - x_1)$ (Fig. 5A).
$(x - x_1)^2 = F(y - y_1)$ (Fig. 6A).
Vertex at point (x_1, y_1). Distance from vertex to focus $= F/4$. Latus rectum $= F$.

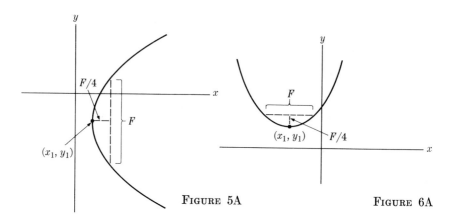

FIGURE 5A   FIGURE 6A

D. Equation of ellipse (Fig. 7A):

$$\frac{(x - x_1)^2}{a^2} + \frac{(y - y_1)^2}{b^2} = 1.$$

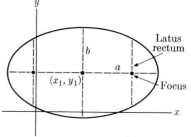

Center at point (x_1, y_1). Major and Minor axes, a and b, parallel to x and y axes. Eccentricity $= \sqrt{a^2 - b^2}/a$, $a =$ major axis. Latus rectum $= 2b^2/a$.

FIGURE 7A

E. Hyperbola (Fig. 8A):

$$\frac{(x - x_1)^2}{a^2} - \frac{(y - y_1)^2}{b^2} = 1.$$

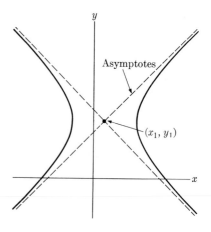

Center at point (x_1, y_1). Axes parallel to x and y axes. Slopes of asymptotes $= \pm b/a$.

FIGURE 8A

F. Rectangular hyperbola (Fig. 9A):

$$(x - x_1)(y - y_1) = \pm k^2$$

Center at point (x_1, y_1). Asymptotes parallel to x and y axes.

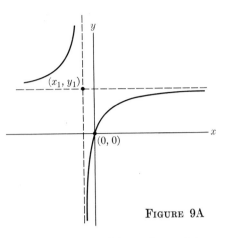

1. If requirement that the point $(0, 0)$ be on curve choosing $-k^2$, then $x_1 y_1 = -k^2$ and it follows that

$$y = \frac{y_1 x}{x - x_1}.$$

FIGURE 9A

2. If in a new coordinate system (u, v) such that $u = 1/x$, and $v = 1/y$ (Fig. 10A), then

$$v = \frac{-x_1}{y_1} u + \frac{1}{y_1} = \frac{-v_1}{u_1} u + v_1,$$

which is an equation of straight line with slope, $-(x_1/y_1) = -(v_1/u_1)$.

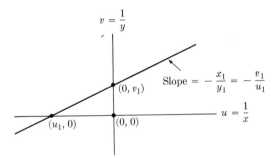

FIGURE 10A

V. DIFFERENTIAL CALCULUS

A. Definition of a function; functional notation:

A variable y is said to be a function of the variable x if there exists a relation between y and x such that for every x (within a range) the value of y is determined. The functional notation representing this may be $y = y(x)$, $y = f(x)$, etc., stating that y is a function of x. If more than one independent variable is involved, the notation $y = y(x, z)$ or $y = y(x_1, x_2, \ldots, x_n)$ is used.

B. The first derivative (Fig. 11A):

Let $y = f(x)$ be a continuous function of x. Let Δx be any change in x and let Δy be the corresponding increment in y. The first derivative of y with respect to x is the limit of the ratio of Δy to Δx as Δx approaches zero in any manner possible. Thus

$$\frac{dy}{dx} = \lim_{\Delta x \to 0} \frac{\Delta y}{\Delta x} = \lim_{\Delta x \to 0} \frac{f(x + \Delta x) - f(x)}{\Delta x} = f'(x).$$

The derivative of a function does not always exist. The derivative of a function is obtained by solving the definition formula for a function or by following the appropriate operation tabulated in Appendix V.D.

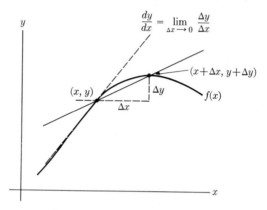

FIGURE 11A

EXAMPLE: $f(x) = x^3 + 5x + 3$.

From the definition:

$$\frac{d}{dx} f(x) = \lim_{\Delta x \to 0} \frac{f(x + \Delta x) - f(x)}{\Delta x}$$

$$= \lim_{\Delta x \to 0} \frac{((x + \Delta x)^3 + 5(x + \Delta x) + 3) - (x^3 + 5x + 3)}{\Delta x}$$

$$= 3x^2 + 5.$$

An identical result is obtained by use of the operation formulas from Appendix V.D taking $f(x)$ term by term:

$$\frac{dx^3}{dx} = 3x^2 \qquad \text{(using D.4)}$$

$$\frac{d(5x)}{dx} = 5 \qquad \text{(using D.2)} \qquad \text{and} \qquad \frac{d(3)}{dx} = 0.$$

Therefore $[df(x)]/dx = 3x^2 + 5$.

C. The second derivative and higher derivatives:

The second derivation of a function is merely the result of taking the derivative of the first derivative.

$$\frac{d}{dx}\frac{df(x)}{dx} = \frac{df'(x)}{dx} = \lim_{\Delta x \to 0}\frac{f'(x + \Delta x) - f'(x)}{\Delta x} = f''(x) = \frac{d^2f(x)}{dx^2}.$$

Higher derivatives are defined in an analogous fashion.

D. Table of derivatives:

1. $\dfrac{d}{dx}(x) = 1,$

2. $\dfrac{d}{dx}(au) = a\dfrac{du}{dx}, \quad a = \text{constant},$

3. $\dfrac{d}{dx}\left(\dfrac{u}{v}\right) = \dfrac{v(du/dx) - u(dv/dx)}{v^2},$

4. $\dfrac{d}{dx}(u^n) = nu^{n-1}\dfrac{du}{dx},$

5. $\dfrac{d}{dx}(e^u) = e^u\dfrac{du}{dx}, \quad e \text{ is defined in Appendix VII},$

6. $\dfrac{d}{dx}(uv) = u\dfrac{dv}{dx} + v\dfrac{du}{dx},$

7. $\dfrac{d}{dx}\sin u = \cos u\dfrac{du}{dx},$

8. $\dfrac{d}{dx}\cos u = -\sin u\dfrac{du}{dx}.$

E. Partial derivatives:

If $z = f(x, y)$ is a function of two variables, x and y, then the derivative of z with respect to x, as x varies while y remains constant, is called the first partial of z with respect to x and is denoted by $(\partial z/\partial x)_y$.

Similarly, $(\partial z/\partial y)_x$ (partial of z with respect to y holding x constant) is denoted in the same way. In general, for $z = f(x_1, x_2, \ldots, x_n)$, the partial derivative may be taken with respect to any one variable, holding the rest constant.

EXAMPLE: $z = 3y^3 + 4x^2 + 2xy,$

$$\left.\frac{\partial z}{\partial x}\right)_y = 8x + 2y, \qquad \left.\frac{\partial z}{\partial y}\right)_x = 9y^2 + 2x.$$

VI. INTEGRAL CALCULUS

A. Indefinite integral:

1. Definition:

$F(x)$ is said to be an indefinite integral of $f(x)$ if the derivative of $F(x)$ is $f(x)$. In general,

$$\int f(x)\, dx = F(x) + C, \quad C = \text{arbitrary constant.}$$

Thus

$$\frac{d(F(x) + C)}{dx} = \frac{dF(x)}{dx} + \frac{dC}{dx} = f(x).$$

2. EXAMPLE: Integrate $(2x + 3)^2\, dx$.

The function $F(x)$ which will give $(2x + 3)^2$ upon differentiation is $\frac{1}{6}(2x + 3)^3 + C$. Thus

$$\frac{d}{dx}\left(\frac{1}{6}(2x + 3)^3 + C\right) = \frac{1}{2}(2x + 3)^2 \frac{d}{dx}(2x + 3) + \frac{dC}{dx}$$

$$= \frac{1}{2}(2x + 3)^2(2) = (2x + 3)^2.$$

3. Table of integrals:

1. $\int df(x) = f(x) + C,$

2. $\int 0\, dx = C,$

3. $\int d(f(x)\, dx) = f(x)\, dx,$

4. $\int af(x)\, dx = a\int f(x)\, dx,$

5. $\int (u \pm v)\, dx = \int u\, dx \pm \int v\, dx,$

6. $\int u\, dv = uv - \int v\, du,$

7. $\int u^n\, du = \frac{u^{n+1}}{n+1} + C, \quad n \neq -1,$

8. $\int \frac{du}{u} = \ln_e u + C$ (ln and e are defined in Appendix VII),

9. $\int e^u\, du = e^u + C,$

10. $\int \sin u\, du = -\cos u + C,$

11. $\int \cos u\, du = \sin u + C,$

12. $\int \frac{dx}{a + bx} = \frac{1}{b}\ln(a + bx) + C.$

B. Definite integrals:

1. Definition:

Let $f(x)$ be continuous for the interval from $x = a$ to $x = b$ inclusive. Divide this interval into n equal parts by the points a, x_1, x_2, ..., x_{n-1}, b, such that $\Delta x = (b - a)/n$. The definite integral of $f(x)$ with respect to x between the limits $x = a$ and $x = b$ is

$$\int_a^b f(x)\, dx = \lim_{n \to \infty} [f(a)\,\Delta x + \cdots + f(x_{n-1})\,\Delta x]$$

$$= [F(x)]_a^b = F(b) - F(a).$$

2. Properties of definite integrals:

$$\int_a^b k f(x)\, dx = k \int_a^b f(x)\, dx, \quad k = \text{constant,}$$

$$\int_a^b f(x)\, dx = - \int_b^a f(x)\, dx,$$

$$\int_a^c f(x)\, dx = \int_a^b f(x)\, dx + \int_b^c f(x)\, dx, \quad \text{where } a < b < c.$$

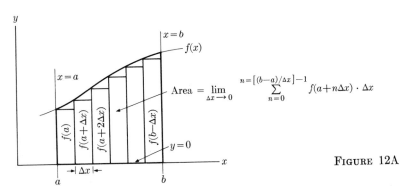

$$\text{Area} = \lim_{\Delta x \to 0} \sum_{n=0}^{n = [(b-a)/\Delta x] - 1} f(a + n\Delta x) \cdot \Delta x$$

FIGURE 12A

3. The definite integral can represent the summation of infinitesimal areas to give the total area under a curve between the limits a and b (See Fig. 12A):

$$\int_a^b f(x)\, dx = \text{area bound by lines } x = a, f(x), x = b, \text{ and } y = 0.$$

The infinitesimal area elements are $dA = f(x)\, dx$.

VII. LOGARITHMS

A. Definition of the natural logarithm, ln:

The natural logarithm is defined, for positive x, as the integral

$$\ln x = \int_1^x \frac{1}{t}\, dt \quad \text{(See Fig. 13A)}.$$

If then $y = \ln x$, the inverse operation is $x = e^y$ where e is the base of the natural logarithm and has the value of $2.71828182845\ldots$

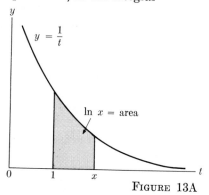

FIGURE 13A

B. Definition of the logarithm to the base 10, $\log_{10} = \log$:

If $10^y = x$, then $\log x \equiv y$.

C. Relation between ln and log:

$\ln 10 = 2.30259\ldots$

Therefore, $2.30259 \log x = \ln x$.

D. Properties of logarithms:

$\ln 1 = 0,$ $\qquad\qquad\qquad$ $\log 1 = 0,$

$\ln e = 1,$ $\qquad\qquad\qquad$ $\log 10 = 1,$

$\ln ax = \ln a + \ln x,$ $\qquad\qquad$ $\log ax = \log a + \log x,$

$\ln \dfrac{x}{a} = \ln x - \ln a,$ $\qquad\qquad$ $\log \dfrac{x}{a} = \log x - \log a,$

$\ln x^a = a \ln x,$ $\qquad\qquad$ $\log x^a = a \log x,$

$\dfrac{d(\ln x)}{dx} = \dfrac{1}{x},$ $\qquad\qquad$ $\dfrac{d(\log x)}{dx} = \dfrac{1}{2.303x},$

$\dfrac{d(\ln u)}{dx} = \dfrac{d(\ln u)}{du}\dfrac{du}{dx} = \dfrac{1}{u}\dfrac{du}{dx},$ $\qquad$ $\displaystyle\int \dfrac{du}{u} = \ln u + C.$

VIII. LOGARITHMIC AND EXPONENTIAL FUNCTIONS

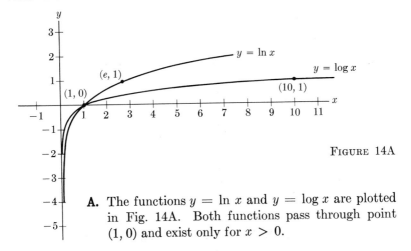

FIGURE 14A

A. The functions $y = \ln x$ and $y = \log x$ are plotted in Fig. 14A. Both functions pass through point $(1, 0)$ and exist only for $x > 0$.

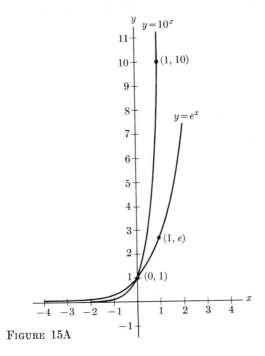

FIGURE 15A

B. The functions $y = e^x$ and $y = 10^x$ are plotted in Fig. 15A. Both functions pass through point $(0, 1)$ and exist for all values of x.

IX. SERIES EXPANSIONS OF FUNCTIONS

$$\ln x = \frac{x-1}{x} + \frac{1}{2}\left(\frac{x-1}{x}\right)^2 + \frac{1}{3}\left(\frac{x-1}{x}\right)^3 + \cdots, \quad x > \frac{1}{2},$$

$$\ln(1-x) = -x - \tfrac{1}{2}x^2 - \tfrac{1}{3}x^3 - \tfrac{1}{4}x^4 - \cdots,$$

$$e^x = 1 + x + \frac{x^2}{2!} + \frac{x^3}{3!} + \frac{x^4}{4!} + \cdots,$$

$$\sin x = x - \frac{x^3}{3!} + \frac{x^5}{5!} - \frac{x^7}{7!} + \cdots,$$

$$\cos x = 1 - \frac{x^2}{2!} + \frac{x^4}{4!} - \frac{x^6}{6!} + \cdots.$$

X. SELECTED PHYSICAL UNITS, DIMENSIONS AND CONVERSION FACTORS

A. Length: dimension $= l$

	m	cm	mm	μ	mμ	A
1 meter (m)	1	10^2	10^3	10^6	10^9	10^{10}
1 centimeter (cm)	10^{-2}	1	10^1	10^4	10^7	10^8
1 millimeter (mm)	10^{-3}	10^{-1}	1	10^3	10^6	10^7
1 micron (μ)	10^{-6}	10^{-4}	10^{-3}	1	10^3	10^4
1 millimicron (mμ)	10^{-9}	10^{-7}	10^{-6}	10^{-3}	1	10
1 angstrom (A)	10^{-10}	10^{-8}	10^{-7}	10^{-4}	10^{-1}	1

B. Volume: dimension $= l^3$

	m^3	l	ml (cc)	μl
1 cubic meter (m^3)	1	10^3	10^6	10^9
1 liter (l)	10^{-3}	1	10^3	10^6
1 milliliter (ml) (cubic centimeter) (cc)	10^{-6}	10^{-3}	1	10^3
1 microliter (μl)	10^{-9}	10^{-6}	10^{-3}	1

C. Mass: dimension $= m$

	kgm	gm	mgm	μgm
1 kilogram (kgm)	1	10^3	10^6	10^9
1 gram (gm)	10^{-3}	1	10^3	10^6
1 milligram (mgm)	10^{-6}	10^{-3}	1	10^3
1 microgram (μgm)	10^{-9}	10^{-6}	10^{-3}	1

D. Time: dimension $= t$

	hr	min	sec	msec	μsec	nsec
1 hour (hr)	1	60	$3.6 \cdot 10^3$	$3.6 \cdot 10^6$	$3.6 \cdot 10^9$	$3.6 \cdot 10^{12}$
1 minute (min)	$1.667 \cdot 10^{-2}$	1	60	$6 \cdot 10^4$	$6 \cdot 10^7$	$6 \cdot 10^{10}$
1 second (sec)	$2.778 \cdot 10^{-4}$	$1.667 \cdot 10^{-2}$	1	10^3	10^6	10^9
1 millisecond (msec)	$2.778 \cdot 10^{-7}$	$1.667 \cdot 10^{-5}$	10^{-3}	1	10^3	10^6
1 microsecond (μsec)	$2.778 \cdot 10^{-10}$	$1.667 \cdot 10^{-8}$	10^{-6}	10^{-3}	1	10^3
1 nanosecond (nsec)	$2.778 \cdot 10^{-13}$	$1.667 \cdot 10^{-11}$	10^{-9}	10^{-6}	10^{-3}	1

E. Force: dimension $= f = mlt^{-2}$

	nt	dyne	
1 newton (nt)	1	10^5	kgm m sec^{-2}
1 dyne (dyne)	10^{-5}	1	gm cm sec^{-2}

F. Pressure: dimension $= fl^{-2} = ml^{-1}t^{-2}$

	nt m^{-2}	dyne cm^{-2}	mm Hg	atm
1 newton per sq. meter (nt m^{-2})	1	10	$7.503 \cdot 10^{-4}$	$9.872 \cdot 10^{-6}$
1 dyne per sq. cm (dyne cm^{-2})	10^{-1}	1	$7.503 \cdot 10^{-5}$	$9.872 \cdot 10^{-7}$
1 mm of Hg (mm Hg)	$1.333 \cdot 10^2$	$1.333 \cdot 10^3$	1	$1.316 \cdot 10^{-3}$
1 atmosphere (atm)	$1.013 \cdot 10^5$	$1.013 \cdot 10^6$	$7.6 \cdot 10^1$	1

G. Energy: dimension $= fl = ml^2t^{-2}$

	joule	erg	ev	cal	kcal	kwh	
1 joule (joule)	1	10^7	$6.242 \cdot 10^{18}$	$2.389 \cdot 10^{-1}$	$2.389 \cdot 10^{-4}$	$2.778 \cdot 10^{-7}$	nt m
1 erg (erg)	10^{-7}	1	$6.242 \cdot 10^{11}$	$2.389 \cdot 10^{-8}$	$2.389 \cdot 10^{-11}$	$2.778 \cdot 10^{-14}$	dyne cm
1 electron volt (ev)	$1.602 \cdot 10^{-19}$	$1.602 \cdot 10^{-12}$	1	$3.827 \cdot 10^{-20}$	$3.827 \cdot 10^{-23}$	$4.450 \cdot 10^{-26}$	
1 grain calorie (cal)	4.186	$4.186 \cdot 10^7$	$2.613 \cdot 10^{19}$	1	10^{-3}	$1.163 \cdot 10^{-6}$	
1 kilocalorie (kcal)	$4.186 \cdot 10^3$	$4.186 \cdot 10^{10}$	$2.613 \cdot 10^{22}$	10^3	1	$1.163 \cdot 10^{-3}$	
1 kilowatt hour (kwh)	$3.600 \cdot 10^6$	$3.600 \cdot 10^{13}$	$2.247 \cdot 10^{25}$	$8.600 \cdot 10^5$	$8.600 \cdot 10^2$	1	

H. Electrical units : mks = meter-kilogram-second system
esu = electrostatic unit system

1. Unit of charge

	coul	statcoul
(mks) 1 coulomb (coul)	1	$2.998 \cdot 10^9$
(esu) 1 statcoulomb (statcoul)	$3.336 \cdot 10^{-10}$	1

2. Unit of current

	amp	statamp	
(mks) 1 ampere (amp)	1	$2.998 \cdot 10^9$	coul sec^{-1}
(esu) 1 statampere (statamp)	$3.336 \cdot 10^{-10}$	1	statcoul sec^{-1}

3. Unit of potential

	v	statv	mv	
(mks) 1 volt (v)	1	$3.335 \cdot 10^{-3}$	10^3	joul coul^{-1}
(esu) 1 statvolt (statv)	$2.998 \cdot 10^2$	1	$2.998 \cdot 10^5$	erg statcoul^{-1}
1 millivolt (mv)	10^{-3}	$3.335 \cdot 10^{-6}$	1	

4. Unit of resistance

	ohm	statohm	
(mks) 1 ohm (ohm)	1	$1.113 \cdot 10^{-12}$	joule sec coul^{-2}
(esu) 1 statohm (statohm)	$8.988 \cdot 10^{11}$	1	erg sec statcoul^{-2}

5. Unit of capacitance

	f	statf	μf	
(mks) 1 farad (f)	1	$8.988 \cdot 10^{11}$	10^6	coul volt^{-1}
(esu) 1 statfarad (statf)	$1.113 \cdot 10^{-12}$	1	$1.113 \cdot 10^{-6}$	statcoul statvolt^{-1}
1 microfarad (μf)	10^{-6}	$8.988 \cdot 10^5$	1	

XI. FUNDAMENTAL CONSTANTS IN SELECTED UNITS

Avogadro's number (N_0) $= 6.025 \cdot 10^{23}$ (gm mole)$^{-1}$

Boltzmann's constant (k) $= 1.3804 \cdot 10^{-16}$ erg ($^\circ$K)$^{-1}$

$= 1.3804 \cdot 10^{-23}$ joule ($^\circ$K)$^{-1}$

$= 8.616 \cdot 10^{-5}$ ev ($^\circ$K)$^{-1}$

Gas constant (R) $= N_0 k = 8.316 \cdot 10^7$ erg (gm mole)$^{-1}$ ($^\circ$K)$^{-1}$

$= 8.317$ joule (gm mole)$^{-1}$ ($^\circ$K)$^{-1}$

$= 1.987$ cal (gm mole)$^{-1}$ ($^\circ$K)$^{-1}$

$= 8.206 \cdot 10^{-2}$ liter atm (gm mole)$^{-1}$ ($^\circ$K)$^{-1}$

Speed of light (c) $= 2.998 \cdot 10^8$ m sec^{-1}

Planck's constant (h) $= 6.625 \cdot 10^{-27}$ erg sec

$= 6.625 \cdot 10^{-34}$ joule sec

$= 4.134 \cdot 10^{15}$ ev sec

Charge on electron (ϵ) $= 1.60207 \cdot 10^{-19}$ coul

$= 4.80301 \cdot 10^{-10}$ statcoul (esu)

Faraday (F) $= N_0 \epsilon = 9.652 \cdot 10^4$ coul equiv^{-1}

Atomic mass unit (amu) $= 1.6503 \cdot 10^{-24}$ gm (based on C^{12})

Mass of electron $= 9.1085 \cdot 10^{-28}$ gm

Mass of proton $= 1.6724 \cdot 10^{-24}$ gm

Mass of neutron $= 1.6747 \cdot 10^{-24}$ gm

INDEX

386

Charge, electron and proton, 14
Chemical potential
in active transport, 324
of a crystal, 235
definition of, 219, 222
of a gas, 232
gradients in diffusion, 290
of ions, 235–236
measurement of, 255–256
in osmotic pressure, 275
as partial molar free energy, 221
and pH, 260
of a solute, 234
of a solvent, 235
useful work, 231
Chemical reaction(s)
coupling of, 252–255,
321–323, 362–364
cycles, 365–368
equilibria (see Equilibrium)
flux, 333–335
free energy of, 252–255
mechanism (see Kinetics,
Enzymes)
sequences, 365–368
Chitin, 162, 169, 171
Cholesterol, 183
Chondroitin sulfate, 169
Chromatography, 79–80
Chromoprotein, 76
Chromosomes, 128
Cistron, 138, 145
Clathrates, 52–53
Coacervation, 2
Coenzyme, 362
Collagen, 201
Component, thermodynamic
definition of, 207
Conductance
ionic radius measurement, 297
limiting, 296–298
in membranes, 306
and mobility, 297
Control mechanisms, 365–368
Cosubstrate, 362
Coulomb's law, 29
Counter-ion, 57
Coupled reactions, 252–255,
321–323, 362–364
Covalent bond, 26, 32–36
partial ionic character, 35–36,
38–39
Covalent radius of atoms, 33–34
Creatine
kinase, 254
phosphoryl-, 254–255
Crick, W. H. C., 117, 137,
139–141
Crystal, structure determination
by x-rays, 6
Cysteine, 66, 70, 139
Cystine, 66, 70, 139
Cytidine, 112
Cytoplasm, 130–131
Cytoplasmic streaming, 366
Cytosine, 110–112, 118, 133

Denaturation, enzyme, 349, 357

protein, 271
Deoxyribose nucleic acid
(see DNA)
Detergents, anionic, 178
cationic, 178–179
Dielectric constant, 29, 32, 42,
47, 49
Diffusion, 103, 288–298
coefficient(s), 103–104
definition, 293
table of, 294
of electrolytes, 294–298
energy dissipation in, 291
flux, 293–295
frictional forces in, 291–292
of ions across membranes,
305–309
mobility in, 292
molecular basis of, 288
potential, 295–296
single-file, 308
thermodynamic forces in,
289–291
velocity in, 292
Diiodotyrosine, 68, 71
Diisopropylfluorophosphate
(DFP), 70
Diphosphopyridine nucleotide
(DPN), 255
Dipolar ion, 62, 268
Dipole, electric, 36–41
induced, 40–41
interactions, 36–42
transient, 40–41
water as a, 48–49
Disaccharases, 168
Disaccharides, 167–168
Dispersion interactions,
London, 40–42
Disulfide bonds, 82, 99
DNA, 110–124
base pairs, 117–118
base ratios, 116, 117, 122
base sequence, 117–118,
130–131
denaturation, 122
in genetic mechanisms, 118,
120–121, 128–132, 135,
137–140
helix, 117–121
helix-coil transition, 122
melting curve, 123
melting temperature, 122
molecular weight, 117
nucleotides, 114
renatured, 124
replication, 137, 138
conservative, 138
dispersive, 138
semiconservative, 138
structure, 115, 119, 120
as template, 130–131, 137–
140
in viruses, 152–153
DNP(dinitrophenyl)-protein,
80–81

Edman method, 81

Electrical neutrality, law of,
279, 305
Electrical potential
in Gibbs-Donnan equilibrium,
284
gradient, 290–291
in liquid junction, 296, 298
across membranes, 279,
305–307, 316
Electrochemical concentration,
definition, 307
Electrochemical potential
definition of, 231
gradients in diffusion, 294–
295
of ionic species, 236
and membranes, 279, 284
in unidirectional fluxes, 307
Electron, 14
orbitals, 17, 20–25
shells and subshells, 17, 21–26
Electronegativity, 35, 39
Electrophoresis, 104–105
Electrophoretic mobility, 105
Endoplasmic reticulum, 197,
366
Energy (see also individual
forms of)
of activation, 342
barrier, 345
of bonds, 28–32, 35
functions, 220–222, (see also
individual functions)
level of electrons, 17–25
units of, 211
Enthalpy
of activation, 346
and chemical potential, 222
definition of, 221
fundamental equation for,
221–222
Entropy, 214–218
of activation, 346
changes in
natural processes, 215
reversible processes, 215
definition of, 214
function, 215
and information, 216
statistical interpretation of,
215
Envelope, viral, 152
Enzyme(s), 9, 61 (see also
names of)
activation, 361–364
and activation energy, 352
activator complex, 362
active site, 349, 357, 364
activity
effect of pH, 364–365
effect of temperature, 364
apo-, 350
as biological catalysts, 9,
349–350
denaturation, 349, 357
and genes, 367
in genetic control, 133
holo-, 350

INDEX

Newton's law of motion, 291
Nirenberg, M., 142, 143
Noble gas, anesthetic action, 53
structures of atoms, 25–26
Nonequilibrium process, 208, 215, 228, 288–298
N-terminal residues, 83
Nucleic acids,
components of, 113 (see also DNA, RNA)
pentose structures in, 112
in protein biosynthesis, 136
structure of, 115
ultraviolet absorption of, 117
Nucleon, 14
Nucleus
atomic, 14
cell, 195–196
Nucleoprotein, 76, 110, 152–153
Nucleosides, 113
composition of, 114
formulas of, 112
Nucleotides, 110–116
in alanyl-s-RNA, 133
composition of, 114
of DNA, formula, 114
of RNA, formula, 115

Ochoa, S., 142, 143
Optical activity, 163–166
Optical isomers, 69
Optical rotation, 163–166
Orbitals,
bond, 33, 39
electron, 17, 20–25
Osmotic pressure
colloid, 277, 284–285
derivation of, 274–277
ideal membranes, 274, 309
and molecular weight determination, 278
nonideal membranes, 310–311
of polysaccharides, 170–171
van't Hoff approximation, 276, 310
virial coefficients in, 277
in water transport, 309–311
Oxygen binding, 99
Oxygen transport, 61
Oxytocin, 73–74, 82

Partial ionic character, 35–36, 38–39
Partial molar free energy, 221
Partial molar volume, 275
Pauli exclusion principle, 23–24
Pauling and Corey, 88, 89
Pectins, 169
Peptide, bond, 71
formation, 71
group dimensions, 90
structure, 72
Permeability, coefficient, 303
and membrane structure, 311–313
and distribution coefficient, 313

Perutz, M. F., 96
pH, 53–57
buffering, 265, 270
definition, 53, 260
effect on enzymes, 364–365
isoelectric, 105, 267–268
theory of measurement, 280–281
titration curves, 262, 267, 271
of pure water, 54, 261
Phase, definition of, 207
Phenylalanine, 65, 70, 99
Phenylthiohydantoin (PTH) method, 81
Phosphatides, 184–185
Phosphoprotein, 75
Phosphoric acid, 266–267
Photon, 19
pK, of acids (table), 266
definition of, 56, 261
and standard free energy, 261
of water dissociation, 260
Planck's constant, h, 19, 346
Plant viruses, 151, 152
Plasma proteins, 105–107
Polarizability, 40
Polymers, 60
origin of, 2
Polynucleotide, 116
poly A, 121, 122
poly (A + U), 121
poly U, 121–122, 133
Polypeptides, 73
configuration, 88
in hemoglobin, 97
molecular weights of, 73
in myoglobin, 97
synthesis of, 134, 135–137
Polyribosome, 135
Polysaccharides, 162, 168–172
Polysome, 135–137
Pressure (see Hydrostatic, Osmotic, Vapor)
Proline, 66, 70, 99, 139
Protein biosynthesis, 131–137
DNA in, 120–121, 130–132, 135, 137–140
mechanism of, 136
ribosomes in, 135–137
RNA in, 132–137
Proteins, carbohydrate-containing, 75
charge, 57
conjugated, 75
contractile, 61
definition of, 60
denaturation of, 61
disulfide bonds in, 99
and enzymatic activity, 61, 349–350
fractionation of, 79
as hormones, 61
hydrogen bonds in, 90 (see also Hydrogen bonds)
hydrolysis of, 60–61, 79
in liberation of energy, 61
lipid-containing, 75

molecular weight
determination of, 100–104, 279
nucleic acid-containing, 76
of plasma, 105, 107
primary structure of, 78
purification of, 79
secondary structure of, 78
specificity of, 61
as structural elements, 61
structural parameters of, 106
structure determination by x-rays, 7
tertiary structure of, 78, 92, 99
titration curves of, 271
in viruses, 152–159
Proteolipids, 75
Proton, 14 (see also Hydrogen ion)
mobility in water, 54–55
Purines, 110–111
Pyranose, 166
Pyrimidines, 110–111
Pyruvate, 255

Quantum numbers, 21–24
Quantum theory, 19

Radiation, electromagnetic, 17–20
nuclear, 15
Radioactive isotopes, 15, 16 (see also Isotopes)
Radioactivity, 15
Raoult's law, 248–250, 277
Reaction sequences, 365–366
Refractive index, 18
Resistive forces, 291–292
Reversible process, 207, 228
Ribonuclease, 84, 294
amino acid sequence of, 84
Ribose nucleic acid (see RNA)
Ribosomes, 130, 131, 135–137, 143, 196–198
RNA, 110, 113–116, 124–125
chain configuration of, 125
in genetic mechanism, 129, 132–137, 142–144
messenger, 135–137, 197
nucleotides, 115
in plant viruses, 152
in protein synthesis, 131
soluble, 132–135
structure, 124
as template, 135–137
transfer, 132–135
in viruses, 124–125, 152–153

Sanger, F., 80
Schlieren optical system, 101, 104
Sedimentation, 101
Sedimentation coefficient, 102
Serine, 65, 70, 75
Sickle-cell, anemia, 145
hemoglobin, 145
Soap, 178–179

389